Microcomputer
Interfacing

Lexington Books Series in Computer Science
Kenneth J. Thurber, General Editor

Microcomputer Interfacing

Principles and Practices

G. Jack Lipovski
University of Texas

LexingtonBooks
D.C. Heath and Company
Lexington, Massachusetts
Toronto

Library of Congress Cataloging in Publication Data

Lipovski, G. Jack
   Microcomputer interfacing.

   1. Microcomputers. 2. Computer interfaces. I. Title.
TK7888.3.L49   001.64'404   79-9683
ISBN 0-669-03619-6

Copyright © 1980 by D.C. Heath and Company

Published simultaneously in Canada.

Printed in the United States of America.

International Standard Book Number: 0-669-03619-6

Library of Congress Catalog Card Number: 79-9683

Dedicated to my wonderful wife

Belle

Contents

List of Figures

List of Tables

Preface

The microcomputer has changed so many aspects of engineering that the cliché "microcomputer revolution" appears in numerous magazine articles and learned papers in the field. It is a great tool. Microcomputer-systems designers, however, have had to develop their own foundations, based on trade magazine articles and applications notes, because no available text-books or reference books have specifically developed those foundations. This book aims to teach the principles and practices of microcomputer-systems design in general and interfacing in particular.

This book was developed from a set of notes for a senior-level course in microcomputer design. The course focuses on the combined hardware-software design of microcomputer systems. It emphasizes the principles—the theory—of design because that is as necessary for a solid foundation for system design as is theory in any engineering discipline. Even so, it also emphasizes the practices—the details of how to get a system to work—because microcomputer-system design requires hands-on experience. The difference between a student who merely reads about microcomputers and a student who has worked with one is clear evidence that theory must be taught with practice. Practical experience is desirable in almost any engineering course. This is not always possible. But microcomputer systems are inexpensive enough that the school or the student can afford this hands-on opportunity, and the joy of seeing the principles work is so attractive that the student often cannot get enough of the material. So the course and this book emphasize both the principles and the practices of microcomputer design.

These principles and practices must cover both hardware and software. A purely hardware approach might be more attractive to a seasoned digital-system designer or an electrical engineering student, but that approach leads to ignorant choices that either do not take full advantage of the tremendous power of software or that force unnecessary constraints and therefore higher costs on its development. On the other hand, a purely software approach misses the opportunity to understand how and why things happen and how to take advantage of these things.

A combined hardware-software approach does require more background. The course on which this book is based is the second course of a two-course sequence. The first course teaches basic assembler-language programming. It is really just a standard computer-science course on assembler-language programming, but it is taught with an assembler language of a microcomputer. The second course builds upon that background. It also presumes some background in logic design, such as would be obtained in a standard introductory course on that topic. This book, however, has two chapters that survey the two prerequisite courses. These two chapters can be skimmed as a review of the required background material, or they can be carefully studied as a condensed tutorial if the reader has not had the earlier courses or their equivalent material. The two chapters are comparatively compressed and terse, because they are intended as review or intensive tutorial material preliminary to the main subject of the book, which follows in the later chapters.

The practices discussed in this book are made concrete through detailed discussion of the Motorola M6800 family of microcomputers and the M6809 microprocessor instruction set. These are used as a means to the end of teaching principles and practices in general, rather than for the promotion, sale, or use of Motorola products. Applications, notes, and catalogs are available from Motorola to that end. Specific and detailed discussion encourages and aides the reader in learning through hands-on experience, and it vitally contributes to an enthusiasm for and understanding of the principles. The M6800 family is used primarily because the M6809 is believed to be the most easily taught microcomputer. Its instruction set is as complete as that of any other machine, supporting enough addressing modes and index registers to teach the intelligent use of data structures, and it is symmetrical and comparatively free from quirks and anomalies that detract from the subject under discussion. Nevertheless, detailed comparisons between the M6809 and other well-designed microcomputers clearly show that others may be better than the M6809 for different applications. We do not mean to imply by the selection of the M6809 that it is the best microcomputer for all applications. We want to stress this point to the reader; however, a comparative study of different microcomputers and applications is beyond the scope of this book. On the other hand, the M6800 family, and the M6809 microcomputer in particular, are excellent vehicles for teaching the principles of microcomputer design.

The first two chapters quickly survey the background needed for the remainder of the book. Chapter 1 covers the instruction set of the M6809. It is intended as a survey for a reader who is acquainted with some other assembler language, either of another microcomputer or of a large machine. Chapter 2 covers basic computer organization but confines itself to those aspects of the topic that are particularly germane to microcomputers. For example, basic computer organization traditionally covers floating-point arithmetic, but this chapter does not; and this chapter dwells on tristate buses, although these are not often covered in discussions of computer organization. The rest of the book covers three basic themes: parallel input/output (I/O) ports in chapters 3 and 4, analog components in chapters 5 and 6, and communications devices in chapter 7. The simple parallel I/O port is displayed in chapter 3. Hardware and software aspects are studied side by side, so that the reader need no longer be intimidated by the basic interface. Chapter 4 discusses interrupts and their alternatives. Hardware-software tradeoffs are analyzed, and different techniques are exemplified. Chapter 5 surveys the traditional (voltage) analog components that are commonly used in microcomputer I/O systems. Sufficient information is provided so that the reader can understand the uses, the limitations, and the advantages of analog components and can use this chapter as a springboard to other texts, magazine articles, or discussions with colleagues with a fuller understanding of analog design. Chapter 6 introduces the counter-timer as an interface to frequency-analog signals. Techniques to generate signals with a frequency, or to measure a signal with a frequency, that is analog to some quantity are discussed. Moreover, the hardware-software alternatives to using this most interesting integrated circuit are discussed and evaluated. Chapter 7 describes communications devices. The Universal Asynchronous Receiver Transmitter (UART) and related devices are thoroughly studied, and other communications techniques are described.

This book is intended to be complete in itself, with no additional books necessary. If the reader wishes to skip the problems at the end of each chapter, and to omit doing the laboratory experiments suggested in the text, this book is sufficient. However, we recommend doing the problems and some laboratory experiments, and to do so the reader will need a copy of *The Complete Motorola Microcomputer Data Library*, printed after 1 June 1980. (Earlier printings have an incomplete description of the 6809.) Most readers will either have that book or will want to acquire a copy for further information on the chips that can be interfaced to the M6809. However, our two appendixes on an Intersil UART and a Motorola addressable UART contain material that is not in the *Data Library* and will allow the reader to do all the problems. The reader may also want to refer to *The TTL Data Book for Design Engineers* published by Texas Instruments, Inc. Also, we are planning a laboratory manual (which we hope will be available by December 1980) and a solutions manual, which may be obtained by contacting the author.

Some remarks are necessary on the style of this book. Terms are formally introduced and used as carefully as possible, and an extensive index is provided to help locate explanations of these terms. This is necessary in order to make some sense out of a subject as broad and rich as microcomputer-system design. There is no room for muddy terminology or the use of undefined jargon. Even though the topic is under rapid development and the terminology used in trade journals and manufacturers' applications notes is inconsistent and often contradictory, the terminology used in a text must be clear and consistent. However, a book full of definitions is too hard to read. The first version of the course notes that led to this book tended to be ponderous. Moreover, today's students are more attuned to television colloquialism and are tuned out to "third-person boring," which is often the style of learned textbooks. So we condescend to first-person conversational, and we enjoy it. The "we" in this book stands not only for the author but also for his colleagues, his teachers, and his students, who have taught him a great deal and who have collectively inspired and developed the principles and practices we discuss in the book. But we admit to exploring Webster's *Collegiate* occasionally for just the right word because we enjoy the challenge, and we even allow a pun or two where it does not interfere with the presentation of the material. We cannot deny it—microcomputer design is fun, and we have fun talking about it. Please forgive us if it shows in the style of the book.

Acknowledgments

The author would like to express his deepest gratitude to all the people who have contributed to this book. In addition to a number of students, fellow faculty members, and colleagues in industry who have helped in no small part, special thanks are due to Professor Charles Roth, who taught the course using these notes and who corrected many errors and contributed some of the better problems at the end of each chapter. Deep thanks are given Terry Ritter at Motorola, one of the designers of the M6809, for his extensive review of the manuscript, and for the many corrections and suggestions that make the book so much better. I would like to thank Lance Leventhal and Harold Stone for some fine comments in their reviews of the manuscript; these comments were invaluable. Gratitude is also offered to Professor Terry Wagner and students Ed Upchurch and Jeff Oliver, who proofread some of the chapters. Finally, I acknowledge the support of my secretary, Janelle Dolby, for correcting errors on the text edition, and my technician, Pat Horne, for preparing some of the rough-draft figures. If I omitted anyone, may I just say that throughout the book, the word *we* refers to me and to all of you who have helped in the formation of the ideas and in the generation of this book.

1

Microprocessing

The microcomputer, the microprocessor, and the subject of microprocessing are both quite familiar and a bit fuzzy to most engineers and computer scientists. When we teach a course on microcomputer interfacing, we ask the simple question, "What is a microcomputer?" and we find a wide range of answers. Different readers have different programming skills and backgrounds, too. But clearly we have to understand these concepts quite well to be able to discuss and design interfaces. This chapter is intended to cover the notions of microcomputer and microprocessor programming techniques that are needed in the discussion of interfacing in the rest of the book.

Other interface design books devote as much as half the book to the topics covered in this chapter. The topics covered are very important. The designer has to know a lot about basic computer architecture, programming, and organization. But, on completing this book, the reader should be ready to design good hardware and software for microcomputer interfaces. We will aim for that goal. We shall have to sacrifice material devoted to basics for material needed to design interface systems. There is so much to cover, and so little time and space, that we will offer a concise summary of the main ideas. Many of you have had this material in formal courses, or have absorbed it from your work or from reading those fine trade journals and hobby magazines that are devoted to microcomputers. If you have such a background, this chapter should bring it all together. Some of you can pick up the subject just by reading this condensed material. Others should get an idea of the amount of background they will need to understand the rest of the book. Refer to the books mentioned at the end of this chapter for recommended additional reading. This chapter contains the essential material needed as background for the rest of the book.

In this chapter, the reader is assumed to be fairly familiar with some kind of assembler language on a large or small computer, or to be able to pick it up quickly. In the chapter he should learn the fundamentals of microcomputing software in general, and the programming practices applicable to the M6809 microprocessor in particular. He should become

Portions of this chapter were adapted from the articles, "Digital Computer Architecture," by G.J. Lipovski, and "Microcomputers," by G.J. Lipovski and T.K. Agerwala, in the *Encyclopedia of Computer Science and Technology*, edited by Belzer et al., published by Marcel Dekker, N.Y. Used with permission.

capable of writing programs having on the order of a hundred lines of code and of debugging them with little difficulty. The reader should become familiar with the basic ideas of arithmetic, data structures, and subroutine handling, and he should be well prepared to understand the programs discussed in the remainder of the book that deal with interfacing microcomputers.

1-1 An Introduction to the Microcomputer

Just what are a microcomputer and a microprocessor, and what is the meaning of microprogramming, which is often confused with microcomputers? This section will survey these and other commonly misunderstood terms in digital-systems design. It describes the architecture of digital computers and gives a definition of architecture. Unfortunately, the study of computers is rather heavy with concepts, and therefore with terminology. But then, it is rather light on theorems and formulas. We will offer a lot of concepts and their definitions to help clear up later discussions; but we have a typical "chicken-and-egg" problem when we try to define these ideas without using terms that are not yet defined. So we have had to use some terms that will be properly defined later. This section opts to get the flavor of a few important concepts, so that should not matter. For a solid foundation in microcomputing, it can be reread when the undefined terms are explained. (Note that the index can help you find explanations of terms.)

We observe that the microcomputer is pretty much like other computers except that it is smaller and cheaper. The concept of the computer is presented first, and the idea of an instruction is scrutinized next. These concepts apply to large computers as well as microcomputers. The special characteristics of microcomputers will be delineated last.

1-1.1 Computer Architecture

Actually, the first and perhaps the best paper in computer architecture, "Preliminary Discussion of the Logical Design of an Electronic Computing Instrument," by A.W. Burks, H.H. Goldstein, and J. von Neumann, was written fifteen years before the term was coined. We find it fascinating to compare the design therein with all computers produced to date. It is a tribute to von Neumann's genius that this design, originally intended to solve nonlinear differential equations, has been successfully used in business data processing, information handling, and industrial control, as well as in numeric problems. His design is so well defined that the vast majority of computers in use are based on it, from large computers to microcomputers, and they are called *von Neumann computers.*

The term "architecture" itself was coined in the early 1960s by a group of computer designers within IBM, including Fred Brooks. They coined this term to describe the "blueprint" of the IBM 360 family of computers, from which several different computers with different costs and speeds (for example, the IBM 360/50) would be designed. The *architecture* of a computer is the instruction set and the input/output (I/O) connection capabilities. Computers with the same architecture can execute the same programs and can have the same I/O devices connected to them. This idea of designing a collection of computers with the same "blueprint" has been successfully copied by several manufacturers. Motorola has used this idea in developing the computers we will study in this book: the computers built from the MC6800, the MC6802, and the MC6808 have the same architecture. The association of computer architecture with this level of design has given a strict definition of the term "computer architecture."

The term "computer architecture" has become very popular, however, and has been extended to describe the computer system in general, including the implementation techniques and organization discussed below. In fact, it is difficult to get two computer architects to agree on the definition of computer architecture. While we are frustrated by such vagueness, it is probably due to the rapid evolution of this dynamic and exciting discipline.

The *organization* of a digital system like a computer is usually shown by a block diagram which shows the registers, buses, and data operators in the computer. For example, the MC6800 and MC6802 have the same architecture because they have the same instruction set and can utilize the same I/O devices, but since they are internally a little different, they have different organizations. Incidentally, the organization of a computer is also called its *implementation*. Finally, the *realization* of the computer is the actual hardware interconnection and construction of the computer. For example, the MC6800 and the MC68A00 have the same block diagrams and instruction sets, but the latter may be made with faster transistors to enable it to run twice as fast as the former. (Actually, the MC6800, MC68A00, and MC68B00 are made the same way at the same time. They are then tested. Those that happen to have the fastest transistors so they run the fastest are sold as MC68B00, the next fastest as MC68A00, and the slowest as MC6800.) The MC68A00 has a different realization from the MC68B00. It is entirely reasonable for a company to change the realization of one of its computers by replacing the hardware in a block in its block diagram with a newer type of hardware or for a designer to use a faster realization of a microcomputer. The implementation or organization remains the same while the realization is different. (In this book, whenever we want to discuss an actual realization, we will designate the component using the full and correct part number, like MC6800 or MC68A00, but we are usually interested in the architecture or the organization only. In these cases, we will refer to them as the 6800 (architecture, with no leading letters) or the M6800 (organization, with a leading M). This should help clear up any ambiguity, and yet it looks like a kind of natural shorthand that is easy enough to read.)

As better technology becomes available and as experience with an architecture reveals its weaknesses, a new architecture may be crafted that includes most of the old instruction set and some new instructions. Programs written for the old computer should then be able to run with little or no change on the new one, and more efficient programs may be able to be written using the new features of the new architectures. This new architecture is *upward compatible* to the old one if this property is preserved.

In this book, we will focus on the 6809 architecture, which is upward compatible to the 6800. Some remarks will be provided on the 6800 in order to make the book useful to some readers that have a 6800 based system. These remarks should also be useful to 6809 users who from time to time design systems with the 6800 architecture, such as the M6802 and M6808, and reprogramming some examples shown for the 6809 in the book for the 6800 will provide some very useful problems at the end of many of the chapters. The sections devoted to the 6800 and the problems that use it can be skipped without fear of omitting any fundamental principles.

The architecture of von Neumann computers is disarmingly simple, and the following analogy shows how simple. See figure 1-1 for the terms defined below.

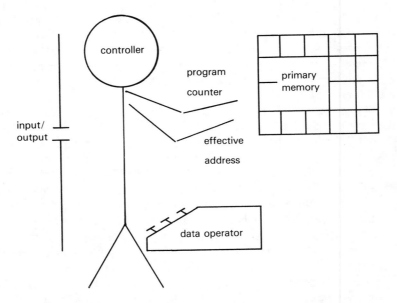

Figure 1-1. Analogy to the von Neumann Computer

Imagine a man in front of a mailbox, with an adding machine and window to the outside world. The mailbox has numbered boxes or slots and is analogous to the *primary memory*, the adding machine is analogous to the *data operator* (arithmetic-logic unit), the man to the *controller*, and the window to *input/output* (I/O). The man's hands *access* the memory. The primary memory is called a *random access memory* (RAM) because the man is free to access words in any order, at random, without having to wait longer for the next word because it is in a different location. Each slot in the mailbox contains a paper that has a string of, say, eight ones and zeroes (*bits*) on it. A string of eight bits is a *byte*. A string of bits in a slot of the memory box, whether or not it is a byte, is called a *word*. In this book, bits in a word are numbered, starting with bit zero on the right end of the word.

With his left hand the man takes out a word from box n, reads it as an instruction, and replaces it. Bringing a word from the mailbox (primary memory) to the man (controller) is called *fetching*. This hand that was on box n, that fetches a word, is analogous to the *program counter*. It is ready to take the word from the next box, box $n + 1$, when the next instruction is to be fetched.

An instruction in the 6809 is a *binary code* like 01001100. Consistent with the notation used by Motorola, binary codes are denoted in this book by a percent sign (%), followed by ones or zeroes. (Decimal numbers, by comparison, will not use any special symbols.) Since all those ones and zeroes are hard to remember, a convenient format is often used, called *hexadecimal notation*. In this notation, a dollar sign ($) is written (to designate that the number is in hexadecimal notation, rather than decimal or binary) and the bits, in groups of four, are represented as if they were "binary coded" digits zero through nine or letters A, B, C, D, E, F, to represent values ten, eleven, twelve, thirteen, fourteen, and fifteen, respectively. For example, the binary code %0100 is the binary code for four, and the binary code %1100 is the binary code for twelve, which is represented as the letter C. The binary code above is represented as $4C. Whether the binary code itself is used, or the simplified hexadecimal code is used, instructions written this way are called *machine coded* instructions because that is the actual code that is fetched from the primary memory of the machine, or computer. This is too hard to use, so a *mnemonic* (which means a memory aid) is used to represent the instruction. The instruction $4C in the 6809 or 6800 actually increments (adds 1 to) accumulator A, so it is written as:

INCA

(The 6809 accumulators and other registers are described in section 1-2.1.)

An *assembler* is a program that converts mnemonics into machine code so that the programmer can write in convenient mnemonics and the output machine code is ready to be put in primary memory to be fetched as an instruction. The mnemonics are therefore called *assembler language instructions*.

While a lot of interface software is written in assembler language, and most examples in this book are discussed using this language, a portion of the software to interface I/O devices is short enough that it is written in machine code. Moreover, quick fixes to programs are often written in machine code. Therefore, in this chapter, we will show the machine code for some assembler-language instructions that are important and that you might have some difficulty picking up on your own.

Many instructions in the 6809 are entirely described by the eight bits in one word. However, some instructions require sixteen or twenty-four bits or more fully to specify them. They are stored in words in consecutive primary memory locations (box numbers) so that when an instruction like that is fetched, each of the words can be fetched one after another.

Now that we have some ideas about the instruction, we resume the analogy to show some things that an instruction might do. For example, an instruction may give the controller directions to take with his right hand a word from a box *m* in the mailbox, copy it into the adding machine destroying the old word in the adding machine, and put the word back in the box. This is an example of an instruction called the *load* instruction. In the 6809, an instruction to load accumulator A with the word at location 256, in decimal, or $100 in hexadecimal, is fetched as three words:

$$\text{\$B6}$$
$$\text{\$01}$$
$$\text{\$00}$$

where the second word is the most significant byte, and the third word is the least significant byte, of the address, and is represented by mnemonics as

LDA $100

in assembler language. The main operation, bringing a word from the mailbox (primary memory) to the adding machine (data operator), is called *recalling* data. The right hand is used to get the word: it is analogous to the *effective address*.

As with instructions, assembler language uses a shorthand to represent locations in memory. A *symbolic address* is a name that means something to the programmer: it is actually some address in memory. For example, location $100 might be called ALPHA. Then the assembler language instruction above can be written:

LDA   ALPHA

(We will be using the symbolic address ALPHA in most of our examples in this chapter, and it will represent location $100. Other symbolic addresses and other locations can be substituted, of course. The way a symbolic address is written as a label, and the way the assembler assigns locations to them, will be discussed when we consider data structures in section 1-3.1.) It is important to remember that symbolic addresses are just representations of numbers, which usually happen to be the numerical addresses of the words in primary memory to which the symbolic addresses refer. As numbers, they can be added to other numbers, doubled, and so on. In particular, the instruction:

$$\text{LDA} \quad \text{ALPHA} + 1$$

will load the contents of the word at location $101 (ALPHA + 1 is $100 + 1) into the accumulator.

Generally, after such an instruction has been executed, the left hand (program counter) is in position to fetch the next instruction in box $n + 1$. For example, the next instruction may give him directions to copy the number in the adding machine into a box in the mailbox, causing the word that was in that box to be destroyed. This is an example of a *store* instruction. In the 6800 or 6809, the store instruction to store accumulator A into location $100 can be written:

$$\text{STA} \quad \text{ALPHA}$$

The main operation in this store instruction, putting a word from the adding machine (data operator) into a box in the mailbox (primary memory), is called *memorizing* data. The right hand (*effective address*) is used to put the word into the box.

Before going on, we point out a feature of the von Neumann computer that is easy to overlook, but is at once von Neumann's greatest contribution to computer architecture and yet a major problem in computing. Both instructions and data are stored in the primary memory, and there is no way to distinguish one from the other, except by which hand (program counter or effective address) is used to get the data. Advantageously, we can use memory not needed to store instructions, if not many are to be stored, to store more data, and vice versa. It is possible to modify an instruction, as if it were data, just before it is fetched, although a good computer scientist would shudder at the thought of it. Nevertheless, through an error (*bug*) in the program, it is possible to start fetching data words as if they were instructions, which generally produces strange results fast.

A *program sequence* is a sequence of instructions that are fetched from consecutive locations one after another. To increment the word at location $100, we can load it into the accumulator, using the LDA instruction, then increment it there, using the INCA instruction, and then put it back, using the STA instruction. This program sequence is written in consecutive lines, as in:

LDA   ALPHA

INCA

STA   ALPHA

Unless something is done to change the left hand (program counter), a sequence of words in contiguous boxes will be fetched and executed as instructions. For example, a sequence of load and store instructions can be fetched and executed to copy a collection of words from one place in the mailbox into another place.

When the man reads the instruction, however, it may direct him to move his left hand to a new location (load a new number in the program counter). Such an instruction is called a *jump*. A similar instruction is used to execute a program, called a *subroutine* which is located in a different part of memory, and then return to the instruction right below this instruction. Such an instruction, a *jump to subroutine*, not only changes the program counter like a jump, but also saves the old value of the program counter so that when the subroutine is finished, the old value of the program counter is restored (to return to the routine right after the jump to subroutine instruction). The last instruction of the subroutine, a *return from subroutine* instruction, causes the program counter to be restored. Subroutines are especially useful in small computers so that common operations that are not instructions can be made into subroutines, because the instructions in a small computer are rather primitive. Moreover, a jump instruction may direct the man in the analogy to jump, for instance, only if the number in the adder is positive. If that number is not positive, the next instruction is later fetched and executed because the left hand is not moved. This is a *conditional jump*. Jumps and conditional jumps permit some instructions to be fetched and executed over and over again. In this way, one can write a program, consisting of a few hundred instruction words, which can move and change thousands of data words. Jumps and conditional jumps are essential for executing the same program sequences over and over again. The forte of the computer is its ability to "massage" large quantities of data under the control of a program that has been stored in its primary memory.

The (*hardware or I/O) interrupt* is an architectural feature that is very important to I/O interfacing. Basically, it is evoked when an I/O device needs service, either to move some more data into the device or out of the device, or when the device detects an error condition. *Handling* an interrupt stops the program that is running, causes another program to be executed to service the interrupt, and then resumes the main program exactly where it left off. The program that services the interrupt (called an *interrupt handler* or *device handler*) is very much like a subroutine, and an interrupt can be thought of as an I/O device tricking the computer into executing a subroutine. However, an interrupt service program is not supposed to disturb the program that was running in any way. The interrupted program should get the same result whenever, or if ever, the interrupt occured. One of the problems in satisfying this requirement is that the interrupt service routine may call up subroutines that are also used by the program that was running. If the subroutine is currently being executed, it is possible for data from the program that was running to get mixed up with data used in the interrupt service routine, so that incorrect results are produced. If this is avoided, then the subroutine is said to be *reentrant* because it can be entered again, even though it has been entered and not finished. This property is important in designing software for interfaces. Related to it, recursion is a property such that a subroutine can call itself as many times as it wants. While recursion is a nice abstract property, it is not useful in interfacing, but recursive subroutines are usually reentrant and that is important.

Most modern computers control interrupts and save the results of operations in a *condition code register*. When a result is obtained, the *zero* bit Z is usually set to one if the result was zero, the *negative* bit N, if the result was negative, the *carry* bit C if an add operation produced a carry, and an *overflow* bit V if an add operation produces an invalid result considered in the two's complement number system because of overflow. These bits can be tested by a later conditional jump instruction. Also, an *interrupt inhibit* bit (also called an interrupt mask bit) I is kept in the condition code; when it is set, interrupts are not permitted. Condition codes are used to generalize the conditional jump capability of the computer, and to control interrupts. The condition code register, accumulators, program counter, and other registers in the controller and data operator are collectively called the *machine state* and have to be saved and restored whenever an interrupt occurs.

In order to facilitate the memorize and recall functions, the effective address can be computed in a number of different ways. These are called *addressing modes*. The 6809 is particularly rich in addressing modes. The different modes, and the reasons for them, will be explained in section 1-2.1.

1-1.2 The Instruction

In this section the concept of an instruction is described from different points of view. The instruction is discussed first with respect to the fetching, decoding, and sequencing of microinstructions that occurs. Then the instruction is discussed relative to hardware-software tradeoffs. Some concepts used in choosing the best instruction set are discussed.

The controller fetches a word or a couple or words from primary memory and sends commands to all the modules to execute the instruction. An instruction, then, is essentially a complex command that can be carried out under the direction of a single word or a couple of words fetched together as an inseparable group from memory.

The bits in the instruction are broken into several fields, which may be the bit code words for the instruction or for options in the instruction, or addresses in primary memory or addresses for some registers in the data operator or I/O device. For example, the instruction LDA   ALPHA may look like the bit pattern 1011011000000000100000000 when it is completely fetched into the controller. The leftmost bit and the fifth to eighth bits from the left, 1,0110, tell the computer that this is a load instruction. It is necessary that each instruction have a different code word, like 1,0110, so that the controller knows exactly which instruction is to be executed just by looking at the instruction word. The second bit from the left may identify the register that is to be loaded: 0 indicates that accumulator A is to be loaded. Bits three and four from the left, 11, indicate the address mode to access the word to be loaded. Finally, the last sixteen bits may be a binary number address: 0000000100000000 indicates that the word to be loaded is to come from word number $100 (ALPHA). Generally, the options, register addresses, addressing modes, and primary memory addresses differ for different instructions. It is necessary to decode the instruction code word, 1,0110, in this example, before it can be known that the second bit from the left, 0, is a register address, the third and fourth bits are address mode designators, and so on.

The instruction is executed by the controller as a sequence of small steps, called *microinstructions*. As opposed to instructions, which are stored in primary memory, microinstructions are usually stored in a small fast memory called *control memory*. A microinstruction is a collection of data transfer *micro-orders* that are simultaneously executed: the *data transfers* that result from these orders are movements of and operations on words of data as these words are moved about the machine. While the control memory that stores the microinstructions is normally written at the factory, never to be rewritten by the user (in read-only memory), in some computers it can be rewritten by the user. The writing of programs for the control memory is called *microprogramming*. It is the translation of the required behavior of an instruction into the control of data transfers that carry out the instruction.

The entire execution of an instruction is called the *fetch-execute cycle* and is composed of a sequence of microinstructions. Access to primary memory being rather slow, the microinstructions are grouped into *memory cycles*. A memory cycle is the period of time during which the memory fetches an instruction, memorizes or recalls a data word, or is idle. A *memory clock* beats out the time signals, one clock pulse per memory cycle. The fetch-execute cycle is then a sequence of memory cycles. The first cycle is the *fetch* cycle in which the instruction code is fetched. If the instruction is *n* bytes long, the first *n* memory cycles are usually fetch cycles. In some computers, the next memory cycle is a *decode* cycle where the instruction code is analyzed to determine what to do next. The 6800 and 6809 do not need a separate cycle for this. The next cycle may be for *address calculations*. Data may be read from memory in one or more *recall* cycles. Then the main function of the instruction is done in the *execute* cycle. Finally, the data may be memorized in the last cycle, the *memorize* cycle.

I/O devices may request an interrupt in any memory cycle; however, the data operator usually has bits and pieces of information scattered around and is not prepared to stop the current instruction. Therefore, interrupts are always recognized at the end of the current instruction, when all the data is organized into accumulators and other registers (the machine state) that are able to be safely saved and restored. The time from when an I/O device requests an interrupt until data that it wants moved is moved, or the error condition is reported or fixed is called the *latency time* or just *latency*. Fast I/O devices require low latency interrupt service. The lowest latency that can be guaranteed is limited to the duration of the longest instruction (and the time to save the machine state), because the I/O device could possibly request an interrupt at the beginning of the execution of such an instruction.

It is conceivably possible to design an instruction so that one can execute a very complicated operation in just one instruction. Also, there are instructions that use certain address modes that operate on addresses to achieve results that would otherwise require additional instructions. On the other hand, it is generally possible to fetch and execute a sequence of rather simple instructions to carry out the same net operation. The program sequence that we discussed earlier can actually be done by a single instruction in the 6809:

INC   ALPHA

It recalls word $100, increments it, and memorizes the result in location $100 without changing the accumulator. If a useful operation is not performed in a single instruction, like INC ALPHA, but rather in a sequence of simpler instructions like the program sequence described above, such a sequence is either a macroinstruction, that is, a *macro*, or it is subroutine. It is a macro if, every time in a program that the operation is required, the complete sequence of instructions is written in place in the program. It is a subroutine if the instruction sequence is written just once, and a jump to subroutine is made to the beginning of this sequence each time the operation is required. In many ways the two concepts—macroinstructions and subroutines—are very similar techniques to get an operation done by executing a sequence of instructions. Perhaps one of the central issues in the design of the architecture of a computer is: what should be made to be instructions or included as addressing modes and what should be left out, to be carried out by macros or subroutines? At the outset, it has been proven that a computer that has just one instruction can do anything that any existing computer can do. It may take a very long time to carry out an operation, and the program may be ridiculously long and complicated, but any operation that any other computer can do can be done by this "minimal" computer. On the other extreme, complex machines for which one instruction is able to execute a high level (for example, FORTRAN) language statement might be desirable from the point of view of most programmers. Such complex instructions create undesirable side effects, however, such as long latency time for handling interrupts. Nevertheless, the issue is efficiency. Instructions are selected so that the operations to be performed by a computer can be translated into programs using those instructions which can be executed as fast as possible (speed) and which take as little room as possible to store the programs (the inverse of program density) without sacrificing low latency. (The related issue of storing data as efficiently as possible is discussed in section 1-3.1.)

The choice of instructions is complicated by the range of requirements in two ways. Some applications need a computer to optimize speed while others need their computer to optimize program density. For instance, if a computer is used like a desk calculator and the time to do an operation is only 0.1 sec, there may be no advantage to doubling the speed because the user will not be able to take advantage of it, while there may be considerable advantage to doubling the program density because the cost of memory may be halved and the cost of the machine may drop substantially. On the other hand, if a computer is used in a computing center with plenty of memory, doubling the speed may permit twice as many jobs to be done, so that the computer center income is doubled, while doubling the program density is not significant because there is plenty of memory left over. Moreover, the different applications that computers are put to require different proportions of speed and density.

To date, there is no known computer that is best suited to every application. Therefore, there is a wide variety of computers with different features, and there is a problem in picking the computer that best suits the kinds of operations to be done by it. Generally, to choose the right computer from a number of computers, a collection of simple well-defined programs that pertain to the expected use of the computer, called *benchmarks*, are set down. Examples of benchmarks are: multiply two unsigned sixteen-bit numbers, move a sequence of words from one location in memory to another, and search for a word in a sequence of words. Programs are written for each computer to effect these benchmarks, and the speed and program density are recorded for each computer. A weighted sum of these values is used to derive a figure of merit for each machine. If storage density is to be studied, the weights used are proportional to the number of times the benchmark (or programs similar to the benchmark) is expected to be stored in memory, and the figure of merit is called the *static efficiency*. If speed is to be studied, the weights are proportional to the number of times the benchmark (or similar routines) is expected to be executed, and the figure of merit is called the *dynamic efficiency*. These figures of merit, together with computer rental or purchase cost, available software, reputation for serviceability, and other factors, are used to select the machine.

In this chapter and throughout the design of software for interfaces, the issue of efficiency continually reappears in the selection of instructions for "good" programs. The 6809 has a particularly rich instruction set, with several alternatives for many important operations. The reader is strongly encouraged to develop the skill of using the most efficient techniques. He should try to select instructions that execute the program in the shortest time, if dynamic efficiency is prized, or that can be stored in the least number of bytes, if static efficiency is desired.

1-1.3 Microcomputers

Microcomputers can be regarded as computers of the kind discussed above that are realized in a particular inexpensive technology. Small computers have been classifed according to the number of bits in a word, the number of words in memory, and the price of the data operator, controller, and memory together. The original classification of micro-, mini-, and midicomputers by Bell in 1970 is given in table 1-1.

The terms have remained although rapid technological improvements have blurred the distinction between these classes and dropped their costs. An *integrated circuit die, or chip*, is a thin sheet of silicon, on the order of 0.04 by 0.04 inches, on which transistors, resistors, and capacitors are constructed, to make the components of digital systems. It is an *LSI* or large-

Table 1-1
Classification of Computers

Class	Memory Words	Cost ($) (1970)	Bits/Word
Micro	8,000	5,000	8 to 12
Mini	32,000	10,000	12 to 16
Midi	65,000	20,000	16 to 24

scale integrated circuit chip if it has on the order of a thousand transistors. Such a die is usually put in a ceramic or plastic container, called a *dual in line package*, about 0.3 by 0.8 inches. See the bottom of figure 1-2. It is now possible to put the controller and data operator on a single LSI integrated circuit or on a small number of LSI integrated circuits. Such a data-operator/controller is called a *microprocessor*. If a memory and I/O module are added to a microprocessor, the result is called a *microcomputer*. The integrated circuits are normally put on a *printed circuit card* like the one shown on the top of figure 1-2, and several cards may be mounted, like pages in a book, on a *motherboard* that acts like the binder in a book to connect the boards together. Microcomputers are characterized at present by very low cost and by the absence of software programs that are available to use on them. For example, single board microcomputers are available (1979) for around $100.00, and more powerful multiple board microcomputers, for about $300.00. The heart of a microcomputer, the microprocessor, is only about $10.00. Minicomputers are characterized by the abundance of software (loaders, debuggers, assemblers, compilers, and the like) available for them. The distinction between minicomputers and microcomputers is blurred by the fact that some architectures are available either as minicomputers (PDP-11/45) or as microprocessors (PDP-11/LSI). The distinction is further blurred by the availability of sixteen-bit microprocessors such as the 68000, and the capability of putting up to 65,000 words of memory in a microcomputer. Moreover, more software is becoming available for microcomputers. At any rate, the terms microcomputer and minicomputer are both commonly used to describe small computers.

Ironically, this superstar of the seventies, the microcomputer, was born of a broken marriage. At the dawn of the decade, we were already putting pretty complicated calculators on LSI chips. So why not a computer? Fairchild and Intel made the PPS-25 and 4004, which were almost computers, but did not have von Neumann architectures. Datapoint Corporation, a leading and innovative manufacturer of terminals and one of the larger users of semiconductor memories, talked both Intel and Texas Instruments into building a microcomputer of their design. Neither Intel nor Texas Instruments was too excited about such an ambitious task, but Datapoint threatened to stop buying memories from them, so they went ahead. The resulting devices were disappointing, both an order of magnitude too slow and too expensive. A recession developed, so Texas Instruments dropped the project, but did get the patent on the microcomputer. Datapoint decided they would not buy it after all because it did not meet their specifications. Even until recently, Datapoint has been unwilling to use microcomputers. Once burned, twice cautious. It is ironic that two of the three parents of the microcomputer disowned the infant. Intel was a new company, and was not so well established that it could drop the project altogether. So they

Source: Motorola, Inc. Reprinted with permission.

Figure 1-2. A Printed Circuit Card and a Dual-In-Line Package

marketed it as the 8008, and it sold. It is also ironic that Texas Instruments
has the patent on the Intel 8008. The 8008 was incredibly clumsy to program, and it took so many additional support integrated circuits that it was
about as large as a computer of the same power that did not use
microprocessors. Some claim it set back computer architecture at least ten
years. But it was successfully manufactured and sold. It was a triumph of integrated circuit technology. It proved that a microcomputer could be a pro-
fitable product as it created a market where none existed before; and the
8080, which was designed to be upward compatible to the 8008, is one of the
most popular microcomputers in the world: in fact it is the microcomputer
copied behind the iron curtain.

We will study the 6809 (and refer to the 6800) in this book; however, the
8080 discussed above, the Fairchild Semiconductor Division F8, the Zilog
Z80, and the MOS Technology 6502 microprocessors are at least as
popular. In addition to these eight-bit word microprocessors, sixteen-bit
word microprocessors like the Texas Instruments 9900, the Intel 8086, the
Zilog Z8000, and the Motorola 68000 promise to be more powerful. We
chose to discuss eight-bit microprocessors in this book because we encourage the reader to build and test some of the circuits we describe, and
eight-bit wide memories and processors are cheaper (especially if you connect power up backwards and pop the ICs), and the same concepts can be
discussed as with sixteen-bit microcomputers. We chose the 6809 because it
has an instruction set that has enough features to illustrate good software
practices. Nevertheless, other microcomputers have demonstrably better
static and dynamic efficiency for certain benchmarks. Even if they have
comparable (or even inferior) performance, they may be chosen because
they cost less, or have a better reputation for service and documentation or
are available, while the "best" chip is more costly, poorly serviced, or
documented, or unavailable. The reader is encouraged to study other
microcomputers too, and to be prepared to use them if the application war-
rants that.

The microcomputer has unleashed a revolution in computer engineering. Briefly stated, as the cost of microcomputers approaches the tens of
dollars range, the computer becomes a mere component. They are appearing as components in automobiles, kitchen applicances, toys, instruments,
process controllers, communication systems, and computer systems. They
should replace larger computers in process controllers much as fractional
horsepower motors replaced the large motor and belt shaft. They are "fractional horsepower" computers. This aspect of microcomputers will be our
main concern throughout the rest of the book, since we will focus on how
they can be interfaced to appliances and controllers. There is, however,
another aspect that we will hardly have time to study, which will be equally
important. They will be used in conventional computer systems. Their

significance in computer systems is only beginning to be appreciated. Consider the following three (slightly overstated) conjectures.

1. The problem of software portability is the problem of getting a program moved from one computer to another. The "software portability" problem is solved! If you buy a software package for $30,000, then that software can be written for a microcomputer, and the firm that wrote and sells the software will give you the microcomputer for free.

2. The solution of large problems will depend only on the patience of the programmer. He could solve these problems on a conventional computer at a high price. Instead, he buys a cheap microcomputer, loads a program on a Friday night, and returns a week later to get his answer. Then he could even throw away the microcomputer and the cost of solving the problem might still be less than on a conventional computer.

3. Future computers will be aggregates of microcomputers. The cost of processing on a microcomputer is so low that a "mess o' micros" will be more economical than a larger processor.

Despite the startling innovations that should result from the microcomputer, the microcomputer, minicomputer, and large computer are generally very similar. In the following subsections the main features of the 6809, which has a von Neumann architecture, are examined in greater detail.

1-2 Instruction Sets of the 6809 and the 6800

A typical machine has six types of instructions and several addressing modes. These different types of instructions and addressing modes are described below in general terms. The types and modes indicate what an instruction set might look like. They also give concrete details about how the 6809 and the 6800 work, which are necessary for the understanding of examples in this book. The first two subsections discuss the 6809, which is the primary microcomputer that is used in the examples throughout the book. The last subsection describes the 6800, which is used in some of the problems at the end of many of the chapters, and should be useful to those readers who have 6800-based systems. The section on the 6800 may be omitted without loss of any important concepts in this book.

This section talks about the instruction set. It does not fully define the instruction set of the 6809 or 6800 because it is easy to get lost in the details. *The Complete Motorola Microcomputer Data Library* (printed after 1 July 1980) or the handy "MC6809 Microprocessor Instruction Set Summary," available from Motorola should be used to specify fully the 6809 instruction set. The only way to really learn an instruction set is to write a lot of programs. It cannot be learned just by reading a book, even one as fine as this.

Nevertheless, some insight can be afforded in a book like this by discussing some useful aspects of the instruction set.

The 6809 is particularly rich in addressing modes. In fact, you can obtain certain operations, which are normally done as instructions, as a result of addressing mode calculations. It is easiest, then, to discuss the addressing modes first, before the instructions are described.

1-2.1 6809 Addressing Modes

The instructions that have been sketched out so far have taken a word from memory where the address of the word is given directly in the instruction. This mode of addressing, called *direct addressing*, is widely used on large computers. By the most commonly accepted definition, direct addressing must be able effectively to address any word in primary memory. The number of bits needed to directly address n words of memory is log $2n$. For a standard sized 65,536-word memory, sixteen bits are required to address each word. If the width of the words is eight bits, an instruction may require twenty-four bits for the instruction code bit pattern and the address. This hurts static efficiency, because a lot of bits are needed, compared to other modes that will be introduced in this section, and it hurts dynamic efficiency, because more time is needed to pick up all those words. Other addressing modes are used to access the most often needed words quickly, and to get to any word in memory somehow, without using as many bits as are needed to address directly all the words of memory. This problem leads to the addressing modes that are especially important in small computers. In the remainder of this section, addressing modes are discussed in general terms to show what might be expected in a computer in general, and what is available on the 6809 in particular. See table 1-2 at the end of this section for a summary of addressing modes.

Motorola calls the direct addressing mode "extended addressing," which you should know if you want to read their literature, but everyone else calls it direct addressing. Motorola uses the term "direct addressing" for a short form of addressing that uses an eight-bit address, which we will call page zero addressing or direct page addressing. Their terminology would be correct, in the classical sense, if they thought of primary memory as being only 256 words. Then direct addressing would just be capable of addressing such a small memory, and addressing more memory would be extended addressing. It seems as though the designers of the 6800 made the assumption that most systems would only require such a small (primary) memory. But, as we now know, garbage fills the container, so if we build a bigger container, it will soon be filled. Thus, we should use the term direct addressing when we use a sixteen-bit displacement as the effective address.

In the following discussion of addressing modes, the bits in the instruction that are used as an address, or that are added to the contents of a register to get the effective address, are called the *displacement*. Also, in the following discussion, an address is calculated the same way for the program counter in jump instructions as for the effective address in such instructions as LDA or STA. Some people get confused about the addressing modes used in jump instructions because they think that JMP ALPHA should take a word from location ALPHA, to put it into the program counter, using direct addressing in the same way as in the instruction LDA ALPHA. No, JMP ALPHA loads the address ALPHA into the program counter. The simple analogy we used earlier in this chapter should make it clear, that the program counter is, like the effective address, a "hand" to address memory, and is treated the same way as the effective address by the addressing modes.

Some techniques solve the problem of improving addressing efficiency by avoiding the calculation of an address to memory. *Implied addressing* is a technique whereby the instruction always deals with the same register or a fixed word in memory, so that no bits are required within the instruction to specify it. An example is a kind of jump to subroutine instruction called the software interrupt SWI (this instruction will be more clearly explained in 1-2.2: it is also called TRAP or SVC). When it is executed, the old value of the program counter is saved in a specific place (to be described later) and the new program counter value is gotten from two specific places (memory location $FFFA, $FFFB). The instruction itself does not have any bits in it where it ought to that indicate the address of the next instruction: the address is implied. Motorola, and others, also call this mode "inherent."

A similar mode uses registers as the source and destination of data for instructions. This is called *register addressing*. The 6809 has accumulators that can be so used, called *accumululator A, accumulator B*, and *accumulator D*. Accumulator D is a sixteen-bit accumulator for two-word data operations and is actually the same as the two eight-bit accumulators A and B joined together. That is, if accumulator A has $3B and accumulator B has $A5, then accumulator D has $3BA5, and vice versa. In some instructions, such as INC, one can increment a word in memory using direct addressing, as in INC ALPHA, or else one can increment a register, such as INCA. Thus, register addressing can be used instead of memory addressing to get data for instructions. This mode substantially improves both static and dynamic efficiency, because fewer bits are needed to specify the register than a memory word, and a register can be accessed without taking up a memory cycle.

Another nonaddressing technique is called *immediate addressing*. Herein, part of the instruction is the actual data, not the address of data. In a sense, the displacement is the data itself. For example, a type of load instruction,

LDA   #$10

actually puts the number $10 into the accumulator. Using Motorola's nota-
tion an immediate address is denoted by a number sign (#). The LDA instruction, with addressing mode bits for immediate addressing, is $86, so
this instruction is stored in machine code thus:

$86

$10

The number $10 is actually the second word (displacement) of the two-word
instruction. This form of addressing has also been called literal addressing.

Page addressing is closely related to direct addressing. Three variations
of page addressing appear in the 6809 and the 6800 and will be discussed
below. Suppose eight bits can be used to give the address inside the instruction. Then 2 to the eighth power or 256 contiguous words can be directly addressed with these bits. A *page* in this example is defined as 256 contiguous
words. Generally, for a subroutine, there are some data that are needed only by that subroutine (*local data*) and there are some data that have to be
shared with other subroutines (*global data*). Page addressing is used to get
the local data and the global data efficiently.

Page relative addressing calculates the effective address by adding an
eight-bit two's complement displacement to the program counter. The local
data can generally be stored in the subroutine program storage area,
therefore it is on the same page as the program counter. By adding the
eight address bits in the instruction to the value in the program counter one
can get the address for local data. The displacement is added to the program
counter at a time when it is actually pointing to the beginning of the next instruction. Page relative addressing is denoted by an address followed by
,PCR as in the instruction:

LDA   ALPHA,PCR

(The way that relative addresses are stored in memory is more easily shown
in the next example, but the same principle is used in this example.) This addressing mode will only work if the data is within − 128 to + 127 locations
from the address of the next instruction after the LDA ALPHA,PCR. Page
relative addressing is commonly used in jump and conditional jump instructions because one often jumps to a location that is fairly close to (on the
same page as) the place where the jump is stored. This kind of jump instruction is often called a *branch*. A location to which we want to branch may
contain the instruction code for LDA ALPHA. To identify such a place to
jump or branch to, we put a label to the left of it, so that the label begins in

the leftmost column, flush against the left margin. Instructions that are not labeled must begin, then, with a space, so the assembler will not mistake an instruction mnemonic for a label. If the above instruction is at locations $200, $201, and $202, it is written:

L LDA   ALPHA

and the label L will be the symbolic address of the instruction, which may be used in jump or branch statements. Since a branch instruction always uses relative addressing, the appendage ,PCR is omitted in such an instruction. For example, a branch to location $200 (L) is denoted:

BRA L

If L is at location $200, and the branch instruction is at location $1F0, then the program counter is at location $1F2 when the address is calculated, and the BRA instruction (whose instruction code is $20) will be assembled and stored in memory as:

$20

$0E

Note that the assembler language instruction uses the actual symbolic address L rather than the difference between the addresses, as in BRA L-$1F2, and the assembler automatically determines the difference between the current program counter address and the effective address, and puts this difference into the second word (displacement) of the instruction. LDA ALPHA,PCR uses this difference for a displacement, like the displacement of BRA.

Similar to page relative addressing, *long relative addressing* has another use. A sixteen-bit (two-word) displacement, considered a two's complement signed number, is added to the program counter, just as in short relative addressing, to get the effective address. This mode does not conserve bits compared to direct addressing and actually takes longer to execute. It is used, however, to permit the entire program to be moved intact from one place in memory to another. Since the instruction and the data move together, their relative address remains unchanged; but the instruction and the data may be farther than −128 or +127 locations apart. Therefore, both page relative and long relative addressing are useful ways to allow the program to function correctly as it is moved to different places in memory. This characteristic is call *position independence*. It means a program can be loaded anywhere in memory and it will run without change, to simplify the loading of programs and subroutines. Moreover, it means that a read-only memory can be loaded with the program, and it will work wherever that read-only memory is addressed. The latter feature permits such programs written in read-only memories to be usable in a larger range of installations, because the addresses need not conflict with others used by other programs, so these kind of programs can be sold in larger numbers and will therefore be less costly. Long relative addresses in instructions like LDA ALPHA,PCR are denoted just like short relative addresses, and the assembler will determine whether a short relative address can be used to conserve bits, or whether a long relative address is needed to reach the data from the instruction. Branch instructions, however, use different instructions for long relative addressing, called long branch instructions:

LBRA L

will use a long relative addressing mode to load the program counter to jump to L. If this instruction (whose code is $16) is at location $10, then when the address is calculated, the program counter will be $13, so L will be at (the contents of PC) + $1ED = $200. The instruction will actually be stored as:

$16

$01

$ED

Stack addressing is also used to store local data. It will be discussed near the end of this section.

Global data in smaller machines is frequently stored on a specific page, generally the page having addresses with the lowest numbers. This data can be recalled by using the eight-bit displacement (filling the high order bits not supplied by the instruction with zero). This mode is called *page zero* addressing. Page zero addressing is used on the 6800, but an extension of it that substantially changes its character is used on the 6809, which will be discussed shortly. Page zero and page relative addressing made possible the inexpensive "minicomputer" by permitting the programmer to get to local or global data easily on a small machine. They are used in microcomputers to improve static and dynamic efficiency.

Although page zero and page relative addressing permit one to access local and global data, one cannot access much of it. For example, if a page is 256 words, then a twenty by twenty word global array cannot be stored entirely on page zero. This is solved by combining page addressing with *indirect addressing*. Indirect addressing is also used to permit data to be moved around easily as we explain shortly. We denote indirect addressing by enclosing the address in square brackets, as in

LDA [ALPHA]

This instruction first goes to location $100 as in the instruction LDA ALPHA, and reads the (sixteen-bit) address from locations $100 and $101. Say it is $500. Rather than putting $500 into the accumulator (if it would fit), as in page zero or in direct addressing, it recalls the word at location $500, putting that word into the accumulator. Location $100 is an indirect address. This makes it easy to move data around. Suppose that quite a few instructions access the data at location $500, but they do so indirectly through $100. Then if the data is moved, say to location $600, only the content of location $100 has to be changed to $600. All the other data accessing instructions will not be changed, since they still access the data indirectly through location $100.

An alternative addressing mode to indirect addressing is *index or pointer addressing*. Herein, a small array (four by sixteen) of fast registers in the controller module, called index registers or pointer registers, are used to obtain the address. In a load instruction using index addressing, some bits (two bits) choose the (sixteen-bit) index register, to which some part of the instruction (say eight or sixteen bits) are added to get the address of the word that is recalled. The word in the index register itself is unchanged by this operation. Note that the index register can be loaded with the address of any word in memory, so that any word can be recalled by means of index addressing. Moreover, without changing the index register contents, any word near that to which the index register points can be recalled by using different values for the displacement (five, eight, or sixteen bits) added to the index register. This makes index addressing quite versatile for handling arrays. In very small machines, however, there are no bits available in the instruction that can be added to the index registers. The address is exactly the contents of the index register. This special simple form of index addressing is called pointer addressing and the index registers are called pointer registers. From its strong resemblance to indirect addressing, pointer addressing is also called "register indirect" addressing. While pointer addressing can be used to recall any word in memory, it is more difficult to use because the register must be reloaded each time a word at a different location is to be recalled or memorized.

Note that index or pointer addressing is an alternative to indirect addressing. For example, indirect addressing can be used to get a word whose address is at ALPHA: LDA [ALPHA]. If the address of the word is in index register X, this is comparable to loading the index register with the address of ALPHA, then loading the accumulator using index addressing. Index or pointer addressing is more efficient if you will access several words using the index register. Indirect addressing is more efficient when you access just one word or a pair of words in the range of the indirect address because it is like simultaneously loading an index register and using it as an address.

In the 6809, four index/pointer sixteen-bit registers are used, called X, Y, U, and S. The S register is a special *stack pointer*. While all index addressing modes can be applied to this register, it has special meaning and, in our own experience, it has to be treated with some respect. The registers can be used in two-word instructions using pointer addressing and in index addressing in which the last five bits are a signed number displacement. These registers can also be used in index addressing using a three-word instruction in which the last eight bits are a two's complement displacement, and using a four-word instruction in which the last sixteen bits are a two's complement displacement. Of these four modes, the first two are obviously shorter, to improve static efficiency, and the first is a little faster, to improve dynamic efficiency also. Additionally, the 6809 has an addressing mode that uses one of the accumulators (A, B, or D) and one of the index registers (X, Y, U, or S) as two pointer registers used to calculate the address. The effective address is the sum of the two's complement number in the accumulator and the two's complement number in the index register. Motorola calls this mode *accumulator indexed*. This is a powerful addressing mode that we will find very useful when we discuss the addressing of arrays later in this chapter.

Pointer addressing is designated by a comma (,) followed by an index register name, as in:

$$\text{LDA} \quad ,\text{X}$$

which loads accumulator A with the word in memory whose address is in index register X. Index addressing is denoted by writing the displacement followed by a comma and the index register name, as in:

$$\text{LDA} \quad \text{ALPHA,X}$$

If index register X has the value 5, then the above instruction will put the word at location $105 into accumulator A. The different index addressing modes are written the same way in assembler language. The assembler will chose the shortest code word with the fastest mode, depending on the value of the displacement. Note that relative addressing uses a similar assembler-language format, as in:

$$\text{LDA} \quad \text{ALPHA,PCR}$$

but in index addressing the assembler-language address, ALPHA in the above example, is put into the displacement. However, in relative addressing, the difference between the symbolic address, ALPHA, and the value of the program counter when the instruction is executed, is put in the displacement of the instruction. Accumulator indexed addressing, using an accumulator like B and an index register like X to compute the address of a word to load into accumulator A is denoted by writing the accumulator used to calculate the address, a comma, and the index register used, as in:

LDA   B,X

If accumulator B has the number 5, and index register X has the number $100, then this instruction will put the word at location $105 into accumulator A.

The 6809 has a fast but less general kind of index addressing. This form of "index addressing" was developed as an extension of the page zero addressing mode in the 6800. An eight-bit *direct page register* can be loaded with any number. When *direct page* addressing is used, the eight-bit displacement is combined with the number in the direct page register, direct page register as the high byte and displacement as the low byte to get the effective address. When power is turned on, the direct page register is cleared, so that the 6809 behaves just like the 6800 using page zero addressing; but the program can load another value into the direct page register. Then this mode of addressing becomes a "quick and dirty" type of index addressing. As with index addressing, any word in memory can be recalled or memorized by putting the high byte of the address in the direct page register and the low byte in the displacement of the instruction that used direct page addressing. This mode turns out to be the fastest and shortest mode. It requires only a two-byte instruction and displacement and is faster than index addressing because the address calculation is done without the use of the adder. When the direct page register is zero, this mode can be used to satisfy the need for global data in the classic tradition through the use of the mode as in the 6800. If this register has a fixed value other than zero, it can also be used for global data. If the programmer keeps changing it, however, he is using it like a "quick and dirty" index register to improve either static or dynamic efficiency, or both. The use of direct page addressing in its general sense as an index mode is a bit hazardous. If it is so used, every program should begin with the assumption that the direct page register has an unknown value in it, and it should therefore be saved and loaded with a known value before the program begins, then restored to its original value when the program is over. If it is left as zero, however, in every program and subroutine, then it can be safely used to store global data.

The assembler-language designation for direct page addressing is the same as for direct addressing, as in:

LDA   ALPHA

If the assembler knows that the symbolic address ALPHA happens to be on the same page as the number in the direct page register (using an "assembler directive'' SETDP), it automatically uses the shorter and faster direct page addressing mode, rather than direct addressing. For example, if the direct page register happens to have a one in it, then the high byte of address ALPHA ($100) is one, so the assembler will code the instruction using the instruction code $96 that has the address mode bits for direct page addressing, and will supply the low byte of the address as the displacement, as in:

$$\$96$$
$$\$00$$

The last major aspect of the addressing mechanisms used in most computers is the *autoincrement/autodecrement*. One soon recognizes that very often, after the ith word is recalled, the $(i + 1)$st word is recalled. Generally, the address is stored in an index register, using index or pointer addressing. Instead of having a separate instruction to add one to the address i, one can have an addressing mode that automatically adds one to it (autoincrement) as the ith word is recalled. Similarly, an addressing mode is found useful which automatically subtracts one (autodecrement) as the ith word is recalled. Autoincrementing or autodecrementing is done either just before (pre) or just after (post) the address is used. The 6809 can decrement by one, or decrement by two, the contents of any index register just before it is used to calculate the effective address, or increment by one or two the value of an index register just after it is used to compute the effective address. The number in the index register after the instruction is over is the value after it has been incremented or decremented by one or two.

Preautodecrement by one is designated by the sign comma dash (,—) before the index register; by two, by the sign comma double dash (,——); and postautoincrement by one, by a comma before and a plus sign after the index register; and by two, by a comma before and two plus signs after the register. For example, if register X had the number eight in it, and that register were used for preautodecrement pointer addressing to recall a word into accumulator A, it would be written:

$$LDA \quad ,-X$$

the index register X would first be decremented to seven, and the word in location seven would be recalled. An instruction using postautoincrementing by two is denoted thus:

$$LDA \quad ,X++$$

If X were six, then the word at location six is recalled to accumulator A and X becomes 8 after the instruction.

Autoincrement, autodecrement, and index addressing have special significance when used with the stack pointer S. A part of memory, called the *stack buffer*, is set aside for a *stack*. The stack pointer S initially contains one plus the largest address of any word in the stack buffer). *Pushing* a word on this stack means preautodecrementing and memorizing the word, as in the instruction:

$$STA \quad , -S$$

and *pulling* (or popping) a word means recalling a word and postautoincrementing, as in the instruction:

$$LDA \quad ,S+$$

Special instructions, to be described in the next section, also push or pull words from this stack. The stack fills out, starting at high addresses and building toward lower addresses, in the stack buffer. If it builds into addresses lower than the stack buffer, a *stack overflow* error occurs, and if it is pulled too many times, a *stack underflow* occurs. If no such errors occur, then the stack has the property that the last word pushed onto it is the first word pulled from it, and is sometimes called a LIFO stack, or last-in-first-out stack.

The jump to subroutine instruction pushes the two-byte return address onto the stack, least significant byte first, and supplies a new value for the program counter using addressing modes available for the instruction, as in a jump instruction. The corresponding return from subroutine instruction pulls two words from the stack, putting them in the program counter. If nobody changes the stack pointer S, or if the net number of pushes equals the net number of pulls (the stack is said to be *balanced*) between the jump to subroutine and the corresponding return from subroutine, then the last instruction will cause the calling routine to resume exactly where it left off when it called the subroutine. This method of handling return addresses allows easy *nesting of subroutines*, whereby the main program jumps to a subroutine, say A, and subroutine A in turn jumps to subroutine B. When the main program jumps to subroutine A, it pushes the return address to the main program onto the stack. When A jumps to subroutine B, it pushes the return address of A onto the stack, on top (in lower memory words than) of the other return address. When B is completed, the address it pulls from the stack is the return address to subroutine A. When A is completed, the address it pulls from the stack is the return address to the main program. Hardware interrupts and the SWI instructions save return addresses and the contents of all the accumulators and index registers (the machine state) by pushing them onto the stack, and a *return from interrupt* instruction pulls them from the stack in reverse order.

The stack in the 6809 is a good place to store local data. It can also be used to supply arguments for a subroutine and return results from it, as discussed in a later section. To save local data, one can push it on the stack.

For instance, if accumulator A has value five, and accumulator B has value two, then after the instructions:

$$STA \quad , -S$$
$$STB \quad , -S$$

are executed, the top word on the stack, which is at the address in the stack pointer, is two, and the next word on the stack, which is at the next higher address, is five. To get the second word on the stack, one can use index addressing, as in:

$$LDA \quad 1,S$$

which will put the number five into accumulator A. Any number of words can be saved by pushing them onto the stack, and they can be recalled or rewritten in any order using index addressing with the S register. Also, they can be pulled from the stack in the reverse order from that in which they were pushed, using postautoincrement addressing with the S register. Moreover, if the subroutine is reentered (see near the end of section 1-1.1), the local data for the first execution of the subroutine is saved on the stack as new local data is pushed on top of it, and the new data is used by the second execution of the subroutine. When the first execution is resumed, it uses the old data. Keeping all local data on the stack this way ensures reentrancy. Note that the subroutine must pull as many words from the stack as it pushed before the return from subroutine instruction is executed or some data will be pulled by that instruction into the program counter—a particularly troublesome program bug.

The stack pointer S must be treated with respect. It should be initialized to point to the high address end of the stack buffer as soon as possible, right after power is turned on, and it should not be changed except by incrementing it or decrementing it to effectively push or pull words from it. Some programmers like to re-use data that has been already pulled from the stack, using an instruction like LDA $-2,S$. This is not safe. If an interrupt occurs, or if subroutines store return addresses or local variables on the stack, such words above the stack pointer will be written over. Words above the stack pointer must be considered garbage and may not be read after they are pulled. Some programmers like to move S to address good data, in order to read the data by pulling it. Woe to those programmers. The stack pointer will generally overwrite the good data with return addresses each time a subroutine is called, or an interrupt (either hardware or SWI) is serviced. Moreover, the tools used to analyze a faulty program (such as breakpoints and trace steps) use interrupts to store return addresses and registers. A program that mishandles the S register may not be able to use these tools to diagnose the faults in it.

One of the most significant features of the 6809 is its ability to use the

Table 1-2
Addressing Modes for the 6809

Address Mode	Example	Length	Use
Implied	SWI	1	Improve efficiency
Register	INCA	1	Improve efficiency
Immediate	LDA #1	2	Initialize registers, provide constant operands
Direct page	LDA ALPHA	2	Store global data (or improve efficiency)
Direct	LDA ALPHA	3	Access any word in memory
Pointer	LDA ,X	2	Improve efficiency
Index	LDA 5,X	2	Address arrays
	LDA $40,X	3	
	LDA ALPHA,X	4	
Index Using S	LDA 3,S	2	Access local data
Accumulator Index	LDA B,X	2	Address arrays
Page Relative	LDA ALPHA,PCR	3	Address local data
	BRA ALPHA	2	Improve efficiency
Long Relative	LDA ALPHA,PCR	4	Free program to be
	LBRA ALPHA	3	placed anywhere
Postautoincrement	LDA ,X+	2	Character strings, stacks
Preautodecrement	LDA ,−X	2	Access stacks
Indirect	LDA [ALPHA]	4	Move variables while running
Indirect Index (S)	LDA [3,S]	3	Improve static efficiency

stack pointer as an index register, with a five-, eight-, or sixteen-bit displacement. This feature makes access to local variables on the stack efficient. Other features of the 6809 make it easy to allocate room for these local variables and to initialize them and delete them. Further, if routine A calls routine B, then routine B can get the A's local variables on the stack by using a suitable offset. This technique is called *dynamic local access*, whereby a subroutine can use the local variables of the routine that calls it, or in general, of any routine that calls a routine, . . . , that calls it. Dynamic local access can even be used to get to the local variables of the main program, which would otherwise be global variables. You should use this concept of local and dynamic local variables on the stack to take full advantage of the 6809.

A final note on addressing concerns the use of indirect addressing with other modes. All modes (except direct page) in the 6809 can be supplemented by indirect addressing. Even implied addressing can be followed by indirect addressing, as when the SWI instruction implies the address of the subroutine, but jumps indirectly through the implied address at locations $FFFA and $FFFB. In general, as noted earlier, indirect addressing is denoted by putting square brackets around the address description of the instruction. A two-word address is always picked up from the location specified by the companion addressing mode and the next higher location, which is used as the effective address. If an address is pushed on the stack, a short instruction like:

$$LDA \quad [3,S]$$

can get a word into accumulator A, if the address is the third and fourth words from the top of the stack. Finally, indirect relative addressing can be used to access local data using a short instruction in a similar way.

1-2.2 6809 Instructions

We now focus on the instruction set of a von Neumann computer in general, and on the instructions in the 6809 in particular. The instructions are grouped together in this section in order to see the alternatives that are available. The lowly but important move instruction is discussed first. The arithmetic instructions and the logical instructions are covered next. Edit instructions, like shifts; control instructions, like jump; and finally, I/O instructions are covered in the remainder of this section.

The simplest is the *move* type of instruction, such as load and store. This type of instruction moves a word to or from a register in the controller or data operator from or to memory. Typically, a third of the instructions in a program are moves. If an architecture has good move instructions, it will have good efficiency for many benchmarks. Table 1-3 lists the move instructions for the 6809. It appears near the end of this section.

We have already discussed the LDA and STA instructions which are in this class. New instructions, PSH, PUL, TFR, EXG, and TST, are 6809 move instructions, and CLR and some instances of the LEA instruction are alternatives to these, so they are move instructions too. Since move instructions move data between controller and data operator registers and memory, it is a good idea to display all these registers first. See figure 1-3.

The load and store instructions can load or store any of the eight-bit registers A or B or the sixteen-bit registers X, Y, U, S, or D, using any of the addressing modes described in the last section. The instruction LDX ALPHA puts the words at locations $100 and $101 into the index register, LDU ,S puts the top two words on the stack in the U index register, and so on. Note that an accumulator or index register can be used in an addressing mode calculation even when that register itself is being changed by the instruction, because in the fetch-execute cycle, the addresses are calculated before the data from memory is recalled and loaded into the register. In particular, the instruction:

$$LDX \quad ,X$$

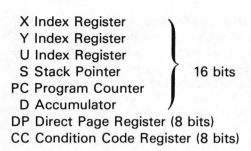

X Index Register
Y Index Register
U Index Register
S Stack Pointer   16 bits
PC Program Counter
D Accumulator
DP Direct Page Register (8 bits)
CC Condition Code Register (8 bits)

a. The Machine State

D is combined A Accumulator (8 bits) and B Accumulator (8 bits)
CC is E, F, H, I, N, Z, V, C Condition Code Bits

b. Breakdown of D and CC Registers

Figure 1-3. Registers in the 6809

is both legal and very useful. If X had the value $100 before the instruction is executed, the instruction gets two words from location $100 and $101, then puts them into the index register. Note that the richness of the addressing modes contributes greatly to the efficiency of the lowly but important move instructions.

The TFR instruction can move a word from any eight-bit register to any other eight-bit register, of the A, B, CC, and DP registers, or alternatively, from any sixteen-bit register to any other sixteen-bit register, of the X, Y, U, S, PC, and D registers. Similarly, the EXG instruction can exchange the two words in any pair of eight-bit registers, or in any pair of sixteen-bit registers. Consider these examples:

TFR   A,B

will move the word from accumulator A to accumulator B, without changing A.

EXG   X,Y

will exchange the contents of index registers X and Y.

The load and store instructions using autoincrement or autodecrement addressing with the S register, can push or pull data on the stack. The PSHS instruction is capable of pushing from one to eight registers on the stack, and the PULS instruction is likewise capable of pulling from one to eight registers from the stack, all in just one instruction. The registers are selected by naming them as operands, and are pushed in a given order—PC, U, Y, X, DP, B, A, CC—regardless of the order they are written as operands, and are pulled in exactly the reverse order by the PULS instruction, regardless of the order of its operands. For instance:

PSHS   A,X

will push the index register X first, least significant byte first, then will push accumulator A. The instruction:

PULS   A,Y

could then pull these words from the stack, putting the top word in accumulator A, and putting the next two words in index register Y. These two instructions make it easy to save registers and restore them, and to set up local variables on the stack. The U index register can also be used like the S register, in the instructions PSHU and PULU. Motorola calls the U index register a user "stack pointer." When we discuss data structures, however, we will point out that the U register is not a particularly good stack pointer, and it can be better used as an index register. Rather, because it is not safe to move the stack pointer S, the U index register can be used when you are tempted to use the stack pointer. For instance, U can point to a few words, and the PULU instruction can be used to load these words into the selected registers, in order to initialize them quickly.

The LEA instructions (LEAX, LEAY, and so forth) are not found in most computers, but are a magnificent little gem in the 6809. They calculate an effective address, using any addressing mode except the first five in table 1-2, but put the effective address in an index register (X, if LEAX or Y if LEAY, and so on), rather than using it to recall a word. Using pointer addressing, or using any form of indirect addressing, it is effectively an instruction to load an index register. For example,

LEAX   ,Y

will put the number in Y into X, and the instruction:

LEAU   [, − −X]

will decrement X by two, then put the word it points to into U. The instruction LDU , − − X will do practically the same thing, though.

The load and store instructions change the condition codes, which can be used in conditional branch instructions. The N bit is set if the moved word is negative and is cleared it if it positive. The Z bit is set if the moved word is zero, and cleared otherwise. The LEAX and LEAY change the Z bit only. The other move instructions discussed above do not change the codes. If you want to set the condition codes as in a load instruction, but you are not particularly interested in moving the word to an accumulator, then the TST instruction can be used. It is like half a load instruction. Finally, as a load instruction with an immediate operand is used to initialize registers, since most initial values are zero, a separate instruction CLR is provided. It may be used rather than LDA#0 to improve efficiency.

The *arithmetic* instructions add, subtract, multiply, or divide the value of the accumulator with the value of a word taken from memory. The 6809 has arithmetic instructions to be used with eight-bit registers, and some arithmetic instructions to be used with sixteen-bit registers. The eight-bit arithmetic instructions are discussed first, then the sixteen-bit instructions. Table 1-4 lists these arithmetic instructions.

The basic eight-bit ADD instruction can add any word from memory into either accumulator A or accumulator B. The instruction is straight-forward, except for the setting of condition codes. The same instruction is used for unsigned additions as for two's complement additions; only the testing of the codes differs between the unsigned and two's complement cases. For example:

ADDA   ALPHA

will add the contents of the accumulator A to word $100 of memory and put the result into accumulator A. Usually, the result is one bit wider than the operands, and the extra leftmost bit is put into the carry flip-flop. For unsigned numbers, the carry is often considered as an overflow indicator; if the carry is one, the result in the accumulator is incorrect because when the word is put back into the (eight-bit wide) memory, the extra ninth bit in the

Table 1-3
6809 Move Instructions

LDA	STA	TFR	LEAS	CLR A
LDB	STB	EXG	LEAX	CLR B
LDD	STD	PSHS	LEAU	CLR
LDX	STX	PULS	LEAY	TST A
LDY	STY	PSHU		TST B
LDS	STS	PULU		TST

carry will not fit and so the result in memory will be incorrect. Also, the carry is used to implement multiple precision arithmetic, which is very important in a microcomputer, as will be discussed shortly. The N and Z condition codes are set just as in the load and store instructions, to reflect that the result of the addition is negative or zero. A half-carry bit is set in this instruction, which is used in decimal arithmetic (to be discussed shortly), and the overflow bit V is set to one if the result is erroneous as a two's complement number. A two's complement overflow will occur if the two numbers being added have the same sign and the result has a different sign. Have you ever added two positive numbers and got a negative number? That's an overflow. Or if you add two negative numbers and get a positive number, that too is an overflow. But if you add two numbers of different signs, an overflow cannot occur. In using these condition codes in branch instructions, we must be careful to test the carry bit after an unsigned binary add, and not the overflow bit, since the carry bit is set if an unsigned overflow occurs, and we must remember to test the overflow bit V after a two's complement add, because it is set if the result is in fact erroneous as a two's complement number.

The *add with carry* instruction ADC is used to effect multiple precision arithmetic. It adds a number from memory into the accumulator and sets the condition codes, as in the ADD instruction, but it also adds in the old value of the carry flip-flop in the least significant bit position. To add the sixteen-bit number at ALPHA (most significant byte at $100 and least significant byte at $101) to a sixteen-bit number at BETA (where BETA is the symbolic address for location $102, most significant byte at $102 and least significant byte at $103), we can execute this program segment:

LDA	ALPHA	GET LEAST SIGNIFICANT BYTE OF FIRST WORD
ADDA	BETA	ADD TO LEAST SIGNIFICANT BYTE OF SECOND.
STA	BETA	PUT BACK IN THE SECOND WORD
LDA	ALPHA + 1	GET MOST SIGNIFICANT BYTE OF FIRST WORD
ADCA	BETA + 1	ADD TO MOST SIGNIFICANT BYTE OF SECOND.
STA	BETA + 1	PUT BACK IN SECOND WORD

(Note that for longer programs, we put comments on the right hand side of each instruction. The reader should develop the habit of writing comments on each line in his program so it can be easily understood later.) In this program segment, the ADD instruction generates a carry, stored in the C condition code bit. The STA and LDA instructions do not change this bit. The ADCA instruction adds the number at BETA + 1 to accumulator A, adds the carry bit in the least significant position, and then produces a new carry to put into the C bit, which is the carry from this add operation. Note that the ADDA instruction might set the carry bit, as if an unsigned overflow occurred, and might set the Z, V, and N bits too, but these are not important and should be ignored. These condition codes are changed again by the ADCA instruction, and they indicate the true sign and overflow bits which should be tested by conditional branch instructions.

The 6809, like most microcomputers, has a similar set of subtract instructions. The instruction:

SUBA   ALPHA

subtracts the word at location $100 from accumulator A, and sets the condition codes as follows. N, Z, and V are set to indicate a negative result, zero result, or two's complement overflow, as in the ADD instruction. The carry flip-flop is actually the borrow indicator; it is set if subtraction requires a borrow from the next higher byte, or if an unsigned underflow error exists because the result, a negative number, cannot be represented as an unsigned number. The *subtract with carry* SBC instruction is used exactly like the ADC instruction to implement multiple precision subtraction.

Subtraction is often used to compare two numbers, sometimes just to see if they are equal. The results are tested in conditional branch instructions. If we are comparing a given number against several numbers, to avoid reloading the given number, we can leave it in an accumulator, and use a *compare* instruction such as CMPA. This instruction is just like the subtract instruction, but it does not change the accumulator so the number in it can be compared to other numbers in later instructions. The condition codes are changed and can be tested by conditional branch instructions. Note, however, that there is no compare with carry instruction to be used with multiple precision comparison; the SBC instruction is used for this application.

Because we often add or subtract just the constant one, or negate a two's complement number, special short instructions are provided to improve efficiency. The instructions INC, DEC, and NEG, can increment, decrement, or negate either accumulator or any word in memory. An unusual quirk of the INC and the DEC instructions: they do not change the carry bit like the add instructions. This makes them useful to count out executions of a "DO LOOP" that has an add operation inside it so that the carry from one execution of the add instruction will not be destroyed by the INC or DEC instructions which allows it to be used in the next execution of the add instruction in the loop. The carry is not needed anyway, since the carry is set after an INC exactly when the Z bit is set, and after a DEC instruction when the number being decremented was zero just before the instruction was executed. Adding a number to itself, that is, doubling it, is an arithmetic left shift ASL, and dividing a two's complement number by two, halving it, is an arithmetic right shift, ASR. The condition codes for ASL are set just as if you had indeed added the number to itself, and the ASR instruction sets N and Z as in the move instructions and shifts the low order bit that is shifted out of the word into the C bit. These edit instructions are also arithmetic instructions, and can be applied to either accumulator or any word in memory.

Two special instructions act on the accumulators only. They enable us to multiply two unsigned eight-bit numbers and to add numbers using the binary coded decimal number representation (BCD). To multiply two eight-bit unsigned numbers, put them in accumulators A and B, and execute the MUL instruction. The sixteen-bit result will be left, most significant byte in accumulator A and least significant byte in accumulator B. To execute arithmetic on binary coded decimal numbers, that is, on two BCD numbers in the left four bits and right four bits of a word, add them with the ADDA instruction or the ADCA instruction, followed immediately by the DAA (decimal adjust accumulator A) instruction. DAA uses the carry and half carry to correct the number so that the sum is the BCD sum of the two numbers being added. Note, however, that accumulator A is an implied address for DAA, and the half carry is only changed by the ADD and ACD instructions, so the DAA instruction only works after the ADDA and ADCA instructions.

The 6809 has several sixteen-bit arithmetic instructions. ADDD will add two words from memory (as if recalled by the LDD instruction) to the D accumulator; SUBD and CMPD will likewise subtract and compare a sixteen-bit number from memory to the D accumulator. These instructions are very useful for sixteen-bit arithmetic, but the eight-bit arithmetic instructions can implement multiple precision arithmetic to handle twenty-four-bit, thirty-two-bit, or forty-bit numbers.

Those marvelous LEA instructions, using index or relative addressing, can add to an index register. For example to increment X, we execute:

LEAX   1,X

but we can add any number to X, instead of one, using this instruction. Note that incrementing S is equivalent to popping words off the stack (destroying them) and decrementing S is equivalent to pushing garbage words onto the stack; these operations are very useful for making room for local variables from the stack at the beginning of a subroutine and deleting them at the end of a subroutine, respectively. For example, the instruction:

LEAS   5,S

will pop five words from the stack, presumably to balance the stack before executing the return from subroutine by popping all the local variables at once. Accumulator index addressing can add variables to an index register. The instruction:

LEAX A,Y

computes an address using the accumulator index mode, adding accumulator A to index register Y, considering both as two's complement numbers, and then puts this number in index register X. On the other hand, the instruction ABX adds the number in accumulator B to index register X, but considers the numbers as unsigned numbers rather than signed numbers in the way that it expands the eight-bit number in accumulator B.

Finally, some computers that have more than one accumulator provide instructions to add one of them to another to improve efficiency. In fact, the 6800 has an instruction, ABA, to add B to A. This type of instruction is missing in the 6809. Rather, the contents of one register can be pushed on the stack, then pulled and added to the other, as in:

PSHS B
ADDA ,S+

Note that instructions other than add can be used, and that an index register can be pushed and added to the D accumulator in a similar way.

A third group of instructions is the *logical* group. See table 1-5. The instruction:

ANDA ALPHA

will logically "and," bit by bit, word $100 in memory to the accumulator. We can "and" into either accumulator A or accumulator B. For example, if the word at location $100 were 01101010 and accumulator A were 11110000, then after such an instruction is executed the result in accumulator A will be

Table 1-4
6809 Arithmetic Instructions

On Accumulators A or B	On Accumulators or Memory	On Sixteen-Bit Registers
ADD	INC	ADDD
ADC	DEC	SUBD
SUB	NEG	CMPD
SBC	ASL	LEAX (and the like)
CMP	ASR	CMPX (and the like)
	(Special: DAA MUL)	ADX

01100000. A "bit test" instruction BIT "ands" an accumulator with a word recalled from memory, but only sets the condition codes and does not change the accumulator. It may be used, like the CMP instructions, to compare a word without destroying it to many words recalled from memory to check to see if some of their bits are all zero. The "and" instruction AND, the "or" instruction ORA, the "bit test" instruction BIT, and the "exclusive or" instruction EOR can work with either accumulator and any word in memory. The complement instruction COM will complement each bit in the accumulator or any word in memory.

The condition codes are often set or cleared. The interrupt mask bit, I, may be set to prevent interrupts and cleared to allow them. The carry bit is sometimes used at the end of a subroutine to signal a special condition to the routine it returns to, and is sometimes cleared before the instructions ADC or SBC, so it is often set or cleared. Therefore, special logical instructions, ORCC and ANDCC, can "or" or "and" a word into the condition code registers instead of one of the accumulators. Also, a special control instruction, clear and wait for interrupt, CWAI will "and" an operand into the condition code register before stopping the computer in anticipation of an interrupt.

The next class of instructions is the *edit* instructions. These rearrange the bits of data without otherwise changing them. The edit instructions in the 6809 are shown in table 1-6, and except for SEX, they can be used to shift or rotate either accumulator or a word in memory that is selected by any of the addressing modes. Most microcomputers have similar shift instructions. A right logical shift, LSRA, will shift the bits in the accumulator right one position, filling a zero bit into the leftmost bit and putting the old rightmost bit into the C condition code register. Similarly, a logical left shift LSLA will shift left, into the C bit, filling with zero. A machine will generally have several different left and right shifts. The 6809 also has arithmetic shifts corresponding to doubling and halving a two's complement number, as discussed in the arithmetic instruction group. However, though there are different mnemonics for each, the LSLA and ASLA instructions do the same thing and have the same machine code. The rotate instructions ROLA

Table 1-5
6809 Logical Instructions

On Accumulators A or B	Special
EOR	COM
ORA	ORCC
AND	ANDCC
BIT	CWAI

and RORA shift in a circular way the nine bits in accumulator A and the
carry bit C one bit to the left, or the right, respectively. They are very useful
for multiple word shifts. For example, to shift the sixteen-bit word in accumulator D (accumulators A and B) one bit right, filling with a zero, we
can execute the program sequence:

LSRA

RORB

The RORB instruction rotates the bit shifted out of accumulator A, which is
held in the C condition code bit, into accumulator B. Since an eight-bit
word is rather inadequate, multiple precision shifting is common in
microcomputers, and the RORA and ROLA instructions are very important. Also, for this reason, microcomputers do not have the multiple shift
instructions like LSRA 5, which would shift accumulator A right five bits
in one instruction. Such an instruction would require saving five bits in the
condition code registers to implement multiple precision shifts. That is too
messy to use, in general. Rather, a loop is set up so that inside the loop one
bit is shifted throughout the whole multiple precision word, and the loop is
executed as many times as the number of bits is to be shifted.

Some computers have more complex edit instructions than the shifts
discussed above, such as instructions to format strings of output characters
for printing. The 6809 has another edit instruction of moderate complexity,
sign extend SEX. This instruction copies the most significant bit of accumulator B into each bit of accumulator A, so that the D accumulator will
have the same two's complement value as the B accumulator had before.

The fifth group of instructions are the *control* instructions that affect
the program counter. See table 1-7. These instructions are very important in
any computer, and are especially important in microcomputers because of
the high cost of memory compared to the cost of the processor. Next to
move instructions, conditional branches are most common, so their performance has a strong impact on the performance of a computer. Also,
microcomputers having such a limited instruction set that is missing such
operations as floating point arithmetic, multiple word shifts, and high level
language (FORTRAN) operations, these "instructions" are implemented as
subroutines to save memory space, rather than as macros. The machine

Table 1-6
6809 Edit Instructions

ASL	LSL	ROL	SEX
ASR	LSR	ROR	

code that is produced by a FORTRAN compiler, in particular, is full of subroutine calls, and very little else. Unconditional jumps and no-operations are considered first, then the conditional branches are considered, and finally the subroutine calls and related instructions will be scrutinized.

The left column of table 1-7 shows unconditional jumps. As noted earlier, the JMP instruction can use any addressing mode, but the effective address is put in the program counter. BRA is preferred because it is shorter, and BRA and LBRA use relative addressing, which may be preferred for position independent code which allows the program to execute properly anywhere in memory. The TFR instruction that moves the number in a sixteen-bit register to PC is also a jump instruction. A rather interesting instruction, SKIP2, unconditionally skips over one or two words, which might be executed as instructions if a jump were made directly to these words. The CMPX instruction using immediate addressing will act this way, except that it will change the condition codes, although that may not be a problem. An example of the use of SKIP2 is given shortly. The *no-operation* instructions do absolutely nothing. Why have them, you may ask? In programs that send signals to the "outside world," real-time programming may use the time to execute a program segment to time the length of a pulse. These instructions provide specific delays for that purpose. NOP delays two memory cycles; branch never, BRN, takes three; and long branch never, LBRN, takes five. Also, if we test a program, these instructions can be put in where we will later insert other instructions, to save room for them.

The 6809 has only conditional branch and conditional long branch instructions, rather than conditional jumps or conditional subroutine calls and conditional subroutine returns (as does the 8080). The conditional (long) branch tests one or more condition codes and branches to another location specified by the displacement if the condition is true, using page (or long) relative addressing.

A set of simple branches can test any one of the condition codes, branching if the bit is set or else branching if it is clear. For example, BCC L will branch to location L if the carry bit is clear, while BCS L will branch there if the carry bit is set. Another set of branches tests combinations of condition codes that indicate two's complement inequalities. This set tests combinations of the Z, N, and V bits. The last set of branches tests combinations of the Z and C bits, to test unsigned number inequalities.

The branches in the second column of table 1-7 test each condition code separately. The (L)BMI and (L)BPL instructions check, the sign bit, and should be used after a load, store, or test instruction to check the sign of a two's complement number that was moved. The (L)BCC and (L)BCS instructions test the carry bit, which indicates an overflow after adding unsigned numbers, or the bit shifted out after a shift instruction. The (L) BVS and (L)BVC instruction tests the V condition code, which is set if an overflow occurs on adding two's complement numbers. The Z bit is also tested easily by an instruction, but since we often execute a compare instruction to set the Z bit if the two numbers are compared as equal, the instruction is called (L)BEQ and the complementary instruction is (L)BNE. These last two instructions are also used in the two's complement and unsigned number branches discussed below.

The branches listed in the middle column of table 1-7 are used after a compare (or subtract) instruction to sense the inequalities of the two numbers being compared as two's complement numbers. The program sequence below shows an example of the branch on greater than instruction, as well as the SKIP2 instruction:

CMPA	ALPHA	COMPARE ACCUMULATOR A TO ALPHA
BGT	L	BRANCH TO L IF ACCUMULATOR A > ALPHA
LDB	#$10	OTHERWISE PUT $10 IN B
SKIP2		AND EXECUTE CMPX #, TO SKIP NEXT 2 WORDS
L LDB	#$20	IF BRANCHED, PUT $20 IN B

If the two's complement number in accumulator A is greater than the number at location ALPHA, then the branch is taken, putting $20 in accumulator B and going onward. If the two's complement number in accumulator A is less than or equal to the number in location ALPHA, the branch instruction is a no-operation (like BRN) and the next instruction is executed, which puts $10 into accumulator B. The next instruction, shown here as SKIP2, is actually the CMPX immediate instruction (which can be generated by a FCB $9C directive, discussed in section 1-3.1), which effectively skips over the instruction LDB $20 by picking both words up as if they were the immediate operand of the CMPX instruction. After this instruction is executed, the rest of the program below this segment is executed, exactly as if the branch were taken and LDB $20 were executed.

The fourth column of table 1-7 shows an equivalent set of branches that sense inequalities between unsigned numbers. By putting BHI in place of BGT in the segment above, one could compare the unsigned numbers in accumulator A against the number at location ALPHA, putting $20 in accumulator B if the register were higher than the word, otherwise putting $10 in accumulator B. The unsigned conditional instructions test combinations of the C and Z bits, and should only be used after a compare of subtract instruction to sense the inequalities of unsigned numbers. To test two's complement numbers after a compare, use the branches in the middle column of table 1-7, and to test the signs of numbers after a load, store, or test, use the BPL or BMI instructions.

As a memory aide in using these conditional branch instructions, remember that signed numbers are greater than or less than, and unsigned numbers are higher than or lower than (SGUH). Also, when comparing any register with a word from memory a branch like BGT branches if the *register is (greater than) the memory word*.

Conditional branches are used in *DO-loops*. A DO-loop repeats a given program segment a given number, say *n*, times. Consider moving 128 words from one area of memory to another, and suppose that index register X points to the lowest address of the area the words are moved from, while Y points to the lowest address of the area the words are moved to.

	LDA	#128	ACCUMULATOR A IS USED AS A COUNTER
L	LDB	,X +	GET A WORD FROM FIRST AREA
	STB	,Y +	PUT THE WORD IN THE SECOND AREA
	DECA		COUNT DOWN
	BNE	L	LOOP 128 TIMES

Note that the first execution of the loop moves the lowest addressed word from the first area to the second area, and increments both pointer registers. The DECA instruction will change accumulator A from $80 to $7F. Since the result is not zero, the BNE instruction will effect a branch to location L, which repeats the loop. Note that the loop is executed $80 times if $80 is put into the accumulator that is used as a counter. An instruction like LDA #$80 is called a *loop initialization*, and instructions like DECA and BNE L are *loop control* program segments. The initialization and control instructions in the example above are used very often, because an accumulator is quite useful as a counter. Alternatively, an index register can be used because it is a sixteen-bit register, or a word in memory can be used if the accumulators are in heavy use. Further, the loop control can use a compare instruction, like CMPX, to test the index register to stop looping when the register points to a final address.

When writing machine code, many programmers have difficulty with relative branch instructions that branch backwards. The technique we found useful is to use sixteen's complement arithmetic to determine the negative number used in the displacement in the branch instruction. The sixteen's complement is to hexadecimal numbers as the two's complement is to binary numbers. The program shown above is listed in machine code below, to illustrate this technique. The program begins at location $200, and the address of each word is shown on the left with the value shown on the right in each line. All numbers are in hexadecimal.

$$
\begin{array}{ll}
200 & 86 \\
201 & 80 \\
202 & E6 \\
203 & 80 \\
204 & A7 \\
205 & A0 \\
206 & 4A \\
207 & 26 \\
208 & xx \\
\end{array}
$$

The displacement used in the branch instruction, the last instruction in the program, is shown as xx. It can be determined as follows. When the branch is executed, the program counter has the value 209, and we want to jump back to location 202. The difference, $209 - $202, is $07, so the displacement should be $- $07. A safe way to calculate the displacement is to convert to binary, negate, then convert to hexadecimal. $07 is 00000111, so the two's complement negative is 11111001. In hexadecimal, this is $F9. That is not hard to see, but binary arithmetic gets rather tedious. A faster way takes the *sixteen's complement* of the hexadecimal number. Just subtract each digit from $F (fifteen), digit by digit, then add one to the whole thing. $- $07 is then ($F - 0), ($F - 7) + 1 or $F8 + 1, which is $F9. That is pretty easy, is it not?

Another important use of conditional branches is the *decision tree*. A rather complex set of tests is often used to determine what to do next. For example, if we want to go to location L1 if index register X is less than $300 and accumulator A is negative, to L2 if X is less than $300 and A is positive, to L3 if X is $300, to L4 if X is greater than $300 and accumulator B is 3, to L5 if X is greater than $300 and B is 6, and to L6 if X is greater than $300 and B is neither 3 nor 6, the program on the next page can be used.

In order to show the flow of control, *flow charts* are often used. A diamond shows a two-way branch or a three-way branch on an arithmetic comparison. Rectangles show program segments. Lines into the top of a diamond or rectangle show which program segments can precede this one, and lines on the bottom of a rectangle show program segments that follow this segment. If a segment is on another page, its label can be shown in a circle. The decision tree shown on the following page can be nicely described as the flow chart in figure 1-4.

	CMPX	#$300	CHECK X AGAINST $300
	BEQ	L3	IF EQUAL, GO TO L3
	BMI	T1	IF LESS, TEST A
	CMPB	#3	IT IS POSITIVE; IF B IS 3
	BEQ	L4	GO TO L4
	CMPB	#6	SEE IF IT IS 6
	BEQ	L5	IF SO, GO TO L5
	BRA	L6	OTHERWISE GO TO L6
T1	TSTA		X IS NEGATIVE; TEST A
	BMI	L1	IF A NEGATIVE, GO TO L1
	BRA	L2	OTHERWISE, A IS MORE, GO TO L2

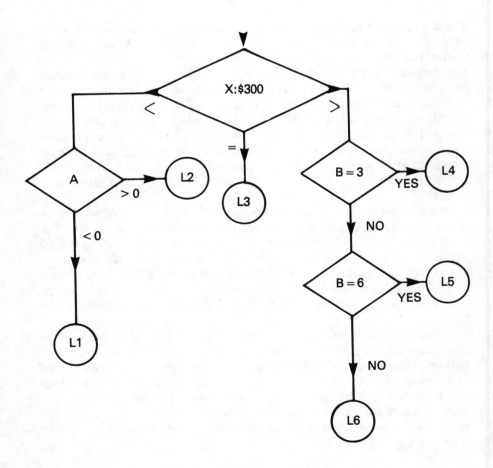

Figure 1-4. A Flow Chart

Flow charts are especially important where complex decision trees are used to analyze data. They are also useful in all programs, and some believe that a flow chart must be written before any part of the program is written. We believe that to be true whenever more than about a hundred lines of code are to be written. In many of the programs used in interfacing, however, comments on each assembler line of code are more useful than flow charts to document the program well. We will be using comments in this book more than flow charts because most segments we write are rather short. Nevertheless, we encourage the reader to write flow charts for longer programs, and for short programs that implement complex decision trees.

The rightmost column of table 1-7 shows subroutine jumps and similar instructions. As with the JMP, the JSR may be replaced either by BSR, which is shorter, or LBSR, which allows position independent code. These instructions not only reload the program counter, but they save its former value, which points to the instruction right below the JSR/BSR/LBSR instruction on the stack. A RTS instruction is used at the end of a subroutine to return to that instruction below the JSR/BSR/LBSR. An interesting variation uses the EXG instruction to exchange the program counter with any index register. The JMP 0,X instruction is used to return to the calling program from the subroutine.

The PULS instruction is able to pull the return address into the program counter to effect a return from subroutine while also returning other values to registers. This makes it easy to save the contents of registers on the stack when you enter and restore them as you return from a subroutine. For example, if the first instruction is PSHS A,X, and the last instruction is PULS A,X,PC, then the registers A and X are saved and restored.

The *software interrupt* instruction (SWI) is a one word "jump to subroutine." This instruction is actually equivalent to the following program segment:

```
        PSHS  CC,A,B,DP,X,Y,U,PC  SAVE ALL REGISTERS
                                  EXCEPT S
        LDX   L,PCR               GET RETURN ADDRESS (POSITION
                                  INDEPENDENT)
        STX   10,S                PUT IN PLACE OF PC SAVED
                                  BY PSHS
        JMP   [$FFF8]
L       NOP
```

(The NOP is not needed, but stands for the next instruction after the SWI instruction.)

The SWI instruction is very useful for testing programs as a *breakpoint*. A breakpoint is used to stop a program that is being tested and to execute a *monitor* program that examines or changes the contents of registers or memory words. Being one word long, it can be inserted in place of any instruction. Suppose we tried to use a JSR instruction to jump to the monitor to replace a single length instruction like INCA, and suppose that the instruction just below the replaced instruction was also jumped to from somewhere else. Since the instruction just below has to be replaced by the second word of the JSR instruction, if the jump to that instruction occurred from somewhere else, it would jump into the middle of the JSR instruction and do some damage. This is a difficult problem to resolve, especially since a breakpoint is often used in a program that does not work right in the first place. A SWI instruction can be used without fear that some jump instruction might happen to jump into the second word, which might happen if the instruction were longer. Saving all the registers automatically, this instruction makes it easy to analyze these registers by examining the top twelve words on the stack. However, this marvelous trick does not work if the program is in read-only memory, because an instruction in that memory cannot be replaced by the SWI instruction.

The SWI instruction is also useful as a convenient subroutine call to execute input/output operations and other complex "instructions" like floating point add. Such a subroutine can be modified and moved, so long as the words in locations $FFF8 and $FFF9 point to the beginning of the subroutine, because the routines that call this subroutine do not have to be modified when the subroutine is changed and moved. A single SWI instruction can be used both for breakpoints and for short special subroutine calls. This is done on the 6800, but the 6809 provides two more instructions for convenient subroutine calls, SWI2 and SWI3. These are exactly like SWI, except they are two words long (and they do not mask interrupts by clearing the I condition code bit, while SWI does this) and they jump indirectly through locations $FFF4 and $FFF5 for SWI2 and $FFF2 and $FFF3 for SWI3. Motorola urges us to use SWI3 for subroutine calls to "packaged software" and to leave SWI2 for subroutine calls written by the "end user." SWI can then be used for breakpoints and only for breakpoints. However, Motorola's current (1979) software for the 6809 (MDOS09) seems to be using only SWI for all functions, not taking advantage of the new instructions SWI2 and SWI3 because they are not used in the 6800. This is done to maintain compatibility with current 6800 programs. Nevertheless, newer software should use the three SWI instructions for different purposes to take full advantage of the machine.

I/O interrrupts on the 6809 will be further discussed in chapter 4. The instructions SYNC and CWAI are used to synchronize the 6809 to interrupts and to wait for them. These will also be discussed there. In this discussion, it is useful to compare I/O interrupts with the SWI instruction. Like SWI, they save the state of the machine, then jump indirectly through locations $FFFC,$FFFD or $FFF8,$FFF9, or $FFF6,$FFF7. The condition code bits E, F, and I govern these interrupts. They will be discussed further in chapter 4.

After completion of a routine that is entered by any SWI or hardware interrupt, the last instruction to be executed is return from interrupt (RTI). It pulls the top twelve words from the stack replacing them in the registers that the interrupt took them from. In particular, RTS should never be used after such a routine. This is a common error, in our opinion, and should always be checked when interrupts and SWIs do not seem to work. (Some slight modifications to the RTI instruction will be discussed in chapter 4.)

The sixth class of instructions is the I/O group. There are a wide variety of approaches used for I/O instructions. Generally, there are word-sized registers in the I/O devices and control logic in them. There are instructions to transfer a word from the accumulator to the register in the I/O device; to transfer a word from the register to the accumulator; and to start, stop, and test the control logic for the device. In the 6800 and 6809 architectures, there are no special I/O instructions; rather I/O registers appear as words in primary memory (*memory mapped I/O*). The LDA instruction serves to input a word from an input register, and STA serves to output a word. Moreover, instructions like INC ALPHA, if ALPHA is the location of a (readable) output register, will modify that register in place so the word is not brought into the accumulator to modify it. CLR, ASR (which happens to be a test and set instruction needed to coordinate multiple processors), and DEC can operate directly on (readable) output registers in a memory mapped I/O architecture. Indirect addressing can be used by programs in read-only memory so that they can work with I/O registers even if those registers are at variable locations. The indirect address can be in read-write memory, and can be changed to the address of the I/O device. That way, a

Table 1-7
6809 Control Instructions

| | | Conditional | | |
Unconditional	Simple	Two's Complement	Unsigned	Subroutine
JMP	(L) BEQ	(L) BGT	(L) BHI	JSR
(L) BRA	(L) BNE	(L) BGE	(L) BHS	(L) BSR
TFR X,PC	(L) BMI	(L) BEQ	(L) BEQ	RTS
SKIP2	(L) BPL	(L) BLE	(L) BLS	PULS . . ., PC
NOP	(L) BCS	(L) BLT	(L) BLO	SWI
(L) BRN	(L) BCC			SWI2
	(L) BVS			SWI3
	(L) BVC			RTI
				SYNC
				CWAI

program in a read-only memory can be used in systems with different I/O configurations. This makes feasible the production of more inexpensive read-only memory software. This aspect of the architecture is centrally important to this book, and will be dealt with extensively in later chapters.

1-2.3 6800 Instructions

If the reader has reason to study the 6800 as well as the 6809, this section is offered to show some of the programming considerations for the former machine. This study is useful because several inexpensive microprocessors are available from Motorola that have the same architecture as the 6800, or are quite similar. These include the 6801 single-chip microcomputer, the 6802, the 6803, and 6808. These machines are particularly useful in minimal cost systems and are therefore the microprocessors chosen for many interface designs. Moreover, it is often necessary to convert a program written for one machine to run it on another machine. This is quite simple on machines like the 6809 and 6800 that are quite similar, but it does illustrate the problem of rewriting software. For this reason several problems at the end of each chapter are offered in which a program shown in the chapter is to be rewritten for the 6800; therefore, the reader may wish to study the 6800 too. This section and the problems that deal with the 6800 may be skipped, however, without sacrificing any important concepts of the principles and practices of microprocessor interfacing.

This section contrasts the 6800 and the 6809. Since the 6809 is upward compatible to the 6800, we will concentrate on the missing instructions and addressing modes of the 6800 that were put into the 6809. For a complete list of instructions, *The Complete Motorola Microcomputer Data Library* should be consulted. As in the former sections, we stress that the best way to learn the 6800 is to write programs for it. This section will just discuss some aspects of the 6800 instruction set that might not be too obvious, yet might be very useful.

The 6800 has a smaller set of registers, shown in figure 1-5. Note that only one index register X is available rather than the X, Y, and U registers of the 6809. Index addressing is only available with this register X and is not available with the stack pointer S. S points to the first free word above (at lower address than) the top word on the stack. Only an eight-bit unsigned number displacement is used in index addressing; autoincrement/autodecrement and zero-, five-, eight-, and sixteen-bit signed displacements are not available. Direct page addressing is fixed to page zero on the 6800, and indirect addressing and page and long relative addressing are not available (except that all conditional jumps are page relative conditional branches). Finally, only accumulators A and B can be pushed and pulled; the index register, in particular, cannot be pushed or pulled by one

A Accumulator

B Accumulator   } 8 bits

CC Condition Codes

X Index Register   } 16 bits

PC Program Counter

a. Registers

Condition Codes are 1, 1, H, I, N, V, C where 1 is the constant 1 bit (not changed)

b. Expansion of the CC Register

Figure 1-5. The 6800 Machine State

instruction; and MUL is not available. Fixes to these limitations are discussed below.

Before we show the missing instructions, we discuss some instructions in the 6800 that are not in the same form in the 6809 and that are particularly useful in building macros or subroutines in the 6800 to replace its missing instructions. These are the SWI, TSX, and INS, INX, DES, and DEX instructions.

The SWI instruction in the 6800 is very useful for fixing up the instruction set. It pushes the program counter and then the index register, least significant bytes first, then the accumulators A and then B, and finally the condition code register CC. The 6800 uses LDAA, LDAB, STAA, and STAB rather than LDA, LDB, STA, and STB used in the 6809. This is only a change in the instruction name, and not in the behavior of the instruction. The instruction TSX in the 6800 is equivalent to the TFR S,X instruction in the 6809; it transfers the contents of the stack pointer to the index register. (Since S points to the next free word above the stack, TSX adds one to S, and puts that in X, so that after the TSX instruction, X points to the top word on the stack.) TSX permits the index addressing modes, available only with the index register, to be used to pick up words from the stack. In particular, after an SWI instruction is executed, and a TSX instruction inside the SWI handler "subroutine" is executed, the instruction:

LDAA   0,X

will put into accumulator A the old value of the condition code register that was saved by the SWI instruction. Using an offset of one rather than zero in the LDA instruction will get the value of accumulator B, using two will get accumulator A, using three will get the high byte of the index register, using four will get its low byte, using five will get the high byte of the program counter, and using six will get the low byte of the program counter that was saved by the SWI instruction. Finally, the 6800 instruction INX is equivalent to the 6809 instruction LEAX 1,X: it increments the index register. INX is actually shorter than LEAX 1,X, being just one byte, but the instruction LEAX 3,X in the 6809 is just as long as the LEAX 1,X instruction in the 6809, while in the 6800 it must be replaced by three INX instructions. Similarly, DEX decrements the index register, INS increments the stack pointer (to delete words from the stack), and DES decrements the stack pointer.

In the following discussions, either an SWI instruction or a subroutine that uses temporary storage words can be used. The use of direct or page addressed temporary storage is generally faster, but is not reentrant, whereas the use of SWI can always be made reentrant because by pushing the registers on the stack it effectively allocates local storage for them on the stack. As an example of these two approaches, consider the replacements for the 6809 instruction ABX, which adds accumulator B to index register X. Using three consecutive temporary storage words at locations TEMP to TEMP + 2, the following subroutine (called by a JSR ABX instruction) can be executed:

```
ABX   STAB   TEMP + 2   SAVE B TO RESTORE AT END
      STX    TEMP       PUT X IN TEMPORARY STORAGE
                        WORDS
      ADDB   TEMP + 1   ADD LOW BYTE TO AC-
                        CUMULATOR B
      STAB   TEMP + 1   PUT BACK LOW BYTE
      LDAB   TEMP       GET HIGH BYTE
      ADCB   #0         ADD CARRY IF GENERATED BY
                        ADDB
      STAB   TEMP       PUT HIGH BYTE BACK
      LDX    TEMP       PUT TWO WORDS IN INDEX
                        REGISTER
      LDAB   TEMP + 2   RESTORE ACCUMULATOR B
      RTS               RETURN FROM SUBROUTINE
```

(The condition codes are not correctly set up in the above replacement, but that is not usually a problem.) Now consider the use of an SWI instruction and look at the SWI handler "subroutine" that follows:

ABXX	TSX		X POINTS TO THE TOP OF THE STACK
	LDAA	4,X	A HAS LOW BYTE OF OLD VALUE OF X
	ADDA	1,X	ADD OLD VALUE OF B
	STAA	4,X	PUT BACK INTO LOW BYTE OF X
	BCC	L	IF NO CARRY SKIP OVER
	INC	3,X	INCREMENTING HIGH BYTE OF OLD X
L	RTI		RETURN FROM SWI HANDLER "SUBROUTINE"

(The address ABXX is put in locations $FFFA and $FFFB so that the SWI instruction will jump indirectly through those words to the routine.) Note that this version is reentrant, because if an interrupt happened to occur while we were in this routine and the interrupt handler used this same routine, then the SWI instruction executed inside the interrupt handler would push new values of B and X on the stack and use them, rather than using the old values that were already there. This is not true of the version that used temporary storage because the interrupt handler would destroy the words in temporary storage that were put there by the routine being executed when the interrupt occurred. While the SWI version appears a bit shorter, if several operations are to be replaced by SWI instructions (and there happens to be only one SWI instruction in the 6800) then the SWI instruction ($3F) has to be followed by a displacement to make it a two-word "instruction." For example, if the second word were zero, as in the machine code:

$$3F$$
$$00$$

the ABX instruction would be executed, but if the second word were one, some other operation like LDA A,X could be executed, and so on. The manner of writing this displacement, and picking it up, will be discussed in section 1-3.2. Once this displacement is obtained, it must be used to jump to the "subroutine" that it indicates. This operation takes a fair amount of time. So using the SWI to replace operations missing in the 6800 takes quite a bit longer than using subroutines called by a JSR instruction, but using SWI instructions makes the routines reentrant by automatically allocating temporary storage on the stack. In the following discussion, we recommend the use of SWI instructions rather than JSR subroutines that use temporary storage. If you are concerned about speed and you do not have to worry about reentrancy, then use the equivalent subroutines that use temporary storage.

Consider now the 6800 SWI routines that replace the 6809 addressing modes not available in the 6800. Direct, page zero, implied, and immediate addressing are available on the 6800. Page and long relative address modes cannot be used to memorize or recall words in LDA or STA instructions. They can be replaced by an SWI instruction, because the program counter is stored as the fourth and fifth words on the stack, which can be accessed by using the TSX instruction, followed by the LDX 4,X instruction. This example is a bit cumbersome so we do not discuss it here, but leave it as a good exercise at the end of the chapter.

If one needs to use a long conditional branch instruction like:

LBEQ L1

in the 6809 (because L1 is beyond the range of a page relative conditional branch), this can be replaced on the 6800 by a short conditional branch testing the opposite condition that skips over a JMP instruction, as in:

BNE   L2
JMP   L1
L2 NOP

(The NOP instruction is not necessary, it stands for the instruction just below the 6809 LBEQ instruction.) Note that the 6809 version is position independent (the program can be put as a whole anywhere in memory) but the 6800 version is not.

Indirect addressing, such as LDA [ALPHA], can often be replaced by index addressing, as in:

LDX   ALPHA
LDAA   0,X

but an instruction such as STX [ALPHA] will not work that way: an SWI instruction can be used to perform that operation. It, too, is a bit messy.

Pointer addressing in the 6800 is actually index addressing with displacement zero. Be careful about index addressing in the 6800, because only positive number displacements in the range 0-255 can be used. Negative displacements and displacements greater than 255 can be handled in one of two ways as follows. An SWI instruction is written to add the A and B accumulator to X, or subtract A and B from X, as in the 6809 instruction LEAX D,X. This instruction is used as often as needed so that when the instruction that would use a negative number displacement or a displacement greater than 255 is executed, X has the actual value of the effective address, and the instruction can use an index address like LDA 0,X. A second way that sometimes works out is to create the effective address in two parts, using index addressing to assemble the parts. An especially important case is the selection of the ith element from a vector of less than 255 one-word elements, as in the high level language statement ALPHA(i). The index i is usually a variable which changes in a DO-loop to select different elements from the vector, and the vector is usually not stored on page zero, so the address ALPHA is a sixteen-bit address. Suppose that one address ALPHA ($100) is broken into two parts ALPHAH ($01) and ALPHAL ($00), and the index i is a variable in accumulator A. Then we can assemble ALPHAH and i in a temporary storage pair of words, or on top of the stack, and then get the words into the index register. Then use index register addressing with a displacement of ALPHAL to calculate the desired effective address. A program segment that uses the stack to be reentrant is shown below:

```
PSHA              PUSH i ON STACK
LDAA  #ALPHAH     CREATE HIGH BYTE OF ADDRESS
                  ALPHA
PSHA              PUT IT ON TOP OF PREVIOUS WORD
TSX               MAKE X POINT TO THAT PAIR OF
                  WORDS
LDX   0,X         GET THOSE TWO WORDS INTO X
INS               DELETE THOSE TWO WORDS FROM
                  THE STACK
INS               TO BALANCE THE STACK
LDAA  ALPHAL,X    GET THE DESIRED WORD
```

Accumulator index addressing is also best handled by an SWI instruction; however, autoincrement/autodecrement addressing is better handled by using the INX and DEX instructions. For example, the 6809 instruction LDA ,X+ is coded in the 6800 as:

```
LDAA  0,X
INX
```

Similarly, autodecrement addressing can be handled using DEX before the instruction.

One of the most serious problems in the 6800 is the fact that only one index register is available, rather than the three in the 6809. Consider the program that moves 128 words from one area in memory to another, which was shown for the 6809 in section 1-2.2 in the discussion of DO-loops. In the 6800, the two addresses needed to get a word from the first area and to put the word in the second area have to be stored in memory. Suppose that ALPHA ($100 and $101) contains the address of the beginning of the first area, and BETA ($102 and $103) contain the address of the second area. Then the 6800 routine would be as follows:

	LDAA	#128	ACCUMULATOR A IS USED AS A COUNTER
L	LDX	ALPHA	GET POINTER ADDRESS TO FIRST AREA
	LDAB	0,X	GET WORD
	INX		INCREMENT POINTER TO FIRST AREA
	STX	ALPHA	PUT IT BACK
	LDX	BETA	GET POINTER TO SECOND AREA
	STAB	0,X	MOVE WORD INTO SECOND AREA
	INX		INCREMENT POINTER TO SECOND AREA
	STX	BETA	PUT IT BACK
	DECA		COUNT DOWN
	BNE	L	LOOP 128 TIMES

Among the missing instructions in the 6800, the most troublesome are the instructions that move data in and out of the index register, such as the 6809 instructions PULS X, PSHS X, TFR D,X and TFR X,D. These can be done using temporary storage and the LDX and STX instructions, but such programs are not reentrant. Reentrant programs using SWI merely rearrange the words on top of the stack, but even that can get messy for the PSHS and PULS operations. The following program segment is an example of an SWI "subroutine" that can replace PULS X. Note the extensive movement of words to delete the two words that were on top of the stack, which are pulled into X. (A shorter reentrant program is possible.)

	TSX		MAKE X POINT TO TOP OF THE STACK
	LDAA	5,X	TOP BYTE OF PROGRAM COUNTER

LDAB	7,X	IS EXCHANGED WITH TOP BYTE
STAB	5,X	OF WORD BEING PULLED
STAA	7,X	
LDAA	6,X	SECOND BYTE OF
LDAB	8,X	PROGRAM COUNTER
STAA	8,X	IS EXCHANGED
STAB	6,X	WITH SECOND BYTE
LDAA	2,X	AND ACCUMULATOR A IS
STAA	4,X	MOVED DOWN
LDAA	1,X	AND ACCUMULATOR B IS
STAA	3,X	ALSO MOVED DOWN
PULA		FINALLY THE CC REGISTER
INS		IS MOVED AND TWO WORDS
INS		ARE DELETED FROM THE TOP
PSHA		WHERE THE CC REGISTER IS PUT
RTI		THEN REPLACE REGISTERS AND EXIT

The 6800 does not have a MUL instruction. This can be replaced by a subroutine call or an SWI instruction. Incidentally, division and multiple precision multiplication operations in the 6809 can be implemented as SWI instructions or as subroutine calls in like manner. The 6800 has an instruction CPX that is like the 6809 instruction CMPX; however, it does not work. It correctly sets the Z bit to test for zero, so it can be followed by a BNE or BEQ instruction, but it does not propagate the carry after comparing the low order two words into its comparison of the high order two words, so the N and V bits are incorrect, and instructions like BGT, BLT, and BLE should not be used in the 6800 after a CPX instruction. To test X against a sixteen-bit number, use an SWI "subroutine." This subroutine is quite tricky because the condition codes have to be modified in memory, the Z bit is easy to mess up, and the SWI instruction will set the interrupt disable bit I, which has a habit of disabling interrupts when you really want them enabled. If you want to write this "subroutine," you had better test it very thoroughly.

The 6800 has nearly the same instruction set as the 6809, so many of the routines in the following chapters can be used without modification in the 6800. Others can be converted using the techniques discussed in this section. You should test your programs by assembling them and running them, however, and be especially careful to watch the condition codes. It is easy to write a program that is almost correct but actually does not work. Testing is the only way to be sure.

1-3 Some Programming Techniques

In our experience, the average student of microcomputer interfacing usually has problems with the three programming techniques studied in this section. The most important technique is the handling of data structures. The first subsection constitutes a brief, microcomputer-oriented discussion of data structures. Another recurrent problem is the handling of subroutines. This is discussed next. Finally, multiple precision arithmetic is especially important in a short word width computer, yet is not well known. This is discussed in the last section.

We do not discuss problems in writing programs larger than one hundred lines long, such as structured and modular programming, high level languages, and documentation. That does not mean we do not think they are important—just that they are beyond the scope of this book.

1-3.1 Data Structures

Data structures are at least as important as programming techniques, for besides the program, the data itself and the structure of that data are the other half of the software. We discussed storage density as a characteristic of an architecture, but we discussed only the amount of memory needed to store the program. We may also have to worry about the storage of data and its impact on static and dynamic efficiency as well as on the size of memory needed to store the data. These considerations about data structures are very important in microcomputers.

A data structure is one view of data among three views. The *information structure* is the view of data as seen by the end user. For instance, the end user may think of his data as a table, like table 1-1 in this book. The *data structure* is the way the programmer sees the same data. This is strongly related to the way that he accesses it but is independent of the details of the size of words and positions of bits. The data structure for our example may be an array of characters that spell out the words in table 1-1. The *storage structure* is the way the information is actually stored in memory, right down to the bit positions. For our example, the table may appear as an array of eight bit words in the machine structure.

The idea of a data structure has been found a bit hard to accept by some very practical engineers. It is a level of abstraction that allows us to make some observations about the way we store things that can be extended over similar kinds of storage techniques. For instance, if we can say something about how to access an array, the same kinds of ideas can be used to access an array of eight-bit words as an array of twenty-four-bit words, even though the programs could be quite different. At the outset, we must stress that a data structure is a kind of template that tells us how data is stored and is also a menu of possible ways that the data can be written or read. Two data structures are different if they have different templates that describe their general structure or if the possible access techniques are different.

In order to discuss examples of storage structures, we introduce the notion of *assembler directives*. These look just like instructions in an assembler language program, but they tell the assembler to do something other than to create the machine code for an instruction. Most of the directives that we need are used to allocate space for data storage; however, two will be used in later examples that do not allocate data. These are briefly discussed here with the other assembler directives.

The NAM statement and the END statement are assembler language directives used to begin and end a program that is to be processed by an assembler. (They can be omitted, but they should be put in.) The program then appears as in:

NAM   PROG1

.

.

.

(your program)

.

.

.

END

The name of the program to the right of the NAM directive is printed on the listing of the program on the top of each page. We use this method to refer to programs in this book, rather than number them like figures, if we want to refer to a program in another section.

Some other assembler directives allocate storage in one way or another. See table 1-8 for a list of directives. The *origin* statement is used to tell the assembler where to put the next word it generates after the ORG. For example, the sequence:

ORG $100

LDA   ALPHA

will put the instruction code word for LDA at location $100 (when the program is loaded in memory) and each succeeding word in consecutive locations following that. By using the ORG directive to insert words further down in memory than the location they should be in without the ORG directive, an area of memory can be left aside to store data.

Table 1-8
Assembler Directives for the 6800 or 6809

Directive	Meaning
NAM N	Declares that the name of this program is N.
END	Terminates the program.
ORG N	Sets the origin to location N, so succeeding code is written, starting at location N.
L RMB N	Allocates N words and designates L as the label of the first word of the area being allocated.
L EQU N	Declares label L to have value N.
L FCB N1,N2	Forms (generates) one byte per argument, assigns label L to the first byte.
L FDB N1,N2	Forms (generates) two bytes per argument, assigns label L to the first byte of the first argument.
L FCC 'ABC'	Forms (generates) ASCII coded characters for each character between single quotes, assigns label L to the address of the first character.

A second directive can be used to allocate an area of memory, the *reserve memory bytes* directive RMB. To reserve $100 words to store data and assign a label L to refer to the first word of the area, write:

$$L \quad RMB \quad \$100$$

This allocates $100 words for some data and lets you refer to it using the label L. The assembler will skip over the $100 words to put its next word $100 words further down (at higher addresses) than it would have. For instance, to load the first word from this area into accumulator A, use LDA L; to load the second word, use LDA L + 1, and so on. Note that accumulator index register addressing can be used to get the ith word (where the zeroth word is really the first word at location L into one of the index registers, such as X, and execute LDA A,X. Incidentally, the number of words can be zero in an RMB directive; this can be used to put a label on a line without putting an instruction on it. Some of the previous examples could use such an RMB 0 rather than the NOP that was used in them.

A third way to allocate words of memory for data is to use the *equate* directive EQU. A directive like:

$$ALPHA \quad EQU \quad \$100$$

can be put somewhere in the program. This will tell the assembler that wherever ALPHA appears in the program, the number $100 is to be substituted. EQU directives are useful ways to tell the assembler where variables are located and are especially useful to label input/output registers in memory and locations to jump to or to branch to that are in other programs.

The ORG, RMB, and EQU directives tell the assembler where areas of data are to be put but do not fill those areas with initial values. The directives that follow will not only provide room for variables, but will also initialize the words with constants when the program is loaded.

The *form constant byte* directive FCB will put a byte in memory for each operand of the directive. FCB 10 will put $0A in a word in memory. The directive:

$$\text{L} \quad \text{FCB} \quad 1,2,3$$

will initialize three words in memory to be:

$$01$$
$$02$$
$$03$$

and will tell the assembler that L is the symbolic address of the first word, whose initial value is $01. *Form double byte* FDB will initialize two consecutive words for each argument. For example, the directive

$$\text{L} \quad \text{FDB} \quad 1,2,3$$

will initialize six consecutive words in memory, as follows:

$$00$$
$$01$$
$$00$$
$$02$$
$$00$$
$$03$$

and will tell the assembler that L is the address of the first word in this area, whose value is $00. The FDB directive is especially useful in putting addresses in memory so they can be used in indirect addressing or can be picked up into an index register. If ALPHA is $100, then the directive:

$$\text{FDB} \quad \text{ALPHA}$$

will generate the following two bytes in memory:

01

00

Finally, *form constant characters* FCC will generate the code words for the letters in the argument of the instruction using the *ASCII code* (listed in appendix A), which encodes each character as an eight-bit byte. The argument can be expressed in different ways, but in this book, we will enclose the letters to be coded and stored in single quotes. The assembler directive:

L   FCC   'ABC'

will generate the following pattern in hexadecimal in memory:

41

42

43

and let the assembler know that the label L refers to the address of the first letter that is stored as the word $41.

Data structures divide into three main categories: indexable, sequential, and linked. Indexable and sequential structures are more important and are discussed here. Linked structures are very powerful but are not easy to discuss in abstract terms. They will be sketched in a concrete example in chapter 3.

Indexable structures include vectors, lists, arrays, and tables. A *vector* is a sequence of elements in which each element is associated with an index i that can be used to access it. To make address calculations easy, the first element is usually associated with the index zero, and each successive element with the next integer (*zero origin indexing*), but you can change the index origin of the vector to one if you are willing to modify the routines slightly. Also, the elements in a vector are considered to be numbers of the same *precision* (number of bits or bytes needed to store an element). We will normally consider one-byte precision vectors, although an example below shows how the ideas can be extended to *n*-byte precision vectors.

To illustrate a vector, suppose that the vector *V* has elements 31, 17, 10. This can be defined in assembler language by the directive:

V   FCB   31,17,10

and we can refer to the first element as *V*(0), which happens to be 31. The same sequence of values could be called the vector *U*, and could be defined in double precision as:

U   FDB   31,17,10

and the first element, now called $U(0)$, is the first two words. To put the ith element of the first vector V into accumulator A, assuming that the integer i is in accumulator A, use the program segment:

```
LDX  #V
LDA  A,X
```

but to put the ith element of the second vector, U, into accumulator D, use:

```
LDX  #U
ASLA
LDD  A,X
```

The ASLA instruction doubles the index to get the address of the first word to be put in accumulator A in the LDD instruction because each element takes two words.

A *list* is like a vector, being accessed by means of an index, but the elements of a list can be any combination of different precision words, characters, or code words, and so on. For example, the list L can have three elements: the double precision number 5, the three characters ABC, and the single precision number 7. This list can be implemented in assembler language as follows:

```
L   FDB  5
    FCC  'ABC'
    FCB  7
```

and would be stored in machine code as follows:

```
                    00
                    05
                    41
                    42
                    43
                    07
```

Indexing can be used to get elements from a list, but since the elements can be different sizes, we cannot use a simple computation on i to get the ith element. To get $L(2)$, which is the single precision number 7, for example, we could execute the instruction LDA $L+5$.

A *linked list* structure is a list where some elements are addresses of (the first word in) other lists. A linked list structure is very flexible and powerful and is widely used in advanced software. It can be useful in some interfacing applications. It is discussed in section 3-2.3 to make it concrete and to show how simple it really is.

An *array* is a vector whose elements are vectors of the same length. We normally think of an array as a two-dimensional pattern, as in:

$$
\begin{array}{ccc}
1 & 2 & 3 \\
4 & 5 & 6 \\
7 & 8 & 9 \\
10 & 11 & 12
\end{array}
$$

If we consider the rows of the array as the elements of a vector of rows, the data structure is called a *row major order* array. This can be implemented in assembler language as follows:

```
A1  FCB        1,2,3
    FCB        4,5,6
    FCB        7,8,9
    FCB      10,11,12
```

and row zero is the vector 1, 2, 3. Alternatively, if the array is considered a vector of column vectors, the structure is a *column major order* array. Here, column zero is the vector 1, 4, 7, 10 and the array can be described in assembler language as

```
A2  FCB      1,4,7,10
    FCB      2,5,8,11
    FCB      3,6,9,12
```

Depending on which order is used, an element from the ith row and jth column can be extracted from an array by a polynomial evaluation. For example, in a row major order array where each row has n one-word elements, the address of the (i, j)th element is:

$$\text{address} = (i \times n) + j + \text{address of A}(0,0)$$

Note that the MUL instruction can be used in the 6809 to compute array addresses. For instance, if n is 3, and i and j are in accumulators A and B respectively, the following routine will put A(i, j) into accumulator A:

```
PSHS        B        SAVE FOR AFTER MULTIPLY
```

```
LDB      #3        PUT n INTO ACCUMULATOR B
MUL                MULTIPLY i IN ACCUMULATOR A
                   BY n
ADDB     ,S+       ADD j
ADCA     #0        PROPAGATE CARRY
LDX      #A1       GET ADDRESS OF A1(0,0) INTO X
LDA      D,X       GET A1(i, j) INTO ACCUMULATOR A
```

Note, however, that sometimes multiplication can be more easily done by shifting left, and possibly adding the original to the shifted numbers. For example, multiplication by four is more efficiently done by two executions of the instruction ASLA. Finally, column major order arrays can be handled in like manner, essentially by exchanging i and j in the above examples.

Row major order arrays are just as useful as column major order arrays; however, if one often picks up consecutive words along the same row, then row major order is preferable since these can be picked up by incrementing an index register rather than adding a constant to it, such as in autoincrement addressing. In general, the reader should be prepared to use either representation of arrays, and to chose the one that allows him to use autoincrementing as much as possible, rather than to allow the impression to grow on him that row major order is natural and column major order is unnatural, or vice versa.

A *table* is to an array as a list is to a vector. It is a vector of identically structured lists (rows). Tables often store characters, where either a single character or a collection of n consecutive characters are considered to be elements of the lists in the table. Index and autoincrement addressing are useful for accessing tables, especially if the tables are stored in row major order. If the index register points to the first word of a row—any row—then the displacement can be used to access words in any desired column. Also, autoincrement addressing can be used to select consecutive words from a row of the table.

The other important class of data structures is sequential structures, which are accessed by relative position. Rather than having an index i to get to any element of the structure, only the "next" element to the last one that was accessed may be accessed in a sequential structure. Strings, stacks, queues, and deques are sequential structures that are important in microcomputers.

A *string* is a sequence of elements such that after the ith element has been accessed, only the $(i + 1)$st element can be accessed (or in some cases the $(i - 1)$th or both). In particular, a string of ASCII coded characters is a *character string* and is used to store text such as the sequence of characters that is put into an assembler, which embodies the program that is to be assembled. Strings are nicely handled by autoincrement addressing (or autodecrement addressing).

When you type on a terminal, the characters you type are usually stored in memory in a character string. You may want to use a typed word as a command to execute a routine, and to use different words to execute different routines. The following routine, which begins at address SRCH, shows how a character string is stored and how it can be compared against another string, to jump to a routine if the two strings are equal. One string, presumably the one typed in the terminal, is stored in memory and the address of the first character in the string is stored in the two words at ALPHA. The string that it is compared against (START) is stored at BETA, which is five characters long. The following routine will jump to STRT if the two strings are equal, otherwise it will go on to execute the next instruction after the label NOGOOD. (We illustrate some of the assembler directives here that we have just discussed, such as NAM, END, and RMB 0).

```
        NAM    SEARCH
        ORG    $100    PUT DATA AFTER LOCATION
                       $100
ALPHA   RMB       2    RESERVE FOR ADDRESS OF IN-
                       PUT STRING
BETA    FCC   'START'  CHARACTER STRING COM-
                       PARED AGAINST
        ORG    $200    PUT PROGRAM AFTER LOCA-
                       TION $200
SRCH    LDX    ALPHA   GET ADDRESS OF STRING
                       TYPED IN
        LDU    #BETA   GET ADDRESS OF STRING TO
                       BE COMPARED
        LDA      #5    SET LOOP FOR 5 EXECUTIONS
LOOP    LDB      ,X+   GET LETTER TYPED IN, MOVE
                       POINTER
        CMPB     ,U+   COMPARE TO EQUIVALENT
                       LETTER, MOVE POINTER
        BNE    NOGOOD  STRINGS NOT EQUAL
        DECA           COUNT DOWN
        BNE    LOOP    UNTIL 5 CHARACTERS COM-
                       PARED
        LBRA   STRT    IF ALL 5 CHECK, THIS IS THE
                       STRING, GO TO STRT
```

NOGOOD RMB   0 IF SOME CHARACTER DIFFERS,
                                                    CONTINUE HERE

        END

Inside the loop, we compare one character from the input string against one character of the string START at a time. If we detect any difference, we exit to label NOGOOD because the user did not type the string START. But if all five characters match up, the user did type the word START, so the program jumps to the routine at label STRT, presumably to start something that the user requested.

Besides character strings, bit strings are important in microcomputers. In particular, a very nice coding scheme called the *Huffmann code* can pack characters into a bit stream and achieve a reduction of up to 75 percent in storage space compared to storing the characters directly in an ASCII character string. This can be used to store characters more compactly and can also be used to transmit them through a communications link more efficiently. As an extra bonus, the encoded characters are very hard to decode without a description of the code, so you get a much more secure communication link using a Huffman code.

The code is rather like Morse code, in that often used characters are coded as short strings of bits, just as the often used letter E is a single dot in Morse code. To insure that the code words are unique and to suggest a decoding strategy, the code is defined by a tree having two branches at each branching point (*binary tree*), as shown in figure 1-6. The letters at each end (leaf) are represented by the pattern of ones and zeroes along the branches from the left end (root) to the leaf. Thus, the character string MISSISSIPPI can be represented by the bit string 111100010001011011010. Note that the ASCII string would take eighty-eight bits of memory while the Huffmann

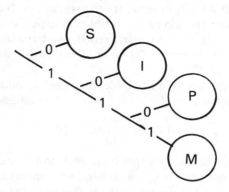

Figure 1-6. A Huffmann Coding Tree

string would take twenty-one bits. When you decode the bit string, start at the root and use each successive bit of the bit string to guide you up (if zero) or down (if one) the next branch until you get to a leaf. Then copy the letter and start over at the root of the tree with the next bit of the bit string. The bit string has equal probabilities of ones and zeroes, so techniques used to decipher the code based on probabilities will not work. It is particularly hard to break a Huffmann code.

Now that we have shown how nice the Huffmann code is, we must admit a few problems with it. To store some text efficiently, the text must be statistically analyzed to determine which letters are most frequent in order to assign these the shortest codes. Note that S is most common, so we gave it a short code word. There is a systematic procedure for generating the best Huffmann code which is presented in almost any book on information theory, but you have to get the statistics of the occurrences of each letter to get that code. Nevertheless, though less than perfect, a fixed code can be used that is based on other statistics if the statistics are reasonably similar. Finally, as we noted, without the decoding tree, you cannot decode the bit string. But if any bit in the bit string is erroneous, your decoding routine can get completely lost. The code has to be sent through a communications link that is pretty free from errors.

A *deque* is a generalized data structure that includes the special cases of the stack and the queue. A deque (pronounced deck) is a sequence of elements that has two ends that we call the top and the bottom. You can only access the top or bottom elements on the deque. You can *push an element on top* by placing it on top of the top element, which makes it the new top element, or you can *push an element on the bottom* making it the new bottom element. Or you can *pull (or pop) the top element* deleting the top element from the deque, making the next to top element the top element, and putting the old top element somewhere else, or *pull (or pop) the bottom element* in like manner.

Deques are theoretically infinite, so that you can push as many elements as you want on either the top or bottom, but practical deques have a maximum capacity. If this capacity is exceeded, we have an *overflow* error. Also, if you pull more elements than you have pushed, an *underflow error* exists.

A deque is implemented in assembler language by allocating an area of N words of memory as a *buffer* for it, such as with an assembler directive:

DEQUE   RMB $10

The buffer is an area of memory that is set aside to be used as the deque expands, which may not be used by any other data or program code. The programmer allocates as much room for the buffer as he believes necessary for the worst case (largest) expansion of the deque, but not more than is necessary.

Two pointers are used to read or write on the top or bottom, and a counter is used to detect overflow or underflow. Though the pointers are usually stored in memory, for simplicity we will assume that index register X points to the top of the deque, index register Y points to the bottom of the deque, and accumulator A contains the number of words in the deque. The idea used to implement the deque is to use autodecrement addressing to push words on the top and autoincrement addressing to pull words from the top of the deque. Similarly, autoincrement addressing can be used to push words on the bottom and autodecrementing can be used to pull words from the bottom (although the index register should then point to the first free word below the deque rather than the bottom word of the deque to use these addressing modes in the 6809). As words are pulled from top or bottom, more space is made available to push words on either the top or bottom. To take advantage of this, we think of the buffer as being a ring or loop of words, so that the next word below the bottom of the buffer is the word on the top of the buffer. That way as words are pulled from the top the memory locations can become available to store words pushed on the bottom as well as words pushed on the top, and vice versa. Then to initialize it, we can execute the following program segment:

CLRA		SET COUNT TO 0
LDX	#DEQUE	INITIALIZE TOP POINTER
LDY	#DEQUE – 1	INITIALIZE BOTTOM POINTER

To push a one-word element from accumulator B on the top (where top means lower address), we can execute the following routine:

	CMPX	#DEQUE	SEE IF POINTER IS ON TOP OF BUFFER
	BNE	L1	IF SO
	LDX	#DEQUE + $11	PUT IT ON THE BOTTOM
L1	INCA		FIND NUMBER OF WORDS IN DEQUE
	CMPA	#$10	COMPARE WITH MAXIMUM NUMBER
	LBHI	ERROR	IF TOO HIGH, THEN JUMP TO ERROR ROUTINE
	STB	, – X	PUT WORD ON TOP OF DEQUE, MOVE POINTER

and to pull a one-word element into accumulator B from the top, use this routine:

```
      DECA                      DECREASE SIZE OF DEQUE
      LBMI          ERROR       IF NEGATIVE, SIGNAL
                                UNDERFLOW ERROR
      LDB           ,X+         GET WORD
      CMPX          #DEQUE+$10  IF AT BOTTOM OF THE
                                BUFFER
      BNE           L2          THEN REPLACE
      LDX           #DEQUE      AT TOP OF BUFFER
  L2  RMB           0
```

Similar routines are used to push and pull the bottom word from the deque. Note that the Y pointer should point to the word below the bottom word on the deque to use the 6809 autoincrement and autodecrement addressing modes.

Note that you cannot really associate the ith word from either end of a deque with a particular location in memory. In fact, in a pure sense, you are only permitted to access the top and bottom words of the deque, and are not permitted to read or write any other word in the deque. In practice, we sometimes access the ith element from the top of the deque or from the bottom of the deque by using a displacement with the pointers that point to the top and bottom words, but this is not a pure deque. We call it an *indexable deque* to give it some name.

A *stack* is a deque in which you can push or pull on only one end. We have already discussed the stack accessed by the stack pointer S, which permits the machine to push or pull words from the top of the stack to save registers for subroutine calls, SWI, and hardware interrupts. Now we consider the stack as a special case of a deque. Actually, the stack in the 6809 is indexable, being a special case of the indexable deque. It is an example of a stack that pushes or pulls elements from the top only. Another stack can be created that pushes or pulls elements only from the bottom of the deque. This is a perfectly good stack, just as one that pushes or pulls only from the top. In fact, if you want to have two different stacks in your memory, it is good to have one that pushes and pulls from the top of this deque, and to have another that pushes and pulls from the bottom of another deque that shares the same buffer space. The reason that this is desirable is that the same buffer can be used for both stacks, as one starts at the top of this buffer (lowest address) and builds downward, while the other starts at the bottom (highest address) and builds upward. A stack overflow exists when the pointer that points to the top of the stack that builds upward is equal to the pointer that locates the bottom of the stack that builds downward. Note that if one stack is shorter, then the other stack can grow longer before an overflow exists, and vice versa. You only have to allocate enough words in the buffer for the maximum number of words that will be in both stacks at the same time.

Note that the U index register is called a user stack pointer, as we noted before. It is designed, however, to push and pull from the top of a deque just like the S stack pointer. Therefore, another register is as good as the U register as a second stack pointer, and U can be used to quickly initialize registers by the PULU instruction. If a second stack is used, another index register should be used to point to the bottom of that deque, and the Y register is a better choice because the LDY and STY instructions happen to be longer than LDX or LDU, and a stack pointer is not loaded as often as other registers.

Programs to push or pull on the two stacks are quite a bit simpler than the general program that operates on the general deque because the pointers do not roll around the top or bottom of the buffer. The 6809 PSHS and PULS and similar instructions push or pull from one stack, while the other uses autoincrement and autodecrement addressing with the Y register, as the operation to push accumulator A is implemented as STA ,Y + and the operation to pull accumulator A as LDA , − Y. Note that Y points one word below the bottom of the deque. This extra stack will be used in the discussion of multiple precision arithmetic functions in 1-3.3. One of the very few weak points of the 6809 is that, while the designers saw the need for two stacks, they did not quite implement the second stack in the most useful way. In particular, it is hard to detect an overflow condition, especially when an I/O interrupt pushes a lot of words on one of the stacks, because we do not know when the two stack pointers cross. It would be rather easy to check this in hardware if the hardware really supported two stacks in an effective manner.

The final structure that is important in microcomputer systems is the *queue*. This is a deque in which we can push data on one end and pull data from the other end. In some senses, it is like a shift register, but it can expand if more words are pushed than are pulled (up to the size of the buffer). In fact, it has been called an elastic shift register. Queues are used to store data temporarily until they are needed, and to use the data in the same order that they were stored in the queue.

Other data structures are important in general programming, such as multidimensional arrays, PL/I structures, trees, partially ordered sets, banyan graphs, and so on. The reader is invited to pursue the study of data structures to improve his programming skills. This section, however, has covered the data structures that we have found most useful in microcomputer interface software.

1-3.2 Subroutines and Arguments

One area of great importance in microcomputer interfacing software that is often inadequately understood is the way that subroutines are called and the ways that arguments are passed into them and results are passed from them. Since the instruction set of a typical microcomputer is rather limited, the kinds of functions usually needed in most applications are implemented as subroutines. In fact, the code that is generated by some high level language compilers is usually almost exclusively subroutine calls, as we noted earlier. The techniques for programming subroutines are discussed in this section.

The main problem in writing good subroutines is the handling of variables. This is discussed first. A "blueprint" for a subroutine call and an example of a subroutine will be presented next. Some important remarks about comments and documentation of subroutines are presented last.

Variables used in subroutines are local or global, or are arguments. *Local variables* are temporary variables used only by the subroutine and not by any other subroutine. Normally local variables are undefined when the subroutine begins execution and may have to be *initialized* before they have known values. This is especially true of reentrant subroutines, and forgetting to initialize variables is a common and insidious bug. In some block-structured languages like ALGOL and PASCAL the program blocks are written so the inner, lower level blocks can access local variables of outer blocks, using the dynamic (run-time) calling sequence. This can be done in assembler-language programs. You can access local variables (called *dynamic local variables*) of routines calling this routine if you know where they are located.

Global variables are variables shared by two or more subroutines. For example, several subroutines may be written to handle a floppy disk, and global variables may be used to keep track of the status of the floppy disk so that all subroutines can access those variables. Global variables are not subroutine arguments, nor are they local or dynamically local variables. Only variables shared by several routines, which are to be located independent of the order of calling subroutines are global variables. One of the problems we often meet regarding global variables is that they are sometimes used to pass arguments. This is like supplying arguments through FORTRAN COMMON. It is too easy to forget to supply one of the critical arguments, and it is easy to use the same location inadvertently to supply an argument to a subroutine that calls another, and for that subroutine to supply an argument to the subroutine that it calls. Finally, such a technique is not reentrant. We recommend against using global variables to pass arguments.

In the 6809, local variables should be stored on the stack, even though relative addressing can also be used to store local variables. This makes the program reentrant and also works when the program and therefore the words picked up by relative addressing are in read-only memory. Note that a variable cannot be stored in a read-only memory unless it is a constant. Relative addressing is useful, though, when large constant data structures, such as character strings, are used in a subroutine. However, short one-word or two-word constants are obviously more efficiently handled as immediate addresses. Finally, in the 6809, global variables should be stored on the direct page if they are short, or their address could be stored on the direct page to be loaded into an index register efficiently, if they would take up too much of the direct page. The ability to use index addressing on the stack in the 6809 encourages the use of dynamic local variables rather than global variables whenever this is possible.

The passing of arguments has two aspects. A conceptual or strategic aspect is associated with how you want the argument treated, and an implementation or tactical aspect is associated with how you actually do it. The conceptual aspect is often covered in courses in computer science. It is especially important in high level languages, because when you program in high level languages you really do not care how the arguments are actually handled, provided that they are handled in a conceptually consistent manner. Even in assembler language, the conceptual aspect is important because you want to know what you are doing in a strategic sense. This is covered first. The implementation aspect is also important to assembler-language programmers because they have to be concerned with how the arguments are passed.

Conceptually, *arguments* or *parameters* are data passed from or to the calling routine to or from a subroutine, like the X in SIN(X). In an implementation, the parameter has either some register in the machine state or some storage location and symbolic address associated with that location inside the subroutine, such as Y; and the register or memory location with its symbolic address used inside the subroutine is called the *formal parameter*. The calling routine has a register or memory location and its symbolic address for the parameter that is usually different each place that the subroutine is called, and the register or memory location with its symbolic address in the calling routine is called the *actual parameter*. For example, at one place in the program we put SIN(ALPHA) and in another we put SIN(BETA) and in another, SIN(GAMMA). ALPHA, BETA, and GAMMA are actual parameters in these examples.

At the conceptual level, arguments are called by value and result, by reference, or by name. In *call by value and result*, the formal parameters inside the subroutine are usually registers, and the values of the actual parameters from the calling routine are actually transferred from the memory locations where they were held in the calling routine to the registers in the subroutine before the subroutine begins to execute its operation and the values of formal parameters in the registers are actually moved to the memory locations of their actual parameters after the subroutine is finished. Any mechanism whereby the actual values (rather than their addresses) are passed to the subroutine or actual results (rather than their addresses) are returned from the subroutine are called by value and result. In general, only parameters passed from the calling routine to the subroutine are moved before the subroutine begins execution, and only the results of the subroutine are copied into the calling routine's actual parameters after the end of execution of the subroutine, but the same formal parameter (register) can be used for input and output.

In *call by reference*, the data itself remains in the calling routine and is not actually moved to another location, but the address of the data is given to the subroutine and the subroutine uses this address to get the data whenever it needs to. Large vectors, lists, arrays, and other data structures can be more effectively called by reference so they do not have to be copied into and out of the subroutine's local variables. Conceptually, arguments passed in call by reference are evaluated just before the subroutine is called and are not reevaluated as the subroutine is executed. If an argument is called by reference, you should normally use it only for input, or only for output, and not both, since input arguments are supposed to behave as if they were evaluated just before the subroutine call, and are supposed to stay that way throughout the subroutine.

The last mechanism, *call by name* allows complex actual arguments to be passed to a subroutine, and these actual parameters are effectively (if not actually) inserted into every occurrence of the corresponding formal parameters inside the subroutine and are reevaluated each time they are met as the subroutine is executed. Call by name is useful when you want to refer to an argument by its address, but you change it in the subroutine, so it has different values at different times in the subroutine. Call by name is also useful when actual parameters are subroutines, for example, as arguments to another subroutine. If you wrote a subroutine called PLOT to plot a graph, you could pass an argument that would be a subroutine like SIN, as in PLOT(SIN), and SIN would be reevaluated each time that the PLOT routine was ready to plot a new point on the graph. If you used call by reference, the argument SIN would be evaluated just once, just before the subroutine was entered, so your plot would be a straight line. Finally, conceptually, call by name is used to handle error conditions. One argument is the address of a subroutine to go to if an error is detected. It is only executed if the error occurs, so it is a call by name argument.

We now consider implementation details of subroutine calls on the 6809. Subroutines are called by the JSR, BSR, and LBSR instructions and use the RTS instruction to return to the main program. The EXG X,PC and JMP 0,X pair and the SWI and RTI pair can also be used to advantage in some cases. The following discussion will primarily use the LBSR instruction to call subroutines because this allows the program to be position independent, but the BSR call can be used to improve efficiency when the address is in range, and the JSR can be used, particularly when some neat addressing mode can be used to calculate the address of the subroutine. Some special remarks on the use of EXG X,PC and SWI calls will be offered near the end of this discussion. The passing of arguments is implemented by means of registers, a stack, or an argument list. We now discuss these techniques with respect to the features of the 6809 that are useful to carry them out.

The 6809 has the X, Y, U, and D (or A and B) registers that can serve to hold arguments or results. While the index registers naturally lend themselves to passing addresses, in call by reference or call by name, these can be transferred to or exchanged with the D register using TFR or EXG instructions, so they can also be used to pass parameters by value. Also, the carry bit in the condition code register can be used to pass a one-bit result that can be used in instructions like (L)BCC and (L)BCS. If a subroutine does not have many arguments, this is usually the best way to pass them. It is easy to understand and to use. Its main disadvantage is that it is not completely general. Most high level languages need a completely general technique because compilers are usually not "smart" enough to pass parameters one way to some subroutines and other ways to other subroutines. Therefore, if you want to use a subroutine that was written to be called by a high level language routine, or if you want to write a subroutine that can be called by an high level language routine, you may have to pass the arguments in one of the ways described below.

The stack provides a completely general mechanism for passing arguments. Suppose the argument X for the subroutine SIN(X) is in accumulator A. To call the subroutine SIN, execute the following program segment:

```
PSHS    A
LBSR    SIN
```

Inside the subroutine, we can get the value of the argument, but the obvious way will not work. Do not execute the instruction:

```
PULS    A
```

This instruction will pull the high byte of the return address into A, rather than the argument that you want. The argument is actually the second word from the top of the stack, so it can be picked up as follows:

```
                      LDA   2,S
```

When the subroutine is finished, the RTS instruction is used to pull the two-word return address from the stack; but we are not through. The argument is still on top of the stack. If the calling routine is itself a subroutine, when it executes its RTS instruction, it will pull the argument from the stack into the program counter and jump to some dangerous place. After the subroutine has returned to the calling routine, the calling routine must remove the argument (balance the stack). A PULS instruction could be used, or if the argument is no longer needed, a LEAS 1,S instruction can delete it. Any number of arguments can be pushed onto the stack this way, and can be accessed inside the subroutine using index addressing with the S register. Values can be passed, as described above, but addresses can also be passed in the same way for call by reference, or subroutine addresses can be passed for call by name. As an example of the latter, the PLOT subroutine may need an argument which is the subroutine of the function to be plotted, such as the SIN routine. To pass the address of the SIN subroutine, we can execute this routine:

```
                LDX    #SIN
                PSHS   X
                LBSR   PLOT
```

(The above example is not position independent, but can be made so.) Inside the PLOT subroutine, to call the SIN subroutine, the instruction:

```
                JSR    [2,S]
```

can be used. Note that when the PLOT subroutine returns to the calling routine, the argument has to be deleted from the stack, so a LEAS 2,S instruction can be used.

Results can be returned on the stack too, but again the obvious way does not work. If, inside the subroutine, you push a result on the stack, then return and expect to pull the result from the stack, the return instruction RTS will pull the result first, which will effect a jump to some unknown place. Rather, a "hole" is inserted for the result on the stack before the subroutine is called, and the result can be put in the hole, in a technique that is the reverse of the one that is used to pass arguments to the subroutine. The calling routine can be written:

```
                LEAS   -1,S
                LBSR   SIN
                PULS   A
```

and the subroutine can put the result in the "hole" by executing the instruction:

$$STA \quad 2,S$$

Note that any number of results can be passed this way. A "hole" for each result must be created before the subroutine is called, and each result must be pulled from the stack (or deleted) to balance the stack after the subroutine has returned to the calling routine. Thus, the stack is a completely general technique for passing arguments and results.

In a similar way a subroutine can use the local variables of the routine that calls it in the same way that global variables are used. A displacement is used with index addressing on S to get farther down the stack to the local variables of the calling routine. Be careful to account for the return address on the stack when determining the displacement.

If a second stack is used rather than the one used to save the return address, then arguments can be pushed on that stack by the calling routine and pulled by the subroutine without fear of messing up the return addresses or having them in the way. This technique is especially useful for arithmetic routines and will be used in section 1-3.3. Also, if the EXG X,PC and JMP 0,X pair are used to call and return from a subroutine, then the stack does not have a return address on it, so you can push or pull on the stack pointed to by the S register without this concern. More will be said on this mode shortly.

The last technique for passing arguments is the *argument list*. It is almost as general as the stack technique and is the most commonly used method for high level language subroutines. A high level language subroutine call, like the FORTRAN statement:

$$CALL \; SUB \; (A,B,C)$$

is most efficiently implemented in assembler language as the following code:

```
LBSR   SUB
FDB    A,B,C
```

(using call by reference). Note that the microprocessor saves what it thinks is the return address, which is the address of the next word below the LBSR instruction, when it executes the LBSR instruction. That turns out to be most fortunate. It helps us get to the argument list, which is the list of addresses created by the FDB directive. To put the value of the word at address C into accumulator B inside the subroutine, execute the following program segment:

```
LDX         0,S    GET THE ADDRESS OF THE ARGU-
                   MENT LIST IN X
LDB         [4,X]  GET THE VALUE OF C INTO AC-
                   CUMULATOR B
```

Note that once one of the index registers, like X, points to the argument list, any argument can be easily obtained by indirect index addressing. If C is the address of an array, that address can be put into an index register so that index addressing can be used to access words in that array, as follows:

```
LDX    0,S    GET ADDRESS OF ARGUMENT LIST
LDU    4,X    GET ADDRESS OF ARRAY INTO U
```

Similarly, values can be passed and arguments can be called by name through the argument list. Note that simple execution of RTS will not work, as the first argument will be executed as an instruction. Rather, if the argument list is six words long, we can execute the following program segment rather than the RTS:

```
PULS   X
JMP    6,X
```

We said that this technique is almost completely general. The only thing wrong with it is that, especially in microcomputers, the program may be stored in read-only memory so that the memory does not have to be loaded each time power is turned on. The argument list in read-only memory cannot be changed. Therefore, if arguments are to be called by value, they cannot be placed in the argument list unless they are the same each time the subroutine is called from that place. That condition does occur sometimes. An example will be discussed with the SWI "subroutine" call shortly. Although it is not completely general, it is faster than the stack approach because the calling routine does not have to set up and delete the arguments. It can be used by subroutines called by high level language programs.

Finally, note that the PULS . . . PC instruction is effectively a return from subroutine that can restore some registers besides PC. This encourages you to save registers that are used in the subroutine other than those used to pass results from the subroutine. For example, if a subroutine uses accumulator B and index registers X and U, the first instruction in the subroutine should be PSHS B,X,U, and the instruction PULS B,X,U,PC should be used in place of RTS. This technique can overcome a lot of errors due to assuming that some registers are not changed by a subroutine when in fact they are changed.

The SWI is an alternative to the usual LBSR subroutine call. The SWI, SWI2, and SWI3 instructions of the 6809 can be attractive because they save all the registers. If you read the optional section on the 6800, you would observe how powerful this can be. And, as discussed there, you may want an argument list to follow the SWI instruction, where one of the arguments (the first) is a call by value argument that tells you exactly which routine you want to execute. The "subroutine call" is written this way:

SWI2

FCB   0

Inside the SWI "subroutine," the (only) argument can be obtained by using the saved PC contents, which are the eleventh and twelfth words from the top of the stack. To put this argument into accumulator A, execute this as the first instruction in the "subroutine":

L   LDA   [10,S]

(The address L is put into locations $FFF4 and $FFF5 so that SWI2 will cause a "jump" to that instruction.) This argument can be used to jump to a number of different routines by jumping through a *transfer vector*, which is a vector of addresses of starting locations of the different routines, such as:

TVEC   FDB   L0,L1,L2,L3,L4

To jump to the *i*th routine where *i* is in accumulator A, double A and add it to the address of the vector, then jump indirectly, as in:

ASLA

LDX   #TVEC

JMP   [A,X]

(The above transfer vector and routine are not position independent, but it is not too hard to make them so.) Note that if the argument after the SWI2 instruction were the number two, we would jump to L2, and so on. This particular argument is likely to be the same actual argument, whenever the subroutine is called from the same place in memory, so it is an example of a call by value that can be stored in a read-only memory argument list. Note that more arguments can be passed in an argument list to an SWI. Finally, note that the RTI instruction will return to execute the arguments as instructions. To avoid that, modify the return address before the RTI to skip over as many words as there are arguments. For instance, to skip over one argument, execute this routine to exit from the SWI:

```
        INC   11,S
        BEQ   L
        INC   10,S
    L   RTI
```

The SWI and the indirect JSR are especially useful for I/O software that you might write to interface your hardware. Suppose that the I/O software has a bug that is discovered after a lot of code has been written that uses it. Fixing that bug may change the sizes and entry points for many of the I/O subroutines. If the SWI "subroutine" technique is used with the transfer vector, only the transfer vector has to be modified, and the other software will still use the same argument. If an (L)BSR subroutine were used, every address in an I/O subroutine call would have to be changed throughout all the programs. SWI "subroutines" are therefore often used for I/O; however, the key aspect of the SWI mechanism is indirect addressing. If you have a transfer vector like TVEC in the above example in a fixed place in memory, the instruction JSR [TVEC + 6] would jump to a (JSR type) subroutine at location L3. If those subroutines were rewritten, only the transfer vector would need to be rewritten, and all the programs that call the subroutines would remain the same. This technique is especially useful when programs are on different read-only memories too. If all subroutine calls to subroutines on a read-only memory JSR indirectly through a transfer vector at the beginning of that read-only memory, then if that read-only memory is changed, the transfer vector can be changed at the same time, and none of the other read-only memories need to be changed to adjust the addresses of the subroutine calls to this read-only memory.

The EXG X,PC and JMP n,X are a useful "subroutine call" and "subroutine return" pair, because they do not leave a return address in the way on top of the stack pointed to by S. However, if a "subroutine" is called this way and it calls another subroutine the same way, the return address is not saved on the stack as it is using the normal technique. The return address can get lost unless the programmer takes care to save and restore it. Moreover, one register is tied up holding the return address. If an argument list is also used, however, that register is ideally suited to pick up the arguments and return past the end of the n word argument list using a JMP n,X instruction. This type of "subroutine" is then quite useful if the "subroutine" does not call other "subroutines," and if it uses an argument list.

We now offer a "blueprint" for calling a subroutine and for writing a subroutine, and a useful example of a subroutine. Thought should be given to the following considerations before anything is written:

1. What are the local and global variables, and what are the arguments and the results? How are the arguments and results to be passed—by value and result, by reference, or by name? Will they be passed in registers, on the stack pointed to by S (or another stack), or through an argument list?
2. Will we use (L)BSR or JSR calls, or should we use SWI calls or EX-G X,PC calls.

When you write the subroutine call, the following sequence of code should appear (although sections that do not pertain may be omitted).

1. Push any arguments to be passed on the stack, and make "holes" for any results to be passed back on the stack.
2. If EXG X,PC is used, load X with the address of the subroutine. Index registers other than X may be used, and relative addressing (LEAX n,PCR) is encouraged to preserve position independence.
3. Jump to the subroutine.
4. Write the argument list, if it is used. Use FDB directives for addresses and two-word operands, FCB for one-word operands, and FCC for character strings. These may be mixed in any order.
5. Pull any values returned on the stack and delete any values passed into the subroutine from the stack.

Inside the subroutine, the following sequences might be expected:

1. If you want to use direct page addressing as a "quick and dirty" index address mode, save the direct page register and any registers that are not supposed to be changed by the subroutine on the stack in the PSHS instruction so you can restore it in step 3 below. Make room on the stack for local variables. We can make room for n variables at once by the LEAS −n,S instruction. Initialize those local variables that may be read before data will be written in them. Note that local variables can be simultaneously allocated and initialized by the PSHS instruction.
2. Your routine can be put next. If argument lists are used, set up an index register, such as U, to point to the beginning of the list, as in LDU 0,S. The index register can be used for some other operation, but must be reloaded with the address of the argument list each time an argument is needed. If it is set up, a call by value one-word argument can be put into accumulator A by the instruction LDA n,U and a call by reference argument by LDA [n,U], where n is the position of the argument in the list. Also, a lot of arguments can be picked up and the argument pointer moved past them by the execution of the PULU instruction.

Arguments called by name on the stack can be picked up by LDA *n*,S and those called by reference by LDA [*n*,S], where *n* is the position of the argument on the stack. (Remember that the return address is (usually) on the stack.) Temporary variables can be pushed and pulled using PSHS and PULS if they are pulled in the order reverse of that in which they are pushed. When you use this method to store temporary variables, remember to account for them in the displacement *n* of instructions like LDA *n*,S.

3. When you are ready to leave a subroutine, delete all local variables from the stack first. We can delete *n* local variables by the instruction LEAS *n*,S. If you saved the direct page register or other registers so you could change them, restore them, using PULS. Then use the return (RTS, RTI, or JMP *n*,X) that corresponds to the call. Note that the PULS instruction can pull the program counter too, so an RTS may not be necessary. If an argument list is used, remember to move the program counter ahead of the argument list before returning. Several techniques for this have been shown above. If the RTS or RTI should be used to exit a subroutine, but you use a (L)BRA or JMP to jump to an error routine and you do not return, then remember to balance the stack by deleting the return address and other registers saved on the stack too.

The subroutine that we will now write conveys a very important concept, so we get to kill two birds with one stone. (A further reason for using a rather complex example will be given at the end of this discussion.)

The routine to be written *hashes* a character string into an address. That is, it converts any string of characters that you may type on a terminal into a number from zero to nineteen, and that number is used as an address. The important property of the hash routine is that when you pass the same character string to it, you always get the same number to use as an address. The actual computations that are done inside the routine are not really important as long as they are done the same way each time. Generally, the input characters are scrambled together as a restaurant serves hash, hence the term "hash." The routine is usually developed experimentally, though, to separate the character strings into different addresses as evenly as possible. Hashing is used to search for a character string to get information about the string. Hashing helps narrow down the search by starting the search at a place, indicated by the address provided by the routine, that is close to where the string starts. In particular, the hashing routine described below is the actual routine that Motorola uses in its MDOS software to search the directory of a disk. (In fact, if you know some of the terminology used with disks, this hash routine determines which sector of the directory the string is (probably) on. That sector is read, and the string is compared to all those strings on the sector. When a matching string is found, the track and sector number that begins the file is read from words that are next to the string.)

This subroutine needs a character string. Suppose its length is variable (the Motorola routine fixes the length to ten). We will not want to pass the string by value if it is of variable length. It should be passed by reference. We can provide the address of the first character of the string. To account for the variable length, we can supply the length as a call by value parameter. The result is a small number, so it can be returned in a register. The parameters can be passed in an argument list to enhance storage efficiency. The length, which will go into an accumulator, and the address, to go into an index register, can be picked up by a PULU instruction. When this is done, the length is the first argument. The calling routine to hash a ten-character string, at location ALPHA, will then be written:

```
LBSR   HASH
FCB    10
FDB    ALPHA
```

The hash subroutine is shown below. Of importance to this discussion on subroutines, the first two lines pick up the arguments and the last line returns past the argument list. The result is left in accumulator B.

When you read this subroutine, you might wonder about some characteristics that affect the way you use it. These should be supplied as comments. Comments can be put on a full line in assembler language by beginning the line with a star (*). Comments for a subroutine should (must) have the following information:

1. A brief description of the meaning of the subroutine should enable the reader to determine if this subroutine is the one he is looking for.
2. A list of all arguments, what they mean, whether they are called by value and result, by reference, or by name.
3. An example of a subroutine call, identifying which arguments are passed on the stack, through the argument list, or in registers by showing a clear example, and identifying whether (L)BSR, SWI, or EXG X,PC calls are to be used.
4. A list of all other registers, global memory words, and temporary storage locations that are changed or destroyed by the subroutine.
5. A description of any error conditions and how they are reported, and any abnormal exits from the subroutine that may be taken to handle errors.

Finally, all subroutines should be position independent and reentrant unless there is good reason to not have these features. If either feature is lacking, note this in the comments at the beginning of the subroutine.

HASH	PULS	U	GET RETURN ADDRESS, POINTS TO THE ARGUMENT
	PULU	A,X	RECOVER COUNT, ADDRESS OF STRING, AND MOVE U
	CLRB		CLEAR THE PLACE WHERE WE COMPUTE THE RESULT
LOOP	PSHS	B,CC	SAVE RESULT AND CONDITION CODES ON STACK
	LDB	,X+	GET A CHARACTER
	SUBB	#$25	MAKE IT UNIQUE
	BPL	NOCLR	IF NEGATIVE
	CLRB		MAKE IT ZERO
NOCLR	PULS	CC	RESTORE CONDITION CODES
	ADCB	,S+	PULL RESULT, ADD TO MODIFIED CHARACTER
	ROLB		DOUBLE, FOLD CARRY BACK
	DECA		DECREMENT COUNT
	BNE	LOOP	UNTIL COUNT BECOMES ZERO, LOOP
	RORB		UNDO LAST ROLB
	PSHS	B	
	RORB		
	RORB		
	RORB		
	RORB		
	ADDB	,S+	
	ANDB	#$1F	CLEAR HIGH THREE BITS
	CMPB	#19	IS IT WITHIN THE DESIRED RANGE?
	BLS	EXIT	IF SO, RESULT IS IN B
	SUBB	#20	PULL IT WITHIN RANGE
	CMPB	#9	IF NOW LOWER THAN 9
	BHI	EXIT	THEN DOUBLE IT
	ASLB		AND THEN
	BITB	#2	EXTEND THE
	BEQ	EXIT	LOWEST BIT
	ORAB	#1	
EXIT	JMP	0,U	U WAS MOVED PAST ARGUMENT LIST BY PULU

An example of a good comment for the above subroutine is given below.

```
****************************************************************

*

* HASH      CONVERTS N LETTER CHARACTER STRING AT
           ADDRESS
*          ADDR INTO A NUMBER FROM 0-19

*

* CALLING SEQUENCE:

*

* LBSR   HASH

* FCB       N CALL BY VALUE

* FDB   ADDR   CALL BY REFERENCE

*

* DESTROYS  CC,A,X,AND U

* RETURNS HASHED ADDRESS IN B
```

We cannot stress enough the need for such comments at the beginning of a subroutine. With them, it is easy to know if, for example, the Y register is untouched by the subroutine, or how to supply an argument and where the result is to be found. Without them, the subroutine program has to be studied thoroughly each time it is used. That is usually too much trouble, as you can appreciate by the above example. Try to understand the subroutine to glean this critical information from it without the use of comments. (We deliberately chose this hash routine to make that point, because it is rather messy inside.)

We have examined different strategies for calling subroutines and passing arguments, and different techniques for implementing those strategies. We should now be prepared to write subroutines for interface software.

1-3.3 Arithmetic Operations

A microcomputer offers some challenging problems in implementing arithmetic operations. An eight-bit word is really very short. Even a sixteen-bit number is often too small. Consider business data processing, for example. If we keep track of money in binary to the penny, an eight-bit unsigned number can keep track of only $2.55, and a sixteen-bit unsigned number, only $655.35. That is not enough for most applications. Von Neumann told us in 1946, in his great paper that begat the computer, that scientific computers need at least forty bits. IBM chose a thirty-two-bit word for its 360/370 and has learned from experience that almost all scientific computations require double precision arithmetic (64 bits) because you do need about forty bits for scientific computation. Sixteen bits is fine for address calculations and for feedback control systems, but is inadequate for just about everything else. So even if the 6809 has sixteen-bit arithmetic instructions, we have to study the effective handling of multiple precision arithmetic. This is offered in this section.

A secondary consideration may be storage density. Rather than having one subroutine for sixteen-bit addition, another for twenty-four-bit addition, and so on, we may want to have only one subroutine that can handle any precision. In fact, with a little effort, we can implement arithmetic functions that are capable of expanding the precision of a number when overflow occurs and of adding numbers of different precision. With this power, there is less need for floating point arithmetic. The resulting routines will be slower than routines optimized for fixed precision, however. Such fixed precision routines can be fairly easily written, though, if the variable precision routines are understood.

About the only method we know that can handle variable precision numbers efficiently is to keep them on a stack (*operand stack*). This stack contains, as elements, numbers of arbitrary size. Conceptually, you can push a number on the stack, or pull a number from it, and you push or pull a whole number regardless of how big it is. We will now discuss how any algebraic formula can be converted into a program of subroutine calls that perform the arithmetic on this stack.

A *dyadic* operation is an operation, like addition, that requires two operands. Any dyadic operation works this way: pull one number from the stack to be used as the first (left) operand, and pull another number from the stack to be used as the second (right) operand. Perform the dyadic operation. Push the result back on the stack. A *monadic* operation is an operation, like negate, that requires one operand. All monadic operations work this way: pull a number from the stack, operate on it, and push the result on the stack. Finally, a *push* operation like push ALPHA copies a number that is stored at location ALPHA, pushing it on top of the stack.

Consider a simple algebraic formula, such as:

$$(A + B)/(C - D)$$

The formula can be evaluated with dyadic operations implemented as the subroutines ADD, SUB, and DIV and the subroutine PUSH that uses a call by reference argument in an argument list to determine what to push, in the following program:

```
LBSR    PUSH
FDB        A
LBSR    PUSH
FDB        B
LBSR     ADD
LBSR    PUSH
FCB        C
LBSR    PUSH
FCB        D
LBSR     SUB
LBSR     DIV
```

The reader should pencil a stack and convince himself that the result of the addition is saved conveniently on the stack as the subtraction is set up, and the results of both are available when the divide subroutine needs them.

The first problem is to find out how to write the program of subroutine calls to implement any arbitrary algebraic formula, and the second problem is to find a way to implement the subroutines that perform the operations. These problems are solved below.

In order to write the subroutines in correct order, the expression that has its operators in the middle (infix expression) has to be converted to one that has its operators at the end of the operands (suffix expression). For example, $A + B$ is written $A B +$. This expression directly represents the subroutine calls: PUSH A, PUSH B, ADD, which are the correct calls to implement the addition operation. (Incidentally, suffix expressions are popularly called Polish or reverse Polish notation, because they were invented by the Polish logician Jan Lucasiewicz.)

One can write the expression in suffix form, then write the subroutine calls, but there is a shorter way of writing arithmetic subroutines using *formula trees*. Figure 1-7a shows the formula tree for a typical dyadic operation, such as addition, and figure 1-7b shows the formula tree for a typical monadic operation like square root. If an argument is evaluated by another formula, the formula tree for that formula is put in place of the formula. A complex expression such as the solution to the quadratic formula is written as follows (to reduce the need for extra symbols and subroutines):

$$\frac{(\sqrt{(B \times B)} - (4 \times (A \times C))) - B}{2 \times A}$$

The expression can be written as the formula tree shown in figure 1-7c.

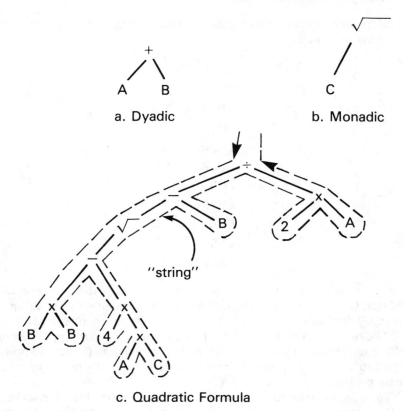

a. Dyadic   b. Monadic

c. Quadratic Formula

Figure 1-7. Some Formula Trees

To write the subroutine calls, wrap a "string" tightly around the tree. See figure 1-7c. Follow the string from left top around the tree to right top, and copy a subroutine call the *last* time you meet a symbol (as you pass it on its right): a PUSH A when you meet a symbol A and a MULT when you meet a ×, and so on. The dyadic operation formula tree produces the subroutine calls described above. The monadic operation formula tree produces the subroutine calls: PUSH C, SQRT. The quadratic formula tree produces the subroutine calls for a 6809 program as shown below:

```
LBSR    PUSH
FDB        B
LBSR    PUSH
FDB        B
```

```
LBSR   MULT
LBSR   PUSH
FDB    FOUR
LBSR   PUSH
FDB     A
LBSR   PUSH
FDB     C
LBSR   MULT
LBSR   MULT
LBSR   SUBT
LBSR   SQRT
LBSR   PUSH
FDB     B
LBSR   SUBT
LBSR   PUSH
FDB    TWO
LBSR   PUSH
FDB     A
LBSR   MULT
LBSR   DIV
```

(The symbolic addresses A, B, C are for the variables in the quadratic formula, and the symbolic addresses FOUR and TWO are for the constants 4 and 2.) Conversion to a formula tree is fairly simple. In fact, if you get used to formula trees, they are easier to write and check than conventional infix expressions. Conversion from a formula tree to the program is mechanical and simple. (Note that this same technique can help you use calculators that use reverse Polish notation.)

We now consider the technique used to implement a variable length number stack on the 6809. To avoid having return addresses in the way a stack different from that pointed to by the S register is used, the operand stack uses the Y index register and builds from low addresses to high addresses in the same buffer space as is used by the stack pointed to by the S register. See figure 1-8. Y points to the word right below (at the next larger address than) the bottom word on the operand stack. The bottom number, call it A, is say three words long, call them A2, A1, A0, where A0 is the least significant word of the number. The bottom number is stored in consecutive locations with A2 at the lowest address, then A1, A0, and then the length of the number, the number three, at the highest address, on the bottom of the operand stack. See figure 1-8. Likewise, another number, call it B, is stored most significant word at lowest address and length at highest address, right above A on the operand stack.

Consider adding the bottom two numbers on the operand stack, assuming they are the same size. Conceptually, you should pull the whole bottom number from this operand stack, pull the next number, add the numbers, then push the whole result on the operand stack. Actually, you can work one word at a time. Add A0 to B0, put the result where B0 was before, then add A1 and B1 with the carry and put the result where B1 used to be, and so on. Note that autodecrement addressing can be used to pick up the words A0, A1, and A2, and that accumulator index addressing, where the accumulator has − (length of A + 1), can pick up the other words, B0, B1, and B2, and put the results back in their place. A subroutine ADD that does just that is shown below:

```
********************************************************************
*
*  ADD     ADDS THE BOTTOM TWO NUMBERS ON THE
           OPERAND STACK
*
*  CALLING SEQUENCE
*
*  JSR ADD
*
*  DESTROYS A,B
*
        ADD     LDA       , − Y    GET LENGTH OF BOTTOM
                                   NUMBER ON OPERAND
                                   STACK

                PSHS      A        SAVE ON STACK TO USE
                                   AS COUNTER

                COMA               GET − (LENGTH OF
                                   NUMBER + 1)

                ANDCC     #$FE     CLEAR CARRY
        LOOP    LDB       , − Y    GET A WORD OF THE
                                   BOTTOM NUMBER
```

```
              ADCB        A,Y   ADD TO CORRESPONDING
                                WORD OF NEXT NUMBER

              STAB        A,Y   PUT THE NUMBER BACK

              DEC          ,S   DECREMENT COUNTER

              BNE        LOOP   ADD ALL WORDS

              PULS       A,PC   DELETE COUNT AND
                                RETURN FROM
                                SUBROUTINE
```

Other dyadic functions can be performed in the same way. Note that subtraction should satisfy the property that the bottom number is subtracted from the next to bottom number correctly to implement formulas that are derived as above, because $A - C$ becomes PUSH A, PUSH C, SUBTRACT. Multiplication and division are quite a bit harder, and will be discussed near the end of this section.

Monadic functions are best implemented using another index register such as U because the Y pointer will have to be left where it was. Consider the left shift function, which doubles a number. The subroutine is shown below:

```
********************************************************************
*
*   LFTSFT                          LEFT SHIFT (DOUBLE) THE
                                    BOTTOM NUMBER
*                                   ON THE OPERAND STACK
*
*   CALLING SEQUENCE
*
*   LBSR LFTSFT
*
*   DESTROYS A,U
*
    LFTSFT    TFR       Y,U   COPY POINTER TO INDEX
                              REGISTER U
              LDA       ,-U   GET LENGTH, MOVE U TO
                              GET LEAST WORD
              ANDCC   #$FE    CLEAR CARRY
    LOOP      ROL       ,-U   ROTATE A WORD
              DECA            OVER ENTIRE LENGTH OF
                              NUMBER
              BNE      LOOP   IN DO-LOOP
              RTS
```

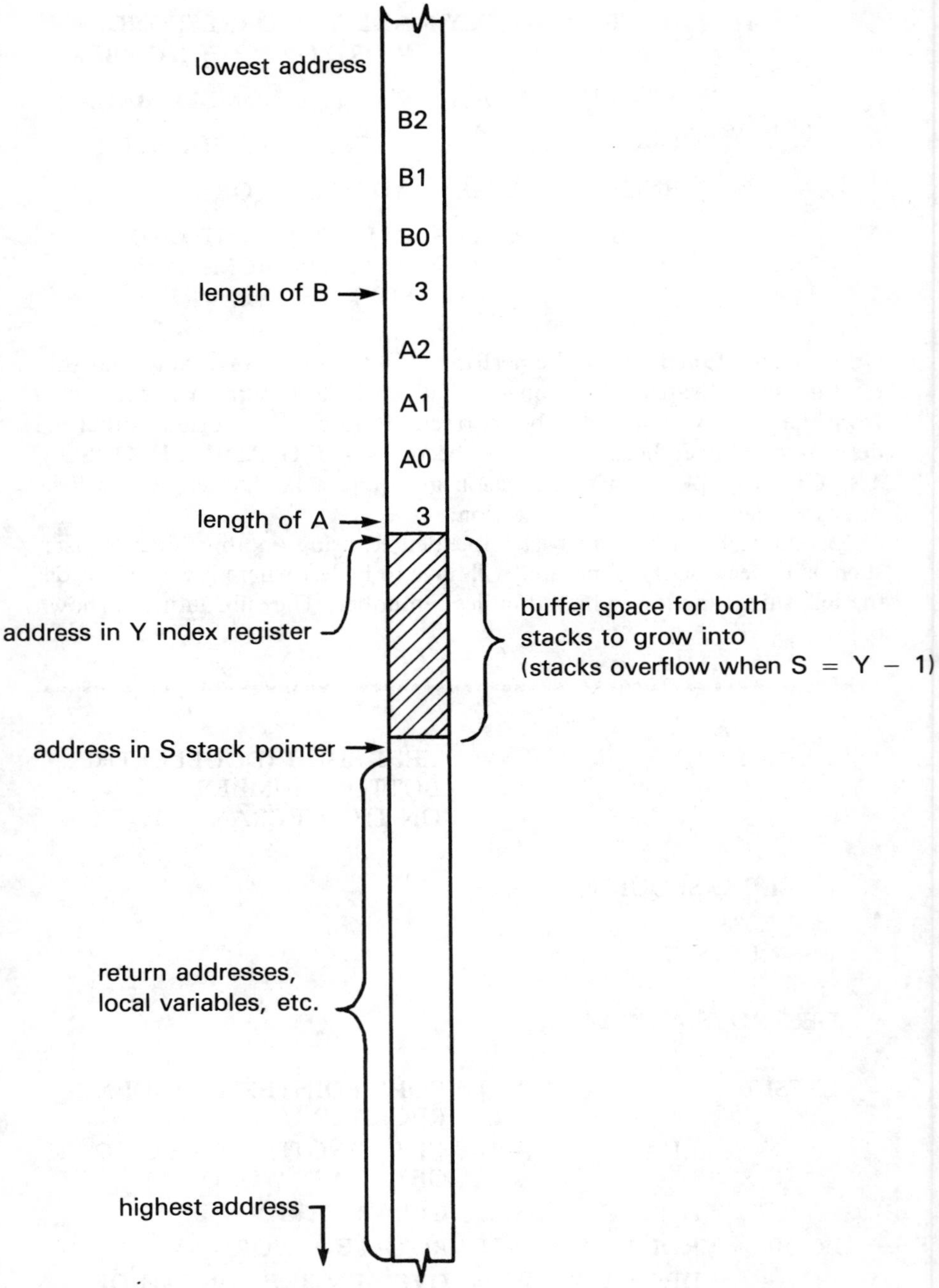

Figure 1-8. The Operand Stack and the Stack Pointed To by S

Note that in a shift right subroutine, you have to start shifting the high order word first, and use autodecrementing.

Generally, the stack can have numbers of different lengths because the length is stored with the number. When two numbers that are to be added just might have different lengths, we can check the lengths of the numbers and expand the smaller one using a routine like the one we used to move 128 words in memory. Also, after an overflow is detected, the result can be expanded in like manner.

Numbers stored in memory other than on the operand stack may or may not have their length stored with them. When you push these numbers onto

```
***************************************************************

*

*    PUSH    PUSHES A NUMBER FROM LOCATION  L  OF
             LENGTH N
*            ONTO THE OPERAND STACK

*

*    CALLING SEQUENCE

*

*        LDA      #N
*        LDU      #L
*        JSR    PUSH

*

*    DESTROYS  B

*

PUSH    PSHS       A    SAVE TO PUT ON BOTTOM OF WORD
LOOP    LDB      ,U +   GET WORD FROM NUMBER BEING
                        PUSHED
        STB      ,Y +   ONTO THE STACK
        DECA            COUNT NUMBER OF WORDS BEING
                        MOVED
        BNE    LOOP     LOOP UNTIL DONE
        PULS       A    RECOVER LENGTH
        STA      ,Y +   PUSH LENGTH LAST
        RTS
```

the operand stack, push the most significant word first, as in the following routine. On calling this subroutine, U points to the most significant word of the number in memory to be pushed, and accumulator A has the number of words in the number to be pushed.

Pulling a number from the stack to be written somewhere else in memory is the opposite of pushing a word. Remember to pull the least significant byte first and to write it at the highest address in the memory location reserved for the number.

Multiplication and division require a little more effort. The problem with multiplication is that if you multiply an n-bit number by an m-bit number you get an $(n + m) =$ bit number. If the sizes of numbers are variable, you have to allocate a variable amount of room for the extra bits produced by multiplication. The best solution to the problem is to treat multiplication as a triadic operation, such as $A + (B \times C)$, where A and C are numbers of the same precision. If you want to perform standard dyadic multiplication, make A zero but push this zero (of the same length as C) on the stack first. You can, however, just as easily execute a simultaneous multiply and add, and this subroutine leaves room, where A and B are stored on the stack, for the final product. Also, the formula trees can be adapted to this triadic operation. The multiply operator has three branches below it, for the A, B, and C in the expression above. The string technique works just fine to convert an arbitrary expression into subroutine calls, even if triadic multiplication operations are used. Finally, division can be a problem because integer divide produces two results, the quotient and the remainder. But the formula tree (now a more general graph called a Hasse diagram) and the string technique can be adapted to this too.

Finally, conversion from one number system to another can be done on the operand stack. The other stack, pointed to by S, is used temporarily to save the whole number on the bottom of the operand stack. One word at a time is pulled from the other stack and the converted number is formed on the operand stack according to the conversion rule. In many cases, the best way to convert from number system A to number system B is not the remainder method suggested in most elementary textbooks, but rather to write the definition of the number system A, such as the decimal number system:

$$N = (((N2 \times 10) + N1) \times 10) + N0$$

but perform the arithmetic in the number system B on the operand stack. It works beautifully.

The use of a variable precision operand stack allows simple and efficient arithmetic in the 6809. We recommend that you use it when you need to. Moreover, studying it will help you write fixed precision routines that you may need if speed is a major concern.

1.4 Conclusions

In this chapter we have surveyed the background in architecture and software that is needed for microcomputer interfacing. The first section covered the bare essentials of the von Neumann computer, the instruction and what it does, and the microcomputer. You will find this background very helpful as you begin to understand the details of what happens in an interface.

The middle section covered the addressing modes and instructions that you may expect in any microcomputer and discussed the ones that are in the 6800 and 6809 in more detail. The general comments in these sections should help you if you want to learn about another machine. The specific comments on the 6809 (and the 6800) should help you read the examples and do some of the experiments suggested in the book. Also, some elementary programming techniques, like decision trees and DO-loops, were presented. While most of you know these techniques, it is absolutely necessary for all of you to be familiar with them.

The final section presented some slightly more complex software techniques, such as the description and handling of data structures, subroutine calling and argument passing techniques, and multiple precision arithmetic techniques. These are the most common techniques that are valuable in interfacing microcomputers.

If you have had difficulty in some sections, we recommend some additional readings. There are plenty of fine books on computer architecture. You may have one already. We encourage you to reread that one again to reinforce the ideas that it presents, rather than to read several new ones superficially. But if you have not read one at all, we recommend *Introduction to Computer Organization and Data Structures* by H. Stone, published by McGraw-Hill in 1972, or any of Stone's later books, because he covers both architecture and data structures together. Additional information on computer architecture can be obtained from my article, "Digital Computer Architecture," in volume 7 of the *Encyclopedia of Computer Science and Technology*. Further information on microcomputers, including a comparison of different microcomputers is available from another article, "Microcomputers," in volume 10 of the same work, edited by Belzer et al. and published by Marcell Dekker. This twenty-volume encyclopedia, incidentally, has many excellent articles, some of which are splendid tutorials, that cover almost every topic in computer science. Further information on the 6809 is rather limited at the time of writing, although several books have been announced that purport to cover it. The *MC6809 Preliminary Programming Manual*, published by Motorola in 1979, is an accurate reference manual on the execution of each instruction in the 6809. Several books are available for the 6800, including paperbacks available in computer hobby stores. The last section can be reinforced by reading any of the many fine books on assembler-language programming, such as *Introduction to Microprocessors: Software, Hardware, Programming* by L. Leventhal, published by Prentice-Hall in 1978. Other fine books are available on these topics, and more are appearing daily. We might suggest contacting an instructor at your local college or university that teaches architecture, microprocessors, or assembler language programming for further more recent books on these topics.

Problems

Note

Problems 1-3 in this chapter and many problems in later chapters are paragraph-correction problems. Use the following guidelines for these problems.

The inclusion of paragraph-correction problems has been found to be a very useful way to help you understand concepts and definitions. The problem numbers of these will be followed by a star (*). The paragraph has some correct sentences and some erroneous sentences. Your task is to rewrite the paragraph so the whole paragraph is correct and has no sentences that do not fit into the theme of the paragraph. If a sentence is already correct, however, you are not supposed to change it, and you are not supposed to use the word "not" or its equivalent to correct the sentence. Consider the first sentence in problem 1. "The architecture is the block diagram of a computer." This is incorrect. It can be made correct by changing "architecture" to "organization," or by changing "block diagram" to "programmer's view" or else "instruction set and I/O connection capabilities." Any one of these corrections would be acceptable. The second sentence is correct as it stands, however, and should not be rewritten. Try to answer these questions without referring to the material in the chapter, then check your answers by looking up the definitions. If you get a couple of sentences wrong, you are doing fine. But if you have more trouble, you should reread the sections that the problem covers.

1.* The architecture is the block diagram of a computer. Von Neumann invented the architecture that is used on microcomputers. In it, the controller is analogous to the adding machine. We "recall" words from primary memory into the controller, using the program counter (left hand). Symbolic addresses are used in assembler languages to represent locations in this memory. A macro is a program in another part of memory that is called by a program, so that when the macro is done, the calling program resumes execution at an instruction below the jump to macro. An I/O interrupt is like a subroutine that is requested by an I/O device. The latency time is the time needed to completely execute an interrupt. To optimize the speed of execution, choose a computer with good static efficiency. A microcomputer is a controller and data operator on a single LSI chip, or a few LSI chips. A chip is called an LSI chip if it has about a hundred transistors.

2.* Addressing modes are especially important because they affect the efficiency of the most common class of instructions, the arithmetic class. Direct addressing has the operand in part of the instruction, called the displacement, and the displacement would be eight bits long for an instruction using it to load an eight-bit accumulator. Page addressing is primarily useful for handling arrays. Indirect addressing allows programs to be position independent. The 6809 has direct page addressing, which is a "quick-and-dirty" index addressing mode. Autoincrement addressing is especially useful for jumping to nearby locations. If we want to move data around in memory during execution of a program, indirect addressing is the only mechanism that can efficiently access single words as well as arrays.

3.* The 6809 has ninety-six bits of register storage, where the D accumulator is really the same as the X index register. The X register serves as an additional stack pointer, and instructions to push or pull can use X. The LEAD instruction will compute an effective address, but put that address in register D. Add with carry is used in multiple precision arithmetic. It can add into accumulator D. The 6809 has a DIV instruction to divide one unsigned number into another number. The DAA instruction can be used after an INCA instruction to increment a decimal number in accumulator A. The SEX instruction is essential for multiple word left shifts. BGT, BLT, BGE, and BLE can be used after comparing two's complement numbers. The SWI instruction is particularly useful as a subroutine call to a fast, short subroutine, because it is a fast instruction.

4. Identify which applications would be concerned with storage density and which would be concerned with speed. Give reasons for your decision. (a) pinball machine game, (b) microwave oven control, (c) home security monitor, (d) fast Fourier transform (FFT) module for a large computer, (e) satellite communications controller.

5. Write the (hexadecimal) code for a BRA L instruction, where the instruction code is at locations $12A and $12B and: (a) L is location $12F, (b) L is location $190, (c) L is location $12A, (d) L is location $120, (d) L is location $103.

6. Suppose X is $208A. Write the shortest, fastest executing (hexadecimal) code for LDA n,X that loads the value of TEMP into accumulator A, where TEMP is: (a) location $208A, (b) location $2095, (c) location $2100, (d) location $2074, (e) location $3076.

7. Suppose a memory is filled as follows, except for the program below: the word at address $WXYZ is $YZ (for example, location $2538 has value $38). Assuming that an address in X never points to the program, what will the value of X be after each instruction is executed in this program:

```
LDX    #$1
LDX    ,X
LDX    4,X
LDX    [,X]
LDX    ,-X
```

8. Suppose the condition code register is clear and the ADDA ALPHA instruction is executed. Give the value in the condition code register if: (a) accumulator A is $77, ALPHA is $77; (b) accumulator A is $C8, ALPHA is $77; (c) accumulator A is $8C, ALPHA is $C8; (d) repeat (c) for SUBA ALPHA.

Note

Problems 9-29 below and many problems in later chapters are programming problems. We recommend the following guidelines for these problems.

Unless otherwise stated, all programming problems should be answered in assembler language, in a format that would be accepted without errors by the Motorola RASM09 assembler (or for the 6800, by the Motorola RASM assembler). Refer to *The Complete Motorola Microcomputer Data Library*, the "M6800 Microprocessor Instruction Set Summary," or the "M6809 Microprocessor Set Summary" for further details on the 6800 and 6809 instruction sets, including timing and lengths of instructions. (Note that the full description of the 6809 does not appear in those books printed before June 1980.) Assume a 1MHZ memory clock for discussions on timing. In all programs that you write to answer questions, each line of code must have some comments which tell the reader what you are doing; but do not just rewrite the instructions in slightly different words as comments. Subroutines must follow the style recommended in section 1-3.2. Unless otherwise noted, you should try to write position independent, reentrant programs with the greatest static efficiency.

9. A forty-bit unsigned number, least significant byte at location N and each next more significant byte at the next higher location, is to be added to another forty-bit unsigned number, least significant byte at M and each next more significant byte at the next higher address. Write (a) the shortest program to add the number at N to the number at M, and (b) the fastest program to add the number at N to the number at M. Neither program need check for overflow.

10. Write a program that will add two single precision vectors:

$$C(I) = A(I) + B(I) \text{ for } I = 0 \text{ to } n - 1$$

where $A(0)$ is at address AR, $B(0)$ is at address BR, $C(0)$ is at address CR, each successive element is at the next higher address, and the number n is in accumulator A, n being less than 256.

11. Write a program to subtract an unsigned decimal number at N from an unsigned decimal number at M. Each number is ten digits stored two digits per byte, and the numbers are oriented as in problem 9. Jump to ERROR if the result is negative.

12. Write a program to convert a ten-digit decimal at location N and the next four locations, oriented as in problem 11, into an ASCII character

string beginning with the first character at location M representing the most significant digit, and next word representing next most significant digit, in the next nine words. Suppress leading zeroes by replacing them with blanks.

13. Write a flow chart and a program that will check each of the five words at location FLAG and the next four locations, and branch to location L0 if the word at FLAG + 0 is negative, L1 if the word at FLAG + 1 is negative, and in general, Ln if the word at FLAG + n is negative. If two words are negative, at the word at FLAG + i and the word at FLAG + j, and i is less than j, then the program will only branch to Li. (This is called a polling sequence.)

14. Write a program and its flow chart to write an n-checkerboard pattern in an area of memory, and then check to see that it is still there after it is completely written. An n-checkerboard pattern is two to the nth words of zeroes, followed by two to the nth words of $FF, followed by two to the nth words of zeroes, and so forth, repeated throughout the memory area. Assume that before the program begins, index register X contains the lowest address in this area, Y contains the highest address, and accumulator A contains the number n. (This pattern is used to check dynamic memories for pattern sensitivity errors.)

15. Write a 6800 assembler language reentrant SWI "subroutine" to compare the value of register A (high byte) and B (low byte) against index register X, setting the condition codes exactly as in the 6809 instruction CMP X.

16. Write a 6800 assembler language reentrant SWI "subroutine" to replace the 6809 instruction PSHS X.

17. Suppose A is a zero-origin five by seven array of triple precision numbers, stored in row major order. Write an assembler-language subroutine to put A[i, j] into location N, N + 1, and N + 2, where the address of A is in X, the address of N is in U, and i and j are in accumulators A and B, on calling this subroutine. Your subroutine should jump to location ERROR if the indexes are outside the range of the array.

18. Suppose a table starting at location TBL has ten rows, and each row has a five-letter ASCII character string followed by a sixteen-bit address, in row major order. Write a routine to jump to the address in the row if the five characters are the same as the five characters at location INSTR and the next four words.

19. Suppose a string of eleven ASCII characters consisting of only the letters S, I, P, and M is stored at location STRNG, as if generated by:

STRNG   FCC   'MISSISSIPPI'

Write a subroutine to convert this (or any other such string) to Huffmann Code, as defined by the coding tree in figure 1-6, and to store the code as a bit string, first bit as most significant bit at location CODE as allocated in:

CODE   RMB   20

Then write a subroutine that decodes such a code at location CODE, using the coding tree in figure 1-6, putting the ASCII string back as it were at location STRNG.

20. Write two subroutines to push and to pull a word from the bottom of a deque, assuming that the word is to be taken from or put into accumulator A and the Y pointer points to the word just below (at the next higher address than) the bottom word on the deque.

21. Write a subroutine that is equivalent to the FORTRAN statement:

$$IF(A) \quad 1,2,3$$

It will jump to FORTRAN line 1 if A is negative, to line 2 if A is zero, and to line 3 if A is positive. It will be called in assembler language passing A in call by value by putting it in accumulator A, and using call by name labels for FORTRAN lines 1, 2, and 3:

> LBSR   IF
> FDB   L1,L2,L3

(Note: you must balance the stack by removing the return address.)

22. A position independent transfer vector can be written:

> L   FDB   L0-L,L1-L,L2-L,L3-L

Write position independent, reentrant programs that will: (a) jump to the subroutine at location L2 through this transfer vector; (b) jump to Li, where i is in accumulator zero, and to ERROR if i is out of range; (c) exit from the routine at Li to the routine at Li + 1 so all routines are done in order, and so that L0 is done after L3. You will jump to this routine each time you finish routine Li. (Note, use long relative addresses, like LEAX L,PCR, to get the address of this table so the calling routine is position independent, provided that the calling routine and transfer vector are moved together and not independent of each other.)

23. A block is defined as the list BLOCK:

> BLOCK   FDB   0
>   FCB   4
>   FCC   'ABC'

Write a subroutine, using the EXG Y,PC instruction to call it, that pushes this block onto the stack pointed to by S, so that the words on the stack are in the same order in memory as they were in the block.

24. Write a formula tree and subroutine call program that will evaluate:

(a) $SIN(X) = X - (X^{**}3/3!) + (X^{**}5/5!) -$
$(X^{**}7/7!) + (X^{**}9/9!)$

(b) $A \times X^{**}3 + B \times X^{**}2 + C \times X + D$

(c) $A \times X + B \times Y + C \times Z$

The subroutines should use the push, dyadic multiply, add, and subtract routines only; and the formula tree and the program should be written so that the maximum number of numbers on the stack at any time is kept to a minimum. Assume that all numbers are signed binary integers (part (a) will have to be scaled by multiplying all coefficients by 9!) of equal length n and that n is in location LEN. Store all coefficients so you will not have to compute them. Expand square ($X^{**}2$), cube ($X^{**}3$) and so on, using multiplication.

25. Write a subroutine to subtract the bottom number on the operand stack from the next bottom number, assuming equal length numbers and no overflows.

26. Write a routine to negate the bottom number on the operand stack.

27. Write a routine to convert the bottom number on the operand stack from binary to binary coded decimal. You may try this strategy. First, pull the number from the operand stack and push it on the stack pointed to by S. Then pull one bit at a time from the latter stack, add it to the (initially zero) number on the bottom of the operand stack, and then double the number on the operand stack. But add the bit and double the number using decimal arithmetic, such as in the ADCA , – Y and DAA instruction sequence.

28. Write the formula trees and subroutine calls in problem 24 assuming that the multiplication routine is triadic, as in $A + B \times C$. Push the constant zero at the right time if you want the equivalent of dyadic multiplication, but try to use triadic multiplication to increase efficiency, and use monadic negation when appropriate. Otherwise, use the guidelines in problem 24.

29. The ADD subroutine in section 1-3.3 (and most of the other "stack" subroutines) can be used as "memory-to-memory" arithmetic routines, which will add one number stored anywhere in memory to another number stored anywhere in memory, as in $C = A + B$, with some simple changes. Rewrite the ADD subroutine for this application. Use Y to point to the source A, X to point to the source B, and U to point to the destination C.

2 Bus Hardware and Signals

The data and address buses are at the heart of the interfacing design problem. This chapter will discuss what a bus is, how data is put onto it, and how data from it is used.

The sections progress inductively. The first section covers basic concepts in digital hardware. These are then used in the next section to describe the control signals on the bus. The final section contains the important discussion on timing in the microprocessor bus.

As in chapter 1, the first two sections of the chapter are a condensed survey of background material that is needed in the remainder of the book. They are a summary of background material on computer organization and realization (as opposed to architecture and software discussed in chapter 1). They lead to the study of bus timing and control, which is very important to the design of interfaces. This experience might show you how important that study is. Microcomputer manufacturers have applications engineers who write applications notes on how to use the chips they manufacture, and who answer those knotty questions that systems designers cannot handle on their own. The author had an opportunity to sit down with Charlie Melear, one of the very fine applications engineers in the microcomponents applications engineering group at Motorola's plant. Charlie told me the two most common problems that designers have are: (1) improper control signals for the bus, whereby several bus drivers are given commands to drive the bus at the same time, and (2) failure to meet timing specifications for address and data buses. These problems will be covered in the last section of the chapter. They come up so often that studying them in depth can save a lot of frustration in the design of interfaces.

This chapter introduces a lot of terminology in order to provide background for later sections and to render the data sheets provided by the manufacturers readable. The terminology is as close as possible to that used in industry: logic diagram conventions conform to those used in *Electronics* magazine and to the Texas Instruments' *The TTL Data Book*, and microprocessor notation conforms to that used in Motorola data sheets. However, some minor deviations have been introduced where constructs appear so often in this book that further notation is useful.

This chapter should provide enough background in computer organization for the remaining sections. After reading the chapter, you should be able to read a logic diagram or the data sheets describing microcomputers or their associated integrated circuits, and you should have a fundamental knowledge of the signals and the timing of signals on a typical microcomputer bus. This chapter should provide adequate hardware background for later chapters; however, if the reader has difficulty with it, additional reading is recommended. As in the last chapter, a list of suggestions will be offered at the end of this chapter for those readers.

2-1 Digital Hardware

The basic notions and building blocks of digital hardware are presented in this section. While most readers have taken a course on digital-hardware design, the traditional course emphasizes minimization of logic gates. Microcomputers interfacing requires an emphasis on buses rather than gates. This section focuses on the digital hardware that can be seen on a typical microcomputer bus. The first subsection presents a clear definition of the terminology used to describe signals and modules connected to a bus. The second subsection considers the kinds of modules you might see there.

2-1.1 Modules and Signals

Before the bus is explained, we need to discuss a few hardware concepts, such as the module and the signal. We deal in abstractions. Rather than working with absolutely fundamental units like electrons and fields, we define abstract things at a level of detail where the concepts can be most readily conveyed.

One of these concepts is the binary *signal*. Although a signal is a voltage or a current, we think of it only as a *high* signal, if the voltage or current is above a predefined threshold, or as a *low* signal if it is below another threshold. We will use the symbols H for high and L for low. A signal is *determinate* when we can know for sure either that it is high or that it is low. Related to this concept, a *variable* is the information a signal carries and has values *true* (T) and *false* (F). For example, a wire can carry a signal L and, being a variable called "ENABLE," it can have a value T, to indicate that something is indeed enabled. We use the expression "to *assert a variable*" to mean to make it true, "to *negate a variable*" to make it false, and "to *complement a variable*" to make it true if it was false, or to make it false if it was true. There are two possible relations betwen signals and variables. In *positive logic*, a high signal represents a true variable, and a low signal, a false variable. In *negative logic*, a high represents a false variable while a low represents a true variable. Signals, which can be viewed on an oscilloscope or a logic analyzer, are preferred when someone, especially a technician, deals with actual hardware. Variables have more conceptual significance, and seem to be preferred by designers, especially in the early stages of design, and by programmers, especially when writing input/output software. Simply put, "true" and "false" are the one and zero of the programmer and the architect and system designer, and "high" and "low" are the one and zero of the technician and IC manufacturer. While we find nothing wrong with using one and zero where the meaning is clear to both speaker and listener, we will use the words true and false when talking about software or system design, and the words high and low when discussing the hardware realization, in order to be as clear as possible in this book.

Two types of variables and their corresponding signals are important in hardware. A *memory variable* is capable of being made true or false, and of retaining this value, but a *link variable* is true or false as a result of functions on other variables. A link variable is always some function of other variables (as the output of some gate). At a high level of abstraction, these variables operate in different dimensions; memory variables are used to convey information through time (at the same point in space), while link variables convey information through space (at the same point in time). Some transformations on hardware, like converting from a parallel to a serial adder, are explained in a satisfying way by this abstract view. For instance, one can convert a parallel adder into a serial adder by converting a link variable that passes the carry into a memory variable that saves the carry. Also, in a simulation program, we differentiate between the types because memory variables have to be initialized and link variables do not.

A *synchronous* signal can be viewed as associated with a periodic variable (for example, a square wave) called a *clock*. The signal or variable is indeterminate except when the clock is asserted. Or alternatively, the value of the signal is irrelevant except when the clock is asserted. Depending on the context, the signal is determinate either precisely when the clock changes from false to true, or else as long as the clock is true. The context depends on the thing that picks up the signal, and will be discussed when we study the flip-flop. This is so in the real world because of delays through circuitry, noise, and transmission line ringing. In our abstraction of the signal, we simply ignore the signal except when this clock is asserted, and we design the system so the clock is asserted only when we can guarantee that the signal is determinate under worst case conditions. Though there are asynchronous signals where there is no associated clock and the signals are supposed to be determinate at all times, most microprocessor signals are synchronous; so in further discussions, we will assume all signals are synchronous. Then two signals are *equivalent* if they have the same (H or L) value whenever the clock is asserted.

The other basic idea is that of the *module*, which is a block of hardware with identifiable input, output, and memory variables. The input variables are the *input ports* and the output variables are the *output ports*. The behavior of a module is often all we are interested in. Modules are *behaviorally equivalent* if for equivalent values of the initial memory variables and equivalent sequences of values of input variables, they deliver equivalent sequences of values of output variables. Thus, we are not concerned about how modules are constructed internally, nor what are the precise voltages, nor about the signals when the clock is not asserted, but only about the signals when the clock is asserted.

In section 1-1.3, we introduced the idea of an integrated circuit to define the term microprocessor. Now, we discuss it further. An integrated circuit is a module that is generally contained in a *dual in-line package*. This is a long rectangular plastic or ceramic package with pins along both the edges (hence the term dual in-line). The pins are the input and output ports. Viewed from the top, one of the short edges has an indent or mark. The pins are numbered counterclockwise from this mark, starting with pin one. Gates are defined in the next section, but will be used here to describe degrees of complexity of integrated circuits. A *small scale integrated circuit*, or SSI, has about ten gates on one chip, a *medium scale integrated circuit* (MSI) has about a hundred, a *large scale integrated circuit* (LSI) has about a thousand, and a *very large scale integrated circuit* (VLSI) has more than ten thousand gates on a chip. SSI and MSI circuits are commonly used to build up address decoders and some input/output modules in a microcomputer; LSI and VLSI are commonly used to implement eight- and sixteen-bit word microprocessors; 4K-bit and 64K-bit memory chips, and some complex input/output chips.

A *family* of integrated circuits is a collection of different types that are made with the same technology and have the same electrical characteristics so they can be easily interconnected with others in the same family. Chips from different families can be interconnected, but this might require some careful study and design. The *low power Schottky*, or LSTTL family, and the *complementary metal oxide semiconductor*, or CMOS family , are often used with microprocessors. Refer to *The TTL Data Book for Design Engineers*, published by Texas Instruments, Inc., for a catalog of LSTTL integrated circuits ICs commonly used in microcomputers. These ICs will be used in examples and problems in this book. The LS family is used where higher speed is required, and the CMOS family where lower power or higher immunity to noise is desired.

A *block diagram* is used to describe hardware organization (see section 1-1.1). It is especially useful for showing how ICs work so that a programmer can get the main ideas without getting involved in the details that do not concern the software. A block diagram shows modules as rectangles, with the most important inputs and outputs shown around the perimeter. Names represent variables rather than signals, functions like AND or OR represent functions on variables rather than signals. An AND function, for example, is one in which the output is T if all the inputs are T. These conventions ignore details that are needed to build the module so that its behavior can be simply explained. The effects of software instructions can be shown nicely on a block diagram: for instance, if the LDX $4000 instruction reads a word from a certain module, then this can be shown as in figure 2-1. Block diagrams are used to show the organization of LSI chips as they appear to the programmer. Block diagrams will appear frequently in the following discussions, and their meaning will be discussed in the accompanying text.

Logic diagrams describe the realization of hardware to the detail needed to build it. In logic diagrams, modules are generally shown as rectangles with input and output ports shown along the perimeter. Logic functions are generally defined for signals rather than variables (For example, an AND function if one whose output is H if its inputs are all H). It is common, and in fact desirable, to use many copies of the same module. This is quite similar to the use of subroutines in software. To encourage software-hardware trade off thinking, we use the same terminology for logic diagrams as is used for subroutines. The original copy, here called the *type*, has a name, the *type name*, and its inputs and outputs are often given *formal parameter names*. The type name is generally put in the middle of the module, unless lack of room indicates putting it above the module, and formal parameter names can be put inside the rectangle close to the termination of the line representing the link. Especially when refering to a copy of a module among several copies, we give each copy a distinct *copy name*, which can be written, in parentheses, in the middle of the module. The variables shown outside the module are *actual parameter names*. Integrated circuits, in particular, are shown this way, and pin numbers are also shown just outside the rectangle for each connection that has to be made. Pins that do not have to be connected are not shown as connections to the module. Figure 2-3 will illustrate some examples of these conventions.

Connections supplying power (positive supply voltage and ground) are usually not shown. They might be identified in a footnote if necessary. In general, in LSI and VLSI N-channel MOS chips such as microprocessors and the input/output chips discussed in these notes, V_{ss} is the ground pin (zero volts), and V_{cc} or V_{dd} is usually positive five volts. You might remember this by a quotation improperly attributed to Churchill: "Ground

Figure 2-1. A Block Diagram Showing the Effect of an Instruction

the SS." For SSI and MSI chips, the pin with the largest pin number is generally connected to positive five volts while the pin kitty-cornered from it is connected to ground. One should keep power and ground lines straight and wide to reduce inductance that causes ringing, and put a capacitor (0.1 microfarad disc) between power and ground to isolate the ICs from each other. These *bypass capacitors* serve to prevent the voltage fluctuations that result when one chip changes its power supply current from affecting the voltage supplied to other chips, as these fluctuations might look like signals to them. Normally, one such capacitor is needed for four SSI chips or one LSI chip, but if the power and ground lines appear to have noise, more capacitors should be put between power and ground.

Negative logic is usually shown in connections to inner modules by a small bubble where the connection touches the rectangle. In inputs and outputs to the whole system described by the logic diagram, negative logic is shown by a bar over the name of the variable. Although it is logically incorrect, common practice accepts a bar over the formal parameter name and a bubble at the end of a line to mean that the line is in negative logic, as if to emphasize the point, rather than to double negate the variable. Ideally, if a link is in negative logic, all its connections to modules should have a bubble. However, since changing logic polarity effects an inversion of the variable, designers sometimes steal a free inverter this way, so if bubbles do not match at both ends, remember that the signal is unchanged, but the variable is inverted, as it goes through the link.

A logic diagram should convey all the information needed to build a module, allowing only the exceptions we just discussed to reduce the clutter. Examples of logic diagrams appear throughout these notes. An explanation of figures 2-2 and 2-3, which must wait until the next section, should clarify these conventions.

2-1.2 Drivers, Registers, and Memories

This section describes the bus in terms of the D flip-flop and the bus driver. These devices serve to take data from the bus and to put data onto it. The memory, a collection of registers, is also introduced.

A *gate* is an elementary module with a single output where the value of the output is a Boolean logic function of the values of the inputs. The output of a gate is generally a link variable. For example, a three-input NOR gate output is true if none of its inputs are true, otherwise it is false. The output is always determined in terms of its inputs. A *buffer* is a gate that has a more powerful output amplifier and is often used to supply the power needed to put signals onto a bus, which we discuss below. In these cases, the gate may be very simple, so that it has just one input, and the output is the complement of the input (inverting buffer) or the same signal as the input (noninverting buffer).

Your typical gate has an output stage which may be connected to up to f other inputs of gates of the same family (f is called the *fan-out*) and to no other output of a gate. If two outputs are connected to the same link, they may try to put opposite signals on the link, which will certainly be confusing to inputs on the link, and which may even damage the output stages. A *bus* (*or buss*), however, is a link to which more than two gate outputs are connected. The gates have to have specially designed output amplifiers so that all but one output on a bus may be disabled. The gates are called *bus drivers*. An upper limit to the number of outputs that can be connected to a bus is called the *fan-in*.

An *open collector gate* or open collector driver output can be connected to a *wire-OR* bus, (the bus has to have a *pull-up resistor* connected between it and the positive supply voltage). If any output should attempt to put out a low signal, the signal on the bus will be low. Only when all outputs attempt to put out a high signal will the output be high. Generally, the gate is a two-input AND gate, the inputs in positive logic, and the output in negative logic. Data on one input is put onto the bus whenever the other input is true. The other input acts as a positive logic *enable*. When the enable is asserted, we say the drive is *enabled*. Since this bus is normally used in negative logic relationship, the value on the bus is the OR of the outputs. This is so common that the bus is called a wire-OR bus.

A *tristate gate* or tristate driver has an additional input, a *tristate enable*. When the tristate enable is asserted (the driver is enabled), the output amplifier forces the output signal high or low as directed by the gate logic. When the enable is not asserted, the output amplifier lets the output float. Two or more outputs of tristate gates may be connected to a *tristate bus*. The circuitry must be designed to insure that no two gates are enabled at the same time, lest the problem with connecting outputs of ordinary gates arise. if no gates are enabled, the bus signal floats: it is subject to stray static and electomagnetic fields. In other words, it acts like an antenna.

Gates are usually shown in logic diagrams as D shaped symbols, the output on the round edge and inputs on the flat edge. See figure 2-2 for the positive logic AND, NAND, and other gates. Even though they are not shown using the convention for modules given above, if they are in integrated circuits, the pin numbers are often shown next to all inputs and outputs.

Gates are usually put into intergrated circuits so that the total number of pins is fourteen or sixteen, counting two pins for positive supply voltage and ground. This yields, for instance, the quad two-input NAND gate, the 7400, which contains four two-input positive logic NAND gates. A typical microprocessor uses an eight-bit wide data bus, where eight identical and

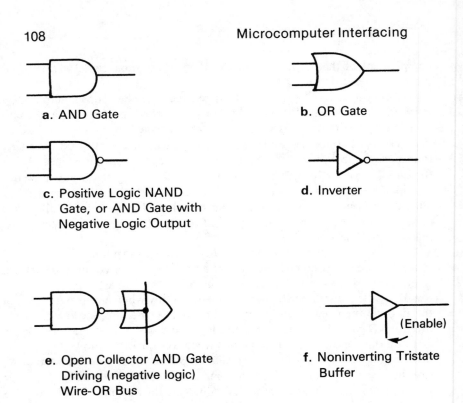

a. AND Gate

b. OR Gate

c. Positive Logic NAND Gate, or AND Gate with Negative Logic Output

d. Inverter

e. Open Collector AND Gate Driving (negative logic) Wire-OR Bus

(Enable)

f. Noninverting Tristate Buffer

Figure 2-2. Some Common Gates

separate bus wires carry one bit of data on each wire. This has engendered octal bus drivers, with eight inverting or noninverting bus drivers that share common enables, in an integrated circuit. The 81LS95 and 81LS96 are popular octal noninverting and inverting tristate bus driver integrated circuits. Figure 2-3a shows a logic diagram of the 81LS95, in which, to show pin connections clearly, the pins are placed along the perimeter of the module exactly as they appear on the dual in line package. A positive five-volt supply wire is connected to pin twenty, and a ground wire, to pin ten. If the signals on both pins one and nineteen are low, the output of the NOR gate will be high, and the eight separate tristate gates will be enabled. For instance the signal input to pin two will be amplified and output on pin three. If either pin one or nineteen is high, the tristate amplifiers are not enabled, and the outputs on pins three, five, . . ., seventeen are allowed to float. This kind of diagram is valuable in catalogues to show most clearly the inputs and outputs of gates in integrated circuits.

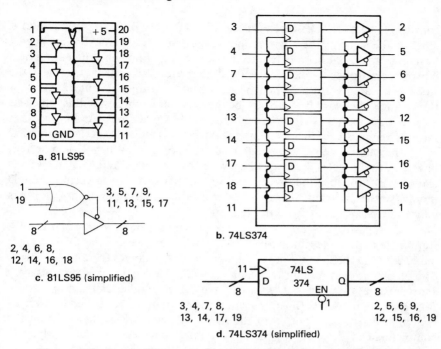

a. 81LS95

b. 74LS374

c. 81LS95 (simplified)

d. 74LS374 (simplified)

Figure 2-3. Logic Diagrams for a Popular Driver and Register

To save effort in drawing logic diagrams, if a number *n* of identical wires connect to identical modules, a single line is drawn with a slash through it and the number *n* next to the slash. If pin connections are to be shown, a list of *n* pin numbers is written. Corresponding pins in the list at one end are connected to corresponding pins in the list at the other end. Commonly, however, the diagram is clear without showing the list of pin numbers. Also, if a single wire is connected to several pins, it is diagrammed as a single line, and the list of pins is written by the line. See figure 2-3c, which shows how the 81LS95 discussed above might be more clearly shown connecting to a bus in a logic diagram. Note the eight tristate drivers with their input and output links are shown by one line and gate symbol. The numeral 8 by the slash indicates the figure should be replicated eight times. The NOR gate output, a single link, connects to the enables of all eight bus drivers.

A *D flip-flop*, also called a (one-bit) latch or (one-bit) transparent latch, is an elementary module with *data input* D, *clock* C, and *output* Q. Q is always a memory variable having the value of the bit of data stored in the flip-flop. When the clock C is asserted (we say the flip-flop is *clocked*), the value of D is copied into the flip-flop memory. The clock input is rather confusing, because it is really just a WRITE ENABLE. It sounds like it must be the same as the microcomputer system clock. It may be connected to such a clock, but usually it is connected to something else such as an output of a controller, which is discussed in section 2-2.1. It is, however, the clock associated with the synchronous variable on the D input of that flip-flop, since the variable has to be determinate whenever this clock is asserted. As long as C is asserted, Q is made equal to D. As long as C is false, Q remains what it was. Note that, when C is false, Q is the value of D at the moment when C changed from true to false. When C is asserted, however, the flip-flop behaves like a wire from D to Q, and Q changes as D changes. D flip-flops are used to hold data that was sent to them on the D inputs, so the data will still be available on the Q output even though it has long since disappeared from the D input.

A *D edge-triggered flip-flop* is an elementary module like the D flip-flop, except that the data stored in it, and available on the Q output, is made equal to the D input only when the clock C changes from false to true. The clock causes the data to change (the flip-flop is clocked) in this very short interval of time. A *D master slave flip-flop* (also called a dual rank flip-flop) is a pair of D flip-flops where the D input to the second is internally connected to the Q output of the first, and the clock of the second is the complement of the clock of the first. Though constructed differently, a D master slave flip-flop behaves the same as the D edge-triggered flip-flop. These two flip-flops have the property that data on their Q output is always the former value of data in them at the time that new data is put into them. It is possible, therefore, to use the signal output from an edge-triggered flip-flop to feed data into the same or another edge-triggered flip-flop using the same clock, even while loading new data. This should not be attempted with D flip-flops because the output will be changing as it is being used to determine the value to be stored in the flip-flops that use the data. When a synchronous signal is input to a D edge-triggered flip-flop, the clock input to the flip-flop is associated with the signal, and the signal only has to be determinate when the clock changes from false to true.

In either type of flip-flop, or in more complex devices that use flip-flops, the data has to be determined (a stable high or a stable low signal) over a range of time when the data is being stored. For an edge-triggered or dual-rank flip-flop, the *setup time* is the time during which the data must be determinate before the clock edge. The *hold time* is the time after the clock edge during which the data must be determinate. For a latch, the setup time is the minimum time at the end of the period when the clock is true in which the data must be determinate, and the hold time is the minimum time just after that when the data must still be determinate. These times are usually specified for worst case possibilities. If you satisfy the set-up and hold times, the device can be expected to work as long as it is kept at a temperature and supplied with power voltages that are within specified limits. If you do not, it may work some of the time, but will probably fail, according to Murphy's Law, at the worst possible time.

In most integrated circuit D flip-flops or D edge-triggered flip-flops, the output Q is available along with its complement, which can be thought of as the output Q in negative logic. They often have inputs, set, which if asserted will assert Q, and reset, which if asserted will make Q false. Set and reset are often in negative logic: when not used they should be connected to a false value, or high signal. Other flip-flops such as set-reset flip-flops and JK edge-triggered flip-flops are commonly used in digital equipment, but we will not need them in the following discussions.

A *one-shot* is rather similar to the flip-flop. It has an input TRIG and an output Q, and has a resistor and capacitor connected to it. The output Q is normally false. When the input TRIG changes from false to true, the output becomes true, and remains true for a period of time T fixed by values of the resistor and capacitor ($T = k \times R \times C$ for some constant k).

The use of eight-bit wide data buses has engendered integrated circuits that have four or eight flip-flops with common clock inputs and common clear inputs. If simple D flip-flops are used, the module is called a *latch*, and if edge-triggered flip-flops are used, it is a *register*. Also, modules for binary number counting (*counters*) or shifting data in one direction (*shift registers*) may typically contain four or eight edge-triggered flip-flops. Note that, even though a module may have additional capabilities, it may still be used without these capabilities. A counter or a shift register is sometimes used as a simple register. More interestingly, a latch can be used as a noninverting gate, or using the complemented Q output, as an inverter. This is done by tying the clock to true. Some popular LS family registers and latches are described in *The TTL Data Book*. The 74LS163 is a popular four-bit binary counter, the 74LS164 and 74LS165 are common eight-bit shift registers, and the 74LS373 and 74LS374 are popular octal latches and registers that have tristate drivers built into them. The 74LS374, shown in Figure 2-3, will be particularly useful in the following discussion of practical buses, since it contains a register to capture data from the bus, as well as a tristate driver to put data onto the bus.

These conventions are used to describe flip-flops in logic diagrams. The clock and D inputs are shown on the left of a square, the set on the top, the reset on the bottom, and the Q on the right. The letter D is put by the D input, but the others need no letter. The clock of an edge-triggered flip-flop is denoted by a triangle just inside the jointure of that input. This triangle and the bubble outside the square describe the clocking. If neither appear the flip-flop is a D flip-flop that inputs data from D when the clock is high; if a bubble, a D flip-flop that inputs data when the clock is low; if a triangle, an edge-triggered D flip-flop that inputs data when the clock changes from low to high; and if both appear, an edge-triggered D flip-flop that inputs data when the clock input changes from high to low. This notation is quite useful because a lot of design errors are due to clocking flip-flops when the data is not ready to be input. If a signal is input to several flip-flops, they should all be clocked at the same time, when the signal will be determinate.

The logic diagram of the 74LS374 is shown in figure 2-3b, as it might appear in a catalog. Note that the common clock for all the edge-triggered D flip-flops on pin eleven makes them store data on their own D inputs when it rises from low to high. Note that when the signal on pin one is low the tristate drivers are all enabled, so the data in the flip-flops is output through them. Using this integrated circuit in a logic diagram, we might compact it using the bus conventions, as shown in figure 2-3d.

An *(i, j) random access memory* (RAM) is a module with i rows and j columns of D flip-flops, and an address port, an input port, and output port. A row of the memory is available simultaneously and is usually referred to as a *word*, and the number j is called the *word width*. There is considerable ambiguity here, because a computer may think of its memory as having a word width, but the memory module itself may have a different word width, and it may be built from RAM integrated circuits having yet a different word width. So the word, and the word width, should be used in a manner that avoids this ambiguity. The output port outputs data read from a row of the flip-flops to a bus and usually has bus drivers built into it. Sometimes the input and output ports are combined. The address port is used to input the row number of the row to be read or written. A *memory cycle* is a period of time during which the memory can write j bits from the input port into a row selected by the address port data, read j bits from a row selected by the address port data to output port, or do nothing. If the memory reads data, the drivers on the output port are enabled. There are two common ways to indicate which of the three possible operations to do in a memory cycle. In one, two variables called *chip enable* (CE) and *read/not write* (R/W) indicate the possibilities; a do-nothing cycle is executed if CE is false, a read if CE and R/W are both asserted, and a write if CE is asserted but R/W is not. In the other, two variables called *read enable* (RE) and *write enable* (WE) are used, when neither are asserted, nothing is done; when RE is asserted, a read is executed; and if WE is asserted, a write is executed. Normally, CE, RE, and WE are in negative logic. The *memory cycle time* is the time needed to complete a read or a write operation and be ready to execute another read or write. The *memory access time* is the time from the beginning of a memory cycle until the data read from a memory is determinate on the output, or the time when data to be written must be determinate on the input of the memory. A popular fast (twenty-nanosecond access time) (4,4) RAM is the 74LS670. (See *The TTL Data Book for Design Engineers*). It has four input ports and four separate output ports; by having two different address ports it is actually able simultaneously to read a word selected by the read address port, and to write a word selected by the write address port. A larger, slower (500-nanosecond cycle time) (1024,1) RAM is the 2102. It has a ten-bit address, a single input and a single output port, and CE, R/W variables that permit it to read or write any word in a memory cycle. A diagram of this chip will appear in figure 2-9a, when we consider an example that uses it in section 2-3.2 in this chapter.

Several cousins to the RAM are used in microcomputers, especially to store fixed data and programs. A *read-only memory* (ROM) is a memory that can be read, but can never be written into. The pattern stored in the memory is determined by a mask used in the final stages of manufacturing the chip. Such ROMs are inexpensive and quite large, but because the mask is rather expensive, they are used where standard patterns can be sold in large quantities. A *programmable read-only memory* (PROM) is a ROM that can be written into (*programmed*) by the designer by burning a fuse inside it for each bit; a fuse is blown if an F is stored, and not blown if a T is stored in a bit. PROMs can be programmed by the designer, but he cannot unblow a fuse. An *eraseable programmable read-only memory* (EPROM) is a PROM that uses static charges on a buried conductor in a dielectric insulation layer, instead of fuses. A charge on the conductor cuts off the current below it, so it acts like a blown fuse. The charges are programmed in a manner similar to programming a PROM, but they can be removed by exposing the insulator to ultraviolet light, which ionizes it. These devices, ROMs, PROMs, and EPROMs, are often used in microcomputer systems to store fixed data and programs.

2-2 Control Signals and Their Sequences in a Microprocessor

One of the main problems that designers face is the control of bus drivers so that at no time will two of them try to drive the same bus. The designer has to be acquainted with control signals and the sequences of control signals that are generated by a microprocessor in order to approach this problem. This section is devoted to the notions of microprogramming and of microcomputer instruction execution that are necessary for the comprehension and explanation of control signals on the microcomputer bus. The first subsection covers the basics of microprogramming to lay the groundwork for the next subsection. That subsection will discuss the way the M6809 actually executes an instruction such as ADDA #5. (The M6800 is internally very similar to the M6809, having fewer buses. The part having to do with the ADDA #5 instruction and the operation of that part is the same in both machines.) With this discussion, you should be able to understand the sequencing of control signals, which is at the heart of the problem of having too many bus drivers enabled on a bus.

2-2.1 Data Transfers and Microprograms

We now look at the control of a bus, by examining the data transfer and the microprogram. *Microprogramming* is the discipline of writing microprograms, which will be explained in this section, in order to convert instructions read by the computer to the actions that carry out those instructions. It will be used in the next subsection to discuss the timing of signals on the M6809 address and data buses. It is an extensive subject, one which can barely be covered in a whole course. This section aims to cover only those aspects that are important in designing microcomputer based systems. One part of a microprogram deals with the control of the machine and the other part deals with the sequence of control, much like jump instructions control a program. We will eschew the study of the sequence. We will concentrate on how the microprogram controls the computer. This aspect presents the best level of detail for explaining the concepts of bus data transfers.

The concept of the data transfer focuses our attention on the data as it moves from module to module. This view is orthogonal to the view of the sequential machine, which concentrates on a module as different data is moved into it. For simplicity, we will discuss data transfers on a single bus, although the idea is more general, and for concreteness we will describe a bus using the integrated circuits discussed above.

Consider a bus to which the outputs of several drivers and the D inputs to several registers are attached. The operation of moving data through this bus, by enabling exactly one of the drivers and clocking one or more of the registers, is a *data transfer*. A data transfer here takes place in a period of time called a *microcycle*. The driver that has been selected to send out the data is enabled throughout almost all of the microcycle, and the clocks of the registers selected to receive the data are asserted so that they copy the data near the end of the microcycle, while the enable is still asserted. Suppose A and B are registers. The data transfer describes the actual movement of data. We note a data transfer thus:

$$A \leftarrow B$$

to mean that in this microcycle, the value that was in B at its beginning is copied into register A at its end.

We offer to clear up some common misconceptions about data transfers. Some worry about clocking two registers at the same time, that this might drain the signal on the bus, perhaps making it too weak to recognize. Actually, a register uses the same amount of signal output from a driver, whether or not it is clocked. It is only important that the number of inputs physically connected to the bus be less than the fan-out of the bus drivers. Usually, tristate gate enables and latch clocks are in the negative logic relations. That is, when off, they are high, and when on, low. This convention is actually a result of the fact that TTL decoders, which usually generate these control signals, are easier to build and are faster if their outputs are in negative logic. If they are asserted (low) throughout the microcycle, or at least during as much of the microcycle as possible, the driver will put data on the bus throughout the cycle and the data will be clocked into the latch throughout the cycle. The value actually stored there will be that value input at the very end, when its clock input rises from low to high as the signal changes from true to false. (The register clocks also use negative logic in order to be interchangeable with latches, but a little gremlin inverts the variable due to the fact that the register is actually clocked by the beginning of the next cycle. Practically speaking, we make sure that the edge that clocks data into the register occurs at the end of the microcycle.)

The enables on the tristate gates and the clocks on the registers are called *control variables* and are generated by a *controller*. The assignment of value(s) to control variable(s) is a *micro-order*. The driver enable variables should have the property that exactly one of them is asserted, the others being false. A collection of variables having the property that only one variable is asserted is called *singular*. For instance, if the variables A,B, and C are singular, they can have the values TFF, or FTF, or FFT. The values TTF or TTT are not permitted (and in a strict sense of the term, FFF is not permitted). The driver enable variables have to be singular, and though they do not have to, the register clock variables are often singular. It is possible to store more compactly and transmit a collection of n singular variables by *encoding* them in binary: that is, each variable is assigned a number from zero to $n - 1$, and the binary number of the asserted variable is stored and transmitted. The binary number is called a *code* for the driver or clock that it enables. This way, for instance, three wires can be used in lieu of eight wires. Ultimately, however, the code has to be *decoded* so that the singular variables are individually available to enable each driver or clock each register. A related idea is that of *recoding* control variables. Suppose a module, such as an integrated circuit, has its control variables encoded so that, for instance, eight sources inside the module can put data onto a bus and only three wires, or pins, are needed actually to send the code into the module to select the source. If the system will only need three of these sources of data, then really only two wires are needed to uniquely identify the source. The n sources are assigned numbers 0 to $n - 1$, and the binary numbers are stored and sent. A *recoder* then converts these codes into the codes actually used by the device. Encoding and recoding can be used to advantage to reduce the cost of the controller, but the operation of decoding or recoding can add some time to the microcycle, slowing down the processor. This may be unacceptable in some cases.

The controller can be built using one-shots, shift registers, and a mess of gates, or it can be designed around a memory. The latter being much easier to describe and becoming more popular, we discuss it here. First, the simpler *horizontal microprogram* technique is discussed. A *control memory* C stores a *microprogram*. One row, say row i, is read out during a microcycle. Each column, say column j, directly feeds an enable or clock control variable. The bit in row i, column j, is true if the jth enable or clock is to be asserted whenever the ith row is read out. Though not necessarily, a counter can provide addresses to read each row out of the memory sequentially, row $i + 1$ right after row i. The microprogram is written for the memory, and the memory is filled with the desired values, so that when it is read out, the data transfers will be executed as desired.

We now give a concrete example of the data transfer and the horizontal microprogram. Consider a simplified bus shown in figure 2-4. Suppose in one microcycle we wish to transfer the variable IN to the register A, and in the next microcycle, to transfer the contents of A into B. (The data in B is always output in link OUT.) This is denoted by the transfers written in two successive lines:

$$A \leftarrow IN$$
$$B \leftarrow A$$

In order to transfer this data, the following micro-orders are given. In the first microcycle, C1 and C2 are asserted. This puts the data IN onto the bus, and then copies this data into register A. In the second microcycle, C3 and C4 are asserted. Consider a slight variation of this microprogram. In one microcycle, the data IN is to be sent to both registers A and B. This is denoted

$$A \leftarrow IN; \; B \leftarrow IN$$

and the two data transfers on the same line are assumed to take place simultaneously, in the same microcycle. Now, to put IN on the bus, C1 is asserted and both C2 and C4 are simultaneously asserted. By this means, the data is copied simultaneously into both registers.

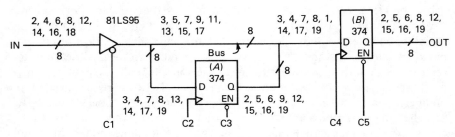

Figure 2-4. A Bus with Control Signals

   Some remarks about timing are now noted. When asserted, C1 and C3 should be held low (since they are in negative logic) for the whole duration of the step. When the edge-trigger clocks C2 and C4 are to be asserted, the rising edge of the signal on pin eleven should arrive towards the end of the step, while C1 or C3 are still asserted. Normally these clock variables are ANDed with a square wave so they are never asserted during the first half of the microcycle, thus there will always be a rising edge at the end of the microcycle even if the variable is asserted in two successive microcycles. This rising edge also has to occur when the data is determinate in order to satisfy the setput and hold times of all the flip-flops that are loading it. The duration of the step must be longer than the delay time for a signal to travel from any output to any input and the setup plus the hold times of the flip-flops loading it. This delay time essentially determines the fastest clock that can be used with the system.

   To continue our example, horizontal microprograms will be shown for the data transfers above. Suppose C1, C2, C3, and C4 are output from the respective columns of control memory, and the transfer A ◄— IN is ordered whenever row five is read, and the transfer B ◄— A whenever row six is read from control memory. Then the control memory will have the following words in rows five and six, respectively:

TTFF
FFTT

Note that if stored in negative logic, the control memory will have in rows five and six:

LLHH
HHLL

We distinguish between the signal and the variable here because, if we were to use one and zero when we write the microprogram on paper, we would write line five as 1100, but when we store it in the control memory, we write the same line as 0011. For the second microprogram, if it is executed when row eight is read, row eight will be:

TTFT

or if the memory stores variables in negative logic:

LLHL

   These concepts are now extended. Suppose a collection of control variables, coming from columns m to n of the control memory are singular. (That is, at most one of the control variables is ever asserted at any given time.) Then we can compress them into fewer variables and columns by encoding them. A decoder module will be needed to decode the codes to obtain the singular control variables needed for the drivers and registers, and the codes are stored in the compressed columns in lieu of the actual singular control signals themselves. Moreover, if recoders are used on the outputs of some columns to further compact the number of columns, the recoded codes are stored therein. This compaction process can be carried to extreme, so that only one code is stored on each row of the control memory, and all control variables are derived from it by a collection of decoders and recoders. Such a microprogram is called *vertical* as opposed to horizontal. Note that in a horizontal microprogram, all control variables have their own columns in the control memory and no decoding or recoding is used. Most microprograms have some decoding and recoding, and are thus between vertical and horizontal microprograms.

We extend our example to show how vertical microprogramming is implemented. Noting that the gate enables C1 and C3 in the previous example must be singular because only one data word can be put on the bus in a microcycle, we can encode them so that the code T orders C1 asserted and the code F orders C3 asserted. Then if the memory stored this code, followed by the clocks C2 and C4, the first microprogram would be stored thus:

$$TTF$$
$$FFT$$

In general, if n control variables are singular, they can be encoded into log n (base 2) bits, to save quite a bit of microprogram storage space. Note that if the clocks were also encoded, another column could be deleted, but the second microprogram would not work because no code would permit both clocks to be enabled simultaneously. A further example is offered to show the concept of recoding. Suppose a microprogram memory has a few rows like the following:

$$TFTTFT$$
$$TTFTTT$$
$$FFFFFF$$
$$FFTFFT$$

in which the leftmost two columns and the rightmost two columns have only the patterns TF . . . FT, TT . . . TT, FF . . . FF, and FF . . . FT and never have any other patterns. Since there are only four patterns, they could be replaced by two (log 4 base 2) columns, and a recoder would be used to recover the original codes. The recoder can be implemented with gates or a small ROM or an equivalent device called a programmable logic array. Suppose we implement the recoder with a ROM having the following pattern:

FFFF

TTTT

TFFT

FFFT

and the original microprogram is then rewritten so that, say, the first two columns generate an address into this ROM, so that the ROM generates the control signals from its columns one to four that were generated from columns one, two, five, and six of the original microprogram. Then the new microprogram would look this way:

TFTT

FTFT

FFFF

TTTF

Using recoding, it is possible to generate the hundreds of control signals needed to run a computer from microprograms with word width of a few tens of bits.

2-2.2 The Fetch-Execute Cycle

Our attention will soon focus upon the data and address buses of a microprocessor. In order to feel comfortable with the signals we see, we first look inside the microprocessor itself to see how it executes a typical instruction.

Recall from section 1-1.2 that an instruction is executed in a period of time called a fetch-execute cycle, which is composed of several memory cycles. The first of these, called the fetch cycle, is used to fetch the first word of the instruction (or the first few words if the instruction takes several words) from memory. The next memory cycles decode and execute the instruction. A memory cycle, the basic time unit of the primary memory connected to the microprocessor, may correspond to one or several microcycles, which are the basic time units for data transfers inside the microprocessor.

We now examine the memory cycles to execute the instruction

ADDA #5

in a microprocessor like the M6809. The instruction takes two words of memory, say from rows 100 and 101. The operation code (op code) that indicates this is an ADDA instruction appears first, then the immediate operand, the number five, appears in the next row.

In the previous section we studied one bus using popular driver and register integrated circuits. To study the microprocessor we would have to know about dynamic logic, where gates leak charges from capacitors to perform logic, and about the unconventional circuits used inside a large integrated circuit. Nevertheless, we can and will use drivers and registers that are behaviorally equivalent to those of the last section in this section. We will ignore the control lines and show only the data buses for clarity. See figure 2-5. The following discussion is actually how the M6809 executes this instruction, within these limitations.

The center of the figure shows the internal buses in the microprocessor itself, while the extreme right side shows the external connections to a typical memory. In the microprocessor, a sixteen-bit address bus AB connects through tristate bus drivers to the sixteen-bit address bus A that sends addresses to memory. The eight-bit data bus DB inside the microprocessor sends data through tristate drivers to, or receives data from a buffer register between the internal eight-bit data bus and the external bus D that connects to the memory. A read/write control signal R/W is asserted when the external memory is requested to read and is false when it should write. Several sixteen-bit registers, including the program counter PC, can put data onto the bus AB, and a sixteen-bit incrementer is able to input data from this bus, increment it, and feed it to PC. Several eight-bit registers, including accumulator ACCA, data bus input DBI, and adder output SUM can put data on the DB bus. The adder adds data on the DB bus to data selected from one of several registers, including ACCA, and inputs the result to register SUM.

In describing the data transfers, we have to use some more notation. PC $\leftarrow$ PC + 1 means that the register PC is loaded with the old value of PC (there at the beginning of the microcycle) plus one. That is, it is incremented. A + B is the binary number sum of the contents of registers A and B. M [PC;] is the row of memory M whose address is the binary number PC.

In the first memory cycle of any instruction, the instruction must be

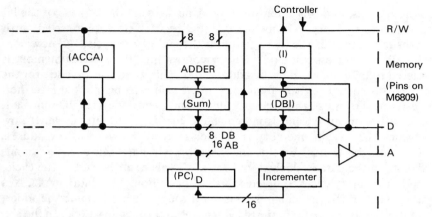

Figure 2-5. The M6809 Microprocessor

fetched into the I register using the address supplied by the PC register, and the PC register must be incremented:

$$PC \leftarrow PC + 1; \quad I \leftarrow M \; [PC;]$$

After the instruction is fetched into I, the controller in the microprocessor begins to decode the instruction to issue micro-orders to carry it out. Each instruction is different. For the ADDA #5 instruction, the second memory cycle will require us to get the immediate operand (the number five) into the DBI register. The operand is recalled using the program counter, since it is stored as the second word of the instruction. The program counter has to be incremented so that it is ready to fetch the next instruction. In terms of data transfers:

$$PC \leftarrow PC + 1; \quad DBI \leftarrow M \; [PC;]$$

Although the addition has not been done, the next instruction is actually fetched as this one is finished. In two halves of the memory cycle where the next instruction is fetched, the following two microcycles take place.

$$SUM \leftarrow ACCA + DBI$$
$$ACCA \leftarrow SUM$$

The next instruction has been fetched and decoded by now. In the next memory cycle, it will be executed.

These data transfers take place in the following way. The fetch cycle always enables the bus drivers of the PC register to put its contents (100) onto the AB bus, and this is put onto the A bus to send the address of the instruction to memory. Meanwhile, the PC register clock is asserted, so it copies the output of the incrementer at the end of the cycle. PC now contains 101. By the assertion of the R/W control line, the external memory is ordered to read the word at the address 100. This word, the op code for the ADDA instruction, is sent by means of the D bus to be clocked into the I register at the end of the cycle. In the second memory cycle, PC sends address 101 to memory, and is incremented, just as in the first cycle. It now becomes 102. Again, memory is ordered to read the word at the address (101) onto the D bus. By this time, the opcode has been decoded as an ADDA, so the data is clocked into the DBI register at the end of the cycle. The last memory cycle completes the add operation. The data in ACCA is put into the adder, the data in DBI is put through the bus DB into the adder, and the sum is clocked into the SUM register in the memory cycle. In the second half of the memory cycle the SUM register drivers put its data onto the DB bus, and ACCA is clocked to input this data.

When we look at the microprocessor, we see only the activity on the address bus A and the data bus D, and on the R/W control. We can sometimes infer the activity inside the integrated circuit microprocessor from these signals, but usually this does not matter. We would only see that in the first memory cycle, the fetch cycle, the contents of the program counter are output on the address bus and the instruction appears on the data bus; and in the second memory cycle, the program counter plus one appears on the address bus as the immediate operand appears on the data bus; and the R/W signal would be high in both cycles. This is what we need to interface to a memory or an I/O device. We need not know that the instruction actually takes three cycles from beginning to end (including the memory cycle that is hidden when the next instruction is fetched), nor which internal registers are used to hold the data from one cycle to the next. If we are aware of these, however, some unusual signals that appear on the buses from time to time make sense.

We can see the address and data bus signals, and the R/W signal, on a *logic analyzer*. This flexible instrument is capable of storing and displaying a sequence of digital signals. A pattern is set up in the logic analyzer, and when this pattern is found on the buses, the data is stored in the logic analyzer for each consecutive clock cycle until the memory in the logic analyzer is full. Then the display can be used to examine the memory to see what happened.

The M6809 has a rich instruction set and a lot of addressing modes. This makes it a challenge to describe the behavior on the buses for each instruction. Even so, it is often necessary to know what is happening on the buses because we need to coordinate them with some other operations, or we need to find out why the system is not working, and this is the only thing that we can look at using a logic analyzer. Table 2-1 presents a breakdown of all the M6809 instructions except CWAI and SYNC and the sequences that honor the interrupts. This table can be used to determine what is happening on the address and data buses and the R/W line in each memory cycle in the execution of each instruction, to establish the timing for I/O operations, to interpret the signals on a logic analyzer, or just to find out exactly how long an instruction takes to be executed. The memory cycles are denoted by letters whose interpretation is given at the bottom of the table. They tell you which register in the M6809 supplies the address, but they do not tell you whether the register is incremented in that memory cycle. Since the contents of the registers are usually fairly far apart as numbers, you can use this rough information to read the logic analyzer. Each instruction is broken into three parts, called the X sequence, the Y sequence, and the Z sequence, which follow each other. The X sequence corresponds roughly to the operation code fetch, the Y to the address calculation, and the Z to the execution of the instruction, but this is only a rough correspondance. Note that some combinations of possibilities from this table are, in fact, illegal. We make no attempt to specify accurately which instructions and addressing modes are illegal in this table. Nevertheless, the table should be very useful for reading a logic analyzer or for determining when the output operation takes place in an I/O routine.

Consider, for example, the ADD immediate instruction that we studied in this section. Looking at table 2-1, we observe that it is not a branch instruction, so we skip to the "all others" part of the table. The X sequence is F,F which means that for two successive memory cycles the program counter is put on the address bus and read command is given in order to fetch the op code and the immediate address. The Y sequence has no memory cycles because the addressing mode is eight-bit immediate, and the Z sequence also has no memory cycles because this is an instruction using an eight-bit accumulator. So the entire fetch-execute sequence is just F,F which means the program counter is used in two consecutive memory cycles to fetch two words. Note that nothing is said about whether the program counter will be incremented, but it will, and you can probably guess that yourself by thinking about the instruction.

Consider some more examples. If LDA ALPHA uses direct page addressing, then the X sequence is F,F, the Y sequence is N,D, and the Z sequence has no memory cycles. The whole sequence is F,F,N,D. The N stands for a null memory cycle: the M6809 is doing something inside the chip itself. In null cycles, the memory is supposed to do nothing: the M6809 will put out $FFFF on the address bus and a read command on the R/W line, which is a harmless read command, in any null cycle. The next cycle is a D cycle, which means that data will be read or written, depending on the instruction (LDA will read data but STA will write data), and the address bus will have the effective address as it is computed by the instruction addressing mode. In general, the D cycle is the one during which input or output operations occur.

Now let us try some harder instructions. ADDD, Y+ + uses autoincrement by two and operates on sixteen-bits. The sequence is F,F,F,N,N,N, D,D,N. Note that three fetches occur, even though only two are needed. The third fetch actually picks up the op code of the next instruction, but does nothing with it. Note that two D cycles are needed to get the sixteen-bit operand. That is obvious if you think about it, even though one D is shown as part of the Y sequence and the other is shown as part of the Z sequence in the table. The table is constructed to make it as easy as possible to put the sequences together, and is not related to architecturally significant components of the fetch-execute cycle in any direct way. Consider RTS. The sequence is F,F,S,S,N. S is a cycle where the stack point S (or the U index register for PULU, PSHU instructions) is used to read or write the word on the stack. STA [ALPHA] using sixteen-bit indirect addressing has the sequence F,F,F,F,F,I,I,N,D. The I cycle is where the indirect address is read. Whenever indirect addressing is used with any of the index registers, as noted at the bottom of the table, put three cycles I,I,N in front of the first D cycle. For instance, if STA ,X has the sequence F,F,F,D then STA [,X] has the sequence F,F,F,I,I,N,D. If LDD ,X+ + has the sequence F,F,F,N,N, N,D,D, then LDD [,X+ +] has the sequence F,F,F,N,N,N,I,I,N,D,D. Note that nothing is said about illegal instruction and address mode combinations: there is no such thing as an RTS instruction with page relative addressing, and there is no such thing as indirect addressing through the direct page even though it would have been quite useful for getting at global arrays. Finally, note that a couple of instructions have an extra fetch cycle at the very beginning. LBCS has the sequence F,F,F,F,N,N, and LDS ALPHA (sixteen-bit direct addressing) has the sequence F,F,F,F,N,D,D. With a little practice, you should be able to determine what each instruction is doing on the address and data buses in each of its memory cycles. This will become very clear when you use a logic analyzer, as we will when we study the timing of I/O operations in section 3-2.1 and the sequence that honors an interrupt in section 4-2.2.

2-3 Interfacing to the Bus

One of the most common problems faced by interface designers is the problem of bus timing and the generation of control signals to the bus. These will be considered in this section.

The first subsection considers the analysis of timing information needed to connect a microprocessor to another device. The second subsection shows a simple example of a complete interfacing design to connect a memory to a microcomputer. The third subsection considers the connection

Table 2-1
6809 Memory-Cycle Sequences (for use with a logic analyzer)

For branches, the FETCH-EXECUTE CYCLE = X, Y, Z where:

X fetches the instruction operation code: X =

F,F,F	long branches, except LBSR, LBRA
F,F	all other branches

Y calculates the address: Y =

N	page relative branches
F,N	long branch if branch not taken
F,N,N,	long branch if branch is taken

Z saves the return address: Z =

D,N,S,S	LBSR, BSR
—	all others

For all others, the FETCH-EXECUTE CYCLE = X, Y, Z where:

X fetches the instruction operation code: X =

F,F,F	load, store, compare Y or load, store, compare S
F,F,F	CMPD, CMPU, SWI2, SWI3
F,F	for all others

Y calculates the address and recalls the operand: Y =

—	8-bit immediate, and implied addresses
F	16-bit immediate addresses
N,D	direct page addresses
F,D	pointer addresses
F,N,D	direct (extended) addresses
F,N,D	5-, 8-bit displacement index addresses
F,N,D	accumulator A, B index addresses
F,N,D	page relative except branches
F,N,N,D	autoincrement or autodecrement by 1
F,N,N,N,D	autoincrement or autodecrement by 2
F,F,F,N,N,D	16-bit displacement index addressing accumulator D index addressing
F,F,F,I,I,N,D	(simple) 16-bit indirect (see below)
F,F,F,N,N,N,D	long relative addressing

Z executes the instruction: Z =

—	instructions using 8-bit accumulator
—	(except TFR, EXG, MUL, ABX)
—	NOP, JMP, LEA, 16-bit load immediate
N	ABX
D	16-bit load and store instructions, except load immediate
D	ANDCC, ORCC
D,N	16-bit arithmetic instructions
N,D	arithmetic and logic instructions on memory
N,S,S	JSR

Table 2-1 *(continued)*

S,S,N	RTS
N,. . .,N	TST (2 Ns) TFR (4 Ns) EXG (6 Ns) MUL (9 Ns)
N,N,S,. . .,S	PSHU, PSHS (one more S than number of words pushed)
N,N,S,. . .,S	PULU, PULS (one more S than number of words pulled)
S,. . .,S	RTI (4Ss if return from FIR, 13 otherwise)
N,S,. . .,S,N,I,I,N	SWI, SWI2, SWI3 (12 Ss)

Where:

—	no memory cycles
F	fetch instruction, address is from the program counter
S	recall or memorize, address is from S (or U)
N	(null operation) recall, address is $FFFF
I	recall a byte of the indirect address
D	recall (normal) or memorize (STA, and the like) a word: address is the one calculated for instruction (or execute N (null) cycle for LEA) and if indirect addressing is used, put I,I,N before the first D cycle (or the last N cycle of a LEA) (These I cycles are show in the sixteen-bit indirect mode.)

of boards to motherboards, the timing of signals through them, and the consideration of control signals that are used to drive this extended bus.

2-3.1 Address and Data Bus Timing

In order to connect memory or input/output registers to the microprocessor the actual timing requirements of the address bus and data bus have to be satisfied. If one uses modules from the same family, such as integrated circuits designed to be compatible with the Motorola MC6809, the timing requirements are usually satisfied automatically; however, when mixing modules from different families or when pressing the capabilities of the modules, one may have to analyze the timing requirements carefully. Therefore, we discuss them in this section.

Timing diagrams are used to show the requirements. A timing diagram is like an oscilloscope trace of the signals, such as is shown in figure 2-6. For collections of variables like the sixteen address lines shown by the trace labeled A two parallel lines indicate that any particular address line may be high or low, but will remain there for the time interval where the lines are parallel. A crossing line indicates that any particular line can change at that time. A line in the middle of the high and low line levels indicates the output is floating because no drivers are enabled, or the output may be changing as it tries to reach a stable value. A line in the middle means the signal is indeterminate: it is not necessarily at half the voltage. (Motorola also uses a cross-hatch pattern like a row of Xs to indicate that the signal is invalid but not tristated, while a line in the middle means the output is in the tristate open circuit mode on the device being discussed. That distinction is not made in this book, because both cases mean that the bus signal is indeterminate and cannot be used.) Causal relationships such as a control variable C causing the address lines to change, are shown by arrows from cause to effect. The cause is usually an edge if the change is made by clocking a register, or a level if the effect is a result of enabling a driver. On the left side of figure 2-6, we indicate that a rising edge of C causes the address lines A to change. Note the circle around the edge showing the cause is the edge. On the right side, we indicate that a low level of signal D causes the address lines to float. Timing is usually shown to scale, as on an oscilloscope, but delays from cause to effect are shown by writing the time by the arrow, and requirements are indicated as dimensions are shown on a blue print. On the left, the addresses change 50 nanoseconds after C rises, and in the middle, we indicate that the address should be stable for more than 150 nanoseconds.

Whether the microprocessor is putting the data into the I register or the DBI register, memory signals are the same. The signals for writing data are similar. We look at a concrete example to show the principles of bus transfers; however, we use approximate numbers for timing. See figure 2-7 for approximate timing relationships of the MC 6809. Accurate timing relationships can be found in the MC6809 data sheets. Other microprocessors have similar timing relationships.

The clock used in memory (called the *E clock* or the *enable*) is shown as trace E: it can be a one-microsecond square wave. The Q *quadrature clock* is like the E clock, shifted ninety degrees. A memory cycle begins and ends when E falls from high to low. The address bus is indeterminate for the first

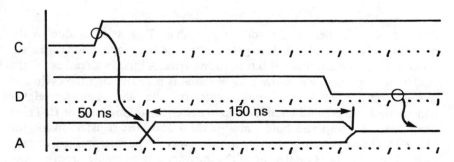

Figure 2-6. Some Timing Relationships

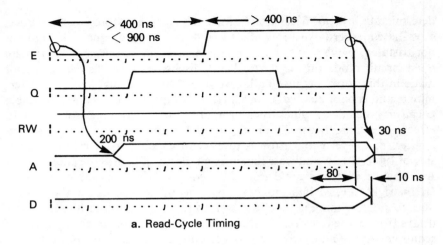

a. Read-Cycle Timing

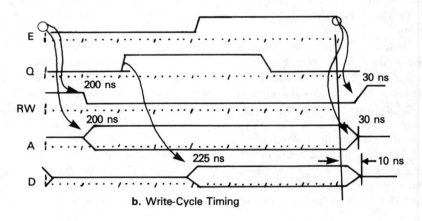

b. Write-Cycle Timing

Figure 2-7. Timing Relationships for the M6809

200 nanoseconds before the address is stable. This delay is due to the propagation of control signals to gate drivers and the propagation of the address through the internal AB bus to the external A bus. In a read cycle, the read/write signal shown in trace R/W remains high through the cycle and the microprocessor expects valid data on the data bus for eighty nanoseconds before and ten nanoseconds after the falling edge of E. These times are the set-up and hold times of the I and DBI registers inside the MC6809. If any data line changes in this interval, the microprocessor may input either an L or H on that line. The memory is responsible for providing valid and constant signals during this interval during the set-up and hold time.

In a write cycle the R/W signal is guaranteed to be low by 200 nanoseconds and can rise 30 nanoseconds after the beginning of the next cycle. Due to delays in the path of the control signal and the delay through the bus driver between the DB bus and D bus (see figure 2-5), the data to be written is put on the D bus and is guaranteed determinate 225 nanoseconds after the rising edge of Q and remains stable for 10 nanoseconds after E falls. These signals are available to use to control the memory. We note, however, that R/W does not have a rising edge whose timing can be depended upon. R/W is *not a timing signal*. You cannot depend on it to satisfy setup and hold times. Such a timing signal is often required, and it can often be obtained by ORing R/W with the complement of E, the E clock (see figure 2-9a).

The use of two clocks in the MC6809 can simplify your logic. If E and Q are one-megahertz square waves with sharp rising and falling edges, and the rising edge of E is 250 nanoseconds after the rising edge of Q, the address and R/W signals are determinate whenever either Q or E are high and the data is determinate when E is high. (If you are studying the MC6800, the Q clock is missing on it, and the timing requirements are a bit harder to satisfy.)

The analysis of timing requirements compares the timing of two parts to be connected, such as the microprocessor and some memory. The object is to verify that data will be available at the receiver when it is needed. One should be aware that the specifications of a part mean that the manufacturer aims to satisfy the specifications and tests some or all of the parts to see that the specifications are met. Some manufacturers just sample the parts, testing a few parts from each batch that is produced, while others (such as Motorola) test each part for most specifications. A design where some requirements are not satisfied may still work because some parts will be better than the specifications require. In fact, if you are willing to take the time or pay the expense, you can *screen the parts* to find out which ones meet your tighter specifications. Nevertheless, if the system fails because the design does not meet the specifications, the designer is blamed. If the design meets specifications but the system fails, we blame the part manufacturer or the part.

A typical memory has timing requirements that must be compatible with those of the microprocessor. To discuss these requirements, we will give the approximate requirements of the very popular 2102, a 1024-bit, one-bit wide random access memory. The same memory is manufactured by different companies—and even by the same company, with different timing requirements. These variations are designated by modifiers, such as in the 2101A-2, or the 2102-1. Requirements are shown for the National Semiconductor 2102-1. See figure 2-8.

The memory has a chip enable CE, read/write R/W, a ten-bit address A, data in DI, and data out DO. See figure 2-8a. The timing requirements

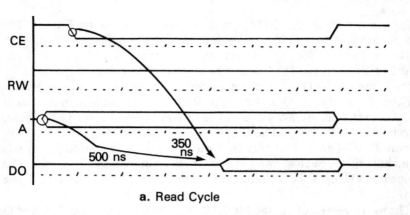

a. Read Cycle

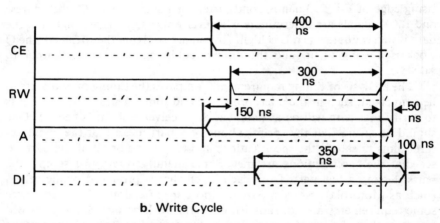

b. Write Cycle

Figure 2-8. Timing Requirements of the National Semiconductor 2102-1

are especially simple. A read cycle begins when the address bus signal becomes stable. Data is available on DO from the bit addressed by A when CE is asserted low, 500 nanoseconds after A is stable or 350 nanoseconds after CE falls, whichever is later. In a write cycle, to prevent writing in the wrong word, the R/W signal should not fall until A has been stable for 150 nanoseconds and should rise at least 50 nanoseconds before the address changes again, but to make sure the word is written, R/W should be low for at least 300 nanoseconds and the chip enable CE should be low for 400 nanoseconds before R/W rises. The data input on DI should be stable 350 nanoseconds before and 100 nanoseconds after the rising edge of R/W. These are the set-up and hold times of the 2102-1. If these requirements are met, the data input in DI will be stored in the bit at the address given by A.

In order to analyze the requirements to see if this 2102-1 is or is not compatible with the M6809, the requirements are compared as follows. For the read cycle, the timing diagrams are referenced to the point where the address bus data is determinate and stable, so we slide the 2102 timing diagrams to the right to match the time when the M6809 output presents a determinate address with the time when the 2102 requires a determinate address to begin its read or write cycle. We verify that the 2102 outputs stable data throughout the interval where the M6809 must receive stable data.

For the write cycle, we observe a slight timing problem and find a way to overcome it. The requirements center on the rising edge of the 2102 R/W signal. The OR gate discussed above could be used to provide R/W to a 2102 memory so that its rising edge occurs at a predictable place, at the end of the write cycle. (This simple solution often works, but in this case, it will not work.) The timing diagram for the 2102 should line up so that the rising edge of R/W corresponds to the falling edge of E for the M6809. We verify that R/W derived with the OR gate from the M6809 is low for at least 400 nanoseconds (note it is low for the last half of the cycle) and that the address is determinate for 150 nanoseconds before R/W falls; however, the data may not be determinate for 50 nanoseconds after the clock rises and the data is not stable for 100 nanoseconds. This is a slight timing problem, which can be fixed by moving the rising edge of the R/W signal so that it occurs at least 100 nanoseconds earlier. The R/W signal for the 2102 is then the R/W signal from the 6809 ORed with a signal that is high for the first 500 nanoseconds, low for the next 400 nanoseconds, and high for the last 100 nanoseconds of every write cycle. Such a signal can be generated by a one-shot that is triggered by the E clock. That changes the timing so that all the requirements are met on the write cycle.

Other solutions are often possible and one is better than the modification discussed above. You can slow down the clock of the M6809, to lengthen the cycle so that stable data will reach the memory earlier, use buffer registers to hold the data going to memory longer, or use a faster version of the 2102. For instance, the Intel 2102A-2 has set-up and hold times of 180 and 0 nanoseconds, and all other requirements are met. We could therefore use the Intel 2102A-2 rather than the National Semiconductor 2102-1 to build a memory for the M6809. Then the R/W signal could be generated by ORing the 6809 R/W signal with the complement of the E clock signal.

We have observed that an analysis of timing requirements can help us select the parts needed to build a system. Surprisingly, a 500-nanosecond memory does not necessarily have adequate timing characteristics to work with a 1-microsecond microcomputer. We reiterate, though, that parts that do not meet specifications on paper may work, some of the time. Nevertheless, if a designer satisfies the requirements and the system does not work, he can blame the parts supplier rather than take the blame himself.

2-3.2 The Design of a (1024,8) Memory for an M6809

The design of a memory for a microprocessor illustrates some of the principles of the previous section and introduces the decoder. While one would expect to purchase a memory subsystem or a complete microcomputer on a printed circuit board rather than build one, the same principles are used in interfacing I/O registers, discussed in the next chapter, and these may be the object of many design travails. Thus, for pedagogical reasons, we consider the design of a memory.

The $(n,1)$ memory such as the 2102 is most common because such a memory uses the least number of pins per bit of memory, and pins are the costliest, most unreliable, and most needed resource in digital systems. Eight (1024,1) memories can be connected as follows to make a (1024,8) memory for an M6809 that would appear at addresses $4000 to $43FF. See figure 2-9. Since 1024 words need 10 bits of address, the low order 10 bits from the address outputs of the M6809 are directly connected to the corresponding address pins of the 2102. The R/W output of the M6809 is ORed with the complement of the E signal to provide R/W for the 2102 (if the 2102 is an Intel 2102A-1, as we observed in the last subsection). The DI and DO pins of each 2102 are connected to one of the data bus pins of the M6809.

The chip enable CE remains as the only signal to consider. It can come from an address decoder that will output a true (low) value whenever an address between $4000 and $43FF is put on the address bus. Analyzing all 1024 of these addresses, we can verify that the low order 10 bits of the addresses can be T or F, but the high order 6 bits must be FTFFFF for all these addresses, and no other addresses than these have such values. (The low order ten bits are decoded, of course, within the memory chips to select the bit to be read or written.) As the address bus is in positive logic, a six-input positive logic AND gate with negative logic output will output a T (L) if each high order address bit (except bit 14) is inverted, and each is input to the gate. This is shown in figure 2-9.

Although the principle is the same, the implementation of address decoders in a typical microcomputer is usually simplified. These simplifications are now discussed.

If one required 2048 words of memory, one could connect two memory modules of the kind designed above to the M6809 as follows. The R/W and ten low order address lines are connected to all 2102 memories, the DI and DO of one 2102 from each memory module are connected to a data bus pin of the M6809, and the CE lines for each module are connected to different decoders. If the first module should hold words $4000 to $43FF, the decoder above will be used for it; if the other module holds words $4400 to $47FF, its decoder would be almost identical—the only difference would be

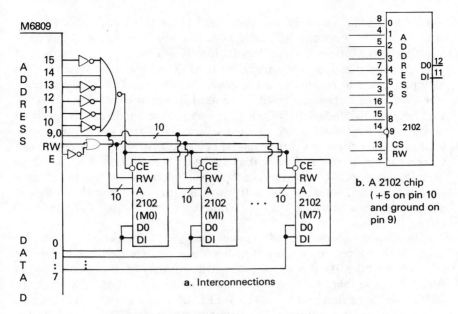

Figure 2-9. A Memory System

that address bit ten would not be inverted on input to this AND gate. Up to sixty-four such memory modules could be connected to an M6809 this way, to build a complete memory for it. Most microcomputers only have as much memory as they will need, and this may be on the order of eight thousand words.

Especially when many modules are used, a decoder integrated circuit is used to decode the high order bits of the address. The 74154 is a popular decoder that can select up to sixteen modules: it has sixteen different circuits like the AND gate in figure 2-9 to select each module. However, the tendency to use a chip just because it is there should be avoided. Most memory modules use the individual gate inside each module rather than a decoder integrated circuit outside the module to enable the memory. This reduces the number of pin connections between modules, and pin connections are much more costly than gates in current technology.

When there is a paucity of modules used, *incompletely specified decoding* may greatly simplify the hardware. Consider the module in figure 2-9 again. If address bit ten is disconnected and its input to the decoder gate tied high, this memory would respond to addresses $4000 to $47FF, and the first word in the memory would respond to addresses $4000 and $4400. If the program uses words $4000 and $4400, they will in fact be the same words. Similarly, $4001 and $4401 would be the same words. But if, say, the words from $4400 to $47FF are never used in the program, then a simpler decoder without bit ten will be adequate. It is possible to extend this technique to delete further decoder inputs. If only one memory module is used with the M6809 and no other module is used (a rather useless system), then all inputs could be eliminated using this technique, and CE could be tied to true (low). Then, the same word in the module would be selected if the address were 0, $0400, $0800, $0C00, $1000, and so on. Incompletely specified decoding can eliminate much of the hardware in a microcomputer that is used to decode addresses. But it should be used only when the program can be trusted not to use addresses that duplicate those that it does use. The technique is especially useful for small microcomputers dedicated to execute a fixed program, which has no software bugs that might use duplicate addresses. It is not as useful for microcomputers used for software development.

We consider an example of an incompletely specified decoder. As we see in the next chapter, input/output registers are implemented as if they were memory modules like the one just designed, but they have just one word in them. Suppose that two memory modules are used, and addresses zero to $03FF are in the first and $FC00 to $FFFF are in the second, and that two one-word memory modules (I/C registers) at addresses $8001 and $8002 can be addressed. The permissible values of address variables are shown in table 2-2 (X is a don't care variable).

Inspection of the permissible addresses indicates that memory module one is selected exactly when address fifteen is false, and memory module two is selected exactly when address fourteen is true. The registers are selected exactly when the two memory modules are not selected, and address lines zero and one distinguish the two registers. Assuming positive logic address signals from the M6809 and negative logic enables on all modules (the most common case) then the enable for the first memory module is address line fifteen, the enable for the other is the inverted address line fourteen, and the register enables are simple logic functions of address lines fifteen, fourteen, one, and zero. The entire decoder can be built from a single 7410 integrated circuit.

2-3.3 Extending the Bus

A microprocessor is capable of driving one regular TTL gate, or about four gates of the LS family, or in the order of ten CMOS gates or other LSI MCS chips designed to be connected to the mircoprocessor. When a larger number of gates are connected, or more than one regular TTL gate is to connect to a microprocessor line, buffers are usually used to raise the drive

Table 2-2
Address Assignments for a Microcomputer

Address line	15	14	13	12	11	10	9	8	7	6	5	4	3	2	1	0
Memory Mod. 1	F	F	F	F	F	F	X	X	X	X	X	X	X	X	X	X
Memory Mod. 2	T	T	T	T	T	T	X	X	X	X	X	X	X	X	X	X
Register 1	T	F	F	F	F	F	F	F	F	F	F	F	F	F	F	T
Register 2	T	F	F	F	F	F	F	F	F	F	F	F	F	F	T	F

capability of that line. Especially when the system is built on several different printed circuit cards, buffers are used to send data between the cards.

Four problems commonly appear in the design of extended buses. The first is the interconnection pattern of the bus drivers: there is a tendency to design straggly buses without planning ahead. The second problem is the satisfaction of timing requirements. The third is the prevention of having more than one bus driver enabled at any time, and the fourth is the suppression of noise.

It is too easy to let the design of a system sort of grow, so that the signals are improperly distributed. Signals like the clock and the R/W signal that is ORed with the complement of the E clock have edges that are used as references to capture data on the buses. These edges usually should arrive at every point in the system at precisely the same time, or as close as possible to that. The difference in time between the arrivals of a signal at different points in the system is called the *skew*. If an output can be connected to f inputs, a tree structure with fan-out f is the best way to distribute a signal: the source of the signal drives f buffers, each of these drives f buffers, and so on. All modules using the signals should be at the leaves of the tree, with the same number of buffers between them and the source. Since buffers, even of the same type, can have significantly different delays, this practice reduces the skew to a minimum, although this minimum skew may still represent a significant problem.

Although the address bus is less time critical, the sixteen address lines are usually distributed using a tree structure, with a pair of octal buffers like the 81LS95 at each branch of the tree. The data bus is not so easy to form because it carries signals bidirectionally, from microprocessor to memory and from memory to microprocessor. A way to implement this type of bus in a tree is to use a pair of buffers like the 81LS95, connected back-to-back so the inputs of one connect to the outputs of the other. Alternatively, a 74LS245 contains a pair of drivers equivalent to two 81LS95s in the above configuration. Only one of the drivers of the two can be enabled at any time, and if several such buffers connect to a node of the tree, only one of the drivers feeding the node may be enabled. In order to determine which drivers to enable, we use some logic that considers the source of the data, which must be at the root or at a leaf of the tree. At most one source may be selected at any time. If a source on a leaf sends data, all rootward going drivers between it and the root are enabled, and in all other branches of the tree the leafward drivers are enabled. The signal will reach all the nodes on the tree in the shortest possible time. In a trivial bus using only one pair of drivers, the microprocessor is at the root and all the devices are connected at the other end of the branch, at the only leaf. The R/W signal is the only one needed because when it is asserted, data flows rootward, and when not, leafward. While the trivial case is by far the most common, the general case is really very simple too.

When buses are expanded using drivers in the above way, we must be aware of the delays through the buffers when we check the timing requirements of memories and other devices. Generally, the longest delay for any signal through the extended bus has to be added to the delays for signals using the bus in the analysis of the timing requirements. Also, the edges of the clock and R/W ORed with the complement of the clock signals may have to be delayed by the same amount as the signal to cancel the skew caused when the signal is sent through such extended buses.

The analysis technique of section 2-3.1 using sliding timing diagrams can be modified to handle extended buses, but a more general technique uses *interval arithmetic*. In many cases, delays can only be specified as a minimum value and a maximum value, which is an *interval* [min, max]. An arithmetic system has been defined for operating on intervals. For example, if one interval [min1, max 1] is added to another interval [min2, max2], the sum is a new interval [min1 + min2, max1 + max2]. For instance, the sum of [1, 5] and [3, 4] is [4, 9]. The negative of an interval [min, max] is [− max, − min]. For instance, the negative of [− 2, 5] is [− 5, 2].

Delays can be specified as intervals and can be added or subtracted using this interval arithmetic. Using this tool skews can be accounted for so that we can be assured that when an edge of a timing signal arrives the set-up and hold times are satisfied.

Consider an example of skewing calculations. Suppose that the data bus from an MC6809 is driven through one 74LS245 and the R/W signal is ORed with the complement of E through one 74LS32 to a National Semi-conductor 2102-1 random access memory chip. Will this satisfy the timing requirements, or will an Intel 2102A-2 be needed, as in the earlier analysis of timing requirements? The problem is to determine the interval of time during which the data from the MC6809 has to be stable so that it is stable at the inputs of the 2102 for the duration of the set-up and hold times of that chip. Intuitively, the MC6809 must supply stable data for an interval of time (T6809) that is larger than the set-up and hold time interval of the 2102 (T2102), to which the delay time through the 74LS32 (T7432) is added and from which the delay through the 74LS245 (T74245) has been subtracted.

A formula can be checked out intuitively as if all intervals were just ordinary numbers. The minimum interval during which the MC6809 must provide stable data is:

$$T6809 = T7432 + T2102 - T74275$$

The intervals are defined so that 0 is the time at which an ideal R/W signal rising edge would appear. The set-up and hold times for a device are [-set-up, hold] and the delays are [min delay, max delay]. If the 74LS245 has a delay between nine and eighteen nanoseconds (the interval [9, 18]), the 74LS32 has a delay between six and eleven nanoseconds (the interval [6,

11]), and the 2102 needs a set-up and hold time of [−350, 100] nanoseconds, the source of the data must make the data stable for a minimum interval of:

$$T6809 = T7432 + T2102 - T74245$$
$$= [6, 11] + [−350, 100] − [9, 18]$$
$$= [6, 11] + [−350, 100] + [−18, −9]$$
$$= [−362, 102]$$

So the data on the output of the MC6809 must be stable 362 nanoseconds before the rising edge of the complemented E signal at the input to the 74LS32 and 102 nanoseconds after that edge. This is not satisfied by the MC6809, so the Intel 2102-1 will have to be used again.

The interval arithmetic method is very general and useful in the analysis of skewing, and in worst case analysis in general. Operations for multiplication, division, and complex functions such as SINE and so on can be defined precisely for intervals, and the execution of these operations is mechanical and clean. Even so, one has to be careful to check intuitively the formula to make sure that it really represents the worst cases by the upper and lower bounds of the interval. Finally, interval arithmetic tends to be a bit pessimistic if two variables appear in two parts of a formula and should cancel. For instance, if the interval A is [1, 2], then A − A is evaluated as [−1, 1] rather than [0, 0] using the rules of interval arithmetic. A-A should be zero. The formula should be written so that each variable appears just once if that is possible, or the answer should be regarded as worse than the worst real case if that cannot be avoided.

The bus that interconnects printed circuit boards is often implemented on a board, called a *motherboard* or *backplane*, into which the other boards are plugged. This bus can be a standard type so that boards made by different manufacturers can be plugged into it. The *S-100* bus is a standard type that is extensively used for Intel 8080 computer systems. It can be used with other systems like the M6809 too. It is called the S-100 bus because it has one hundred pins. Though developed by manufacturers that service the hobby market, this bus has become a standard for the design of small quantity industrial systems because of the large range of "off the shelf" printed circuit boards that can be plugged into it. In fact, the S-100 bus with slight modification has been proposed as an IEEE standard.

The third most troublesome problem in the design of extended buses is control of the bus drivers. If several different boards are plugged into the motherboard or backplane, they are often designed independently of each other at different times. It is easy to design the logic that controls the drivers so that a driver from one of the boards is driving the bus at the same time that another driver is trying to drive the same bus on the backplane. Although this problem can occur on any bus, it is especially troublesome on the backplane bus because boards are often designed at different times. The solution to the problem is good documentation. Each board should be documented to show exactly when it drives signals onto the backplane bus as a function of the addresses on the address bus or other control signals (such as direct memory access acknowledge signals, discussed in chapter 4). When a new board is designed, it should be checked to see if it can ever conflict with an existing board. Also, when no explanation can be found for erroneous behavior on the bus, check all boards again to see if two drivers are driving the bus at the same time.

One of the techniques for controlling bus drivers recommended by Terry Ritter of Motorola is to design all tristate bus drivers to implement *break-before-make* control, using the terminology that describes relay contacts. All tristate bus drivers should be disabled for the first quarter of every memory cycle, when the E and Q clocks are both low. That way, tristate drivers will not drive the bus in different directions while the address and R/W signals are indeterminate.

Many motherboards, especially those for the S-100 bus, use *active terminations*. In order to reduce the electrical noise and ringing on the signals, each line is terminated by connecting it through a (2,000-ohm) resistor to a voltage that is half the positive supply voltage. The resistor absorbs the energy that causes the noise. Half the supply voltage is chosen so that whether the driver is driving the bus high or low about the same amount of power is absorbed by the terminator, and so that if several bus lines are terminated together some being high will supply the current needed by others that happen to be low at that time. This voltage is easily established by an audio amplifier integrated circuit like an LM384, because it automatically sets its output to half the supply voltage. Alternatively, if the board is well-designed, then noise may not be a problem and active terminations may not be needed.

In this subsection, some of the most common problems in interface design have been discussed. Remember to keep the extended bus as much like a symmetrical tree as possible. When confirming the timing requirements, use interval arithmetic. Check the logic that determines which drivers are enabled under which conditions and keep accurate records of these conditions. Finally, use a noise-free mother board, or supply active terminations on it to suppress noise. If you regard this advice, you can avoid many of the most common problems of interface design.

2-4 Conclusions

The microcomputer data and address buses are at the heart of the interface problem. Before it gets on these buses, data inside the microprocessor is unobservable and useless for interfacing. Its form on the bus is, on the contrary, quite important in the design of interface circuitry. This chapter has discussed what address, data, and control signals look like on a typical microcomputer bus and has supported that discussion with a description of some of the mechanisms and components that generate those signals. You should be able to read the data sheets and block or logic diagrams that describe the microprocessor and other modules connected to the bus. You should be able to analyze the timing requirements on a bus. Finally, you should have sufficient hardware background to understand the discussions of interface modules in the coming chapters.

If you have had some difficulty with the discussion on hardware modules and signals, a number of fine books are available on logic design. We recommend *Fundamentals of Logic Design*, second edition, by C.H. Roth, published by West Publishing Co. in 1979, because it is organized as a self-paced course. There are so many good texts in different writing styles, however, that you may find another more suitable. Computer organization is also covered in a number of fine texts, such as *Fundamentals of Microcomputer Architecture* by K.L. Doty, published by Matrix Publishers, or *Computer Hardware and Organization* by M.E. Sloan, published by Science Research Associates. The final section of this chapter, however, is not widely discussed in available texts, but at the time of this writing several books on interfacing are being announced, and we would expect this central problem to be discussed in any good book on interfacing.

Problems

Note

Problems 1-4 are paragraph-correction problems. See the guidelines for these problems in the problem section at the end of chapter 1.

1. *A negative logic signal has a low signal representing a true variable. To negate a variable is to make it low. A synchronous variable is one that repeats itself periodically, like a clock. A family of integrated circuits is a collection of integrated circuits that have the same architecture. A block diagram describes the realization of some hardware to show exactly how to build it. In a block diagram logic functions are in terms of true and false variables. The V_{SS} pin is normally connected to positive five volts on an LSI chip. We normally put bypass capacitors, 0.001 = microfarad capacitors, across power and ground, about every four SSI chips.

2. *A buffer is a gate whose output can be connected to the outputs of other buffers. Open collector drivers can be connected on a bus, called a wire-OR bus, which ORs the outputs in positive logic. When a tristate bus driver is disabled, its outputs are pulled to zero volts by the driver. A flip-flop is a module that copies the variable on the D input when the CLOCK input is high, and leaves the last value in it at other times. The set-up time for a D edge-triggered flip-flop is the time during which the data has to be stable before the edge occurs that clocks the data into the flip-flop. The word width of a microcomputer is the number of bits that are put into the accumulator during a LDA instruction. The memory cycle time is the time from when the address is stable until data can be read from the word addressed, or written into the addressed word. Read-only memories are used to store changing data in a typical microprocessor.

3. *Microprogramming is the programming of microcomputers. A data transfer is the movement of data such as from a register through a driver onto a bus and into another register. A data transfer occurs over a memory cycle. It is caused by asserting control variables that come from the controller. A group of singularly control variables can be encoded in binary to make the controller faster. In vertical microprograms, each control variable appears as the output from a column of the control memory. In designing interfaces for microcomputers, you have to use these control variables from the controller inside the microprocessor to enable the drivers and clock the registers in the interface hardware.

4. *The ADDA immediate instruction begins, as all instructions begin, by recalling the first byte of the instruction code word. The program counter is incremented first, then used as the address to read a word from memory. The second byte of the instruction is then fetched to get the im-

mediate address, which is brought in and added to the accumulator in the same memory cycle. This instruction takes just two memory cycles.

5. The output signals of a gate are defined for each input signal by the table below. What is the usual name for the logic function when inputs and outputs are considered variables if: (a) A, B, and C are positive logic variables; (b) A and B are positive logic and C is negative logic; (c) A and B are negative logic and C is positive logic; (d) A, B, and C are negative logic variables.

A	B	C
L	L	L
L	H	L
H	L	L
H	H	H

6. Using the bus in figure 2-4, write a horizontal microprogram in successive microcycles to successively: (1) put input IN into register B, (2) put input IN into register A, (3) put register A into register B. In the implementation, assume the first column on the left feeds C1, the next feeds C2, the next C3, and the right column feeds C4 (C5 is connected to TRUE). Show the segment of control memory that can be executed sequentially to cause these transfers (a) using block diagram conventions (T, F) and (b) using logic diagram conventions (H, L).

7. Figure 2-10 shows a simple bus. Specify which control signals are asserted, and whether asserted means to make them high or low, to cause each of the following transfers: (a) C ← IN3; (b) D ← C; (c) C ← IN4; (d) D ← IN4; (e) C ← IN3, D ← IN3.

8. A microprogram has been written for the system in figure 2-10 that uses encoded control bits. The control memory, shown below, has four col-

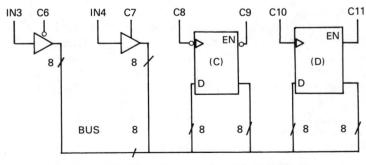

Figure 2-10. A Bus for Problems 7-9

umns and five rows. The leftmost two columns determine which data are transferred onto the bus: C6 is asserted if these bits are FF, C7 if FT, C9 if TF, and C11 if TT. The third column is C8 and the fourth is C10. Write the data transfers, $C \leftarrow IN3$, and the like that occur as each row is read.

FTFT

FFTF

FTTF

FFTT

TTTF

9. Suppose that IN3 of figure 2-10 is connected to OUT of figure 2-4, and IN of figure 2-4 is connected to BUS of figure 2-10. Write a microprogram to exchange the words in registers C and D in figure 2-10. Show (a) the data transfers and (b) the block diagram (T, F) control memory, assuming that the columns from left to right supply the control variables from C1 to C11.

10. Show a microprogram that implements the INCA instruction in the 6809 using the same strategy as in section 2-2.2. Use the bus structure in figure 2-5, except that you will have to put another tristate gate feeding a constant, $01, onto the DB bus. Your microprogram should closely mimic that of the ADDA immediate microprogram, even "fetching" the "second byte of the instruction," which is actually the next instruction in the second memory cycle (the 6809 actually does this). However, do not increment the program counter in the second memory cycle. (a) Show the data transfers, with all transfers that occur in the same microstep written on the same line. Assume that a memory cycle is two microcycles long. (b) Assume that a microprogram memory has columns that enable successively from left to right (1) the ACCA to DB driver, (2) the SUM to DB driver, (3) the DBI to DB driver, (4) the constant $01 to DB driver, (5) the ACCA clock, (6) the SUM clock, (7) the I clock, (8) the DBI clock, (9) the DB to D driver, (10) the PC to AB driver, (11) the PC clock, and (12) the AB to A driver. Show a microprogram segment (six rows, twelve columns, using T, F) that implements the INCA instruction shown as data transfers in part (a). (c) Suppose the leftmost four columns of the memory defined in part (b) are encoded into two columns so that if the two bits are FF, we enable the ACCA to DB driver; if FT, the SUM to DB driver; if TF, the DBI to DB driver; and if TT, the constant $01 to DB driver. Suppose the other eight columns are the same as in part (b). Show a microprogram segment (six rows, ten columns, using T, F) that implements the INCA instruction shown as data transfers in part (a).

11. The output displayed by a logic analyzer is as follows: each next

lower row corresponds to the next consecutive memory cycle, column one gives the R/W signal (R for read and W for write) during the memory cycle, and columns two and three give the values (in hexadecimal) for the address and data buses during the memory cycle. Show the output displayed by such a logic analyzer for each of the following instructions (assume ALPHA is $100, X is $102, Y is $304, S is $600 and PC is $506 and assume location $100 has value $58, location $102 has value $31, and location $305 has value $2A): (a) ADDA ALPHA (extended), (b) ORA 0,X, (c) ANDA, − Y, (d) PSHS X,Y,PC.

12. The 2114 is a (1024,4) random access memory chip that is as easy to use as the 2182, but obviously four times more dense—just two of these can make a (1024,8) memory for a microcomputer. The MCM21L14-20, the MCL21L14-25, the MCM21L14-30, and the MCM21L14-45 are realizations of the 2114, the first listed being the fastest and most expensive and the successive ones being slower and cheaper.

Table 2-2 gives the timing characteristics of the realizations. For definition of the timing characteristics, see figure 2-8. The Read Access time is the delay from when the address is stable until the output data is determinate (500 nanoseconds for the National Semiconductor 2102-1 shown in figure 2-8), the CE-DO Delay is the time from when CE is low until data is determinate (350 nanoseconds in figure 2-8), the Read Hold is the time the data remains determinate after CE becomes high or the address changes, whichever is earlier, the Write Length is the time R/W has to be low (300 nanoseconds in figure 2-8), and the Write Set-up is the time the data has to be stable before R/W rises in a write cycle (350 nanoseconds in figure 2-8). The time from when the address is stable before R/W can be asserted low (150 nanoseconds in figure 2-8), the time the address must remain stable after R/W is negated high (50 nanoseconds in figure 2-8), and the Hold Time that the data must remain stable after R/W rises (100 nanoseconds in figure 2-8) are all zero in all realizations of the 2114. The other times are specified as intervals [min., max.] in table 2-3.

Assuming the 2114 is connected directly to a 6809, which is the cheapest realization that will work with (a) the MC6809, (b) the MC68A09, or (c) the MC68B09 that satisfies all the timing requirements, and for each of the minimum cost pairs that you select, what is the maximum allowable delay on the data bus that could be permitted without violating a timing requirement and how much time is allowed for decoding the address to get the CE signal, assuming the address gets to the decoder when it gets to the memory? (See *The Complete Motorola Microcomputer Data Catalog* for the timing requirements of M6809 chips.)

13. Repeat problem 11 for the different realizations of the 6800. (See *The Complete Motorola Microcomputer Data Catalog* for the timing requirements of the M6800 chips.)

Table 2-3
Timing Characteristics of Several 2114s

Parameter	MCM21L14-20	MCM21L14-25	MCM21L14-30	MCM21L14-45
Read Access	[,200]	[,250]	[,300]	[,450]
CE-DO Delay	[, 70]	[, 85]	[,100]	[,120]
Read Hold	[50,]	[50,]	[50,]	[50,]
Write Length	[120,]	[135,]	[150,]	[200,]
Write Set-up	[120,]	[135,]	[150,]	[200,]

Note

Problems 14 to 20, and many of the problems in later chapters, are hard-ware design problems. We recommend the following guidelines for these problems.

Hardware designs should be minimum cost, where minimum cost means minimum number of chips (where actual chips are specified); and where the number of chips is the same, the minimum number of gates; and then the minimum number of pin connections, unless otherwise noted. Use the integrated circuits in *The TTL Data Book for Design Engineers*, Texas Instruments, Inc. to design circuits, unless otherwise specified. When logic diagrams are requested, use bubbles to represent negative logic and gates representing high and low signals, showing pin numbers where applicable. A logic diagram should describe a circuit in enough detail that it is ready to build. Assume the address and data base are positive logic, and decoder IC outputs and enables are negative logic unless otherwise indicated in the problem or data sheets for the ICs. If timing is required, use *The Complete Motorola Microcomputer Data Library* and assume the E clock is 1 megahertz. When block diagrams are presented, show variables and gates representing true and false values, and show the maximum detail that you can show, unless otherwise stated. (Note that a box with SYSTEM written inside it is a block diagram for any problem below but is not a good answer, so you should understand that we want the maximum amount of detail in your answer that is possible with the information supplied in the question.)

14. Draw a logic diagram of a (1024,8) memory using 2114 chips and 74LS04, 74LS30, and 74LS32 gates so that words in the range $2000 to $2FFF are read and written in this memory. Show all pin connections between these chips and the 6809 so that the logic diagram is detailed enough to build the memory. The pin connections to the SSI chips in *The TTL Data Book*, and those of the eighteen-pin 2114 are: chip select CS (negative logic)—pin 8; R/W—pin 10; ten address bits—pins 1 to 7 and 17, 18; four data pins used

for both input and output of data—pins 11 to 14; +5 volts—pin 18; ground—pin 9. (Note that the address pins are interchangeable with each other, and the data pins are interchangeable with each other because the memory will work correctly if you switch any two of them.)

15. Using just one 74LS10, show a logic diagram that can implement the decoder for the memories and registers selected in table 2-2. For this realization, say (a) what memories or registers will be written into by the instruction STA $9002, (b) what memories or registers are stored into by STA $FFFF, (c) what memories or registers are written into by the instruction STAA $80FF, (d) what memories or registers are written into by the instruction STA $4000, and (e) what five different addresses, other than $8001, access register 1?

16. Show a block diagram for a minimum cost decoder that will select memory module 1 for addresses in the range $0000 to $1FFF, memory module 2 for addresses in the range $F000 to $FFFF, register 1 for address $4000 and register 2 for address $8000.

17. A Z80 microprocessor has negative logic RD and WR control variables instead of the R/W signal and E clock of the 6809. When RD is asserted low, the Z80 has put a stable address on the address bus and wants memory to read the word at this address; when WR is asserted low, the Z80 has put stable data on the data bus and a stable address on the address bus and wants memory to write the data at the address it gave. Show the logic diagram of a decoder (but do not show ICs or pin numbers) using n-input AND gates and inverters to select a 2102 memory whenever an address is presented in the range $5400 to $57FF, and show logic to provide the R/W signal for the 2102 chips. Note that when neither RD nor WR are asserted low, CE should be negated high.

18. Draw the logic diagram for a printed circuit card (1024,8) memory that can plug into a backplane bus. The memory, using 2102s, will respond when the address is in the range $4000 to $43FF, as in figure 2-9. However, it connects to a sixteen-bit positive logic address bus and an eight-bit positive logic data bus, and it receives an R/W signal, which is high if data is being read, all on the backplane, rather than on the 6809 as in figure 2-9. Use the high order bits of the address in the decoder to detect the address as in figure 2-9, but feed the low order address bits and the R/W signal to the memories through 74LS14 inverters on the board to distribute the address over the eight-pin load and feed the data from the backplane to the DO and DI pins of the 2102 and from these pins to the data bus on the backplane through a bidirectional bus amplifier, a 74LS245. You must carefully design the control for the bus drivers. The 74LS245 should drive the backplane bus only when a word is read from $4000 to $43FF, and at no other time. Otherwise, reduce your logic to a minimum.

19. Give the logic diagram for a circuit to control bus drivers for the backplane bus. A printed circuit card has some LSI chip on it (it does not

matter yet which one) whose eight data pins connect to inputs of an 81LS95, called driver A, whose outputs connect to the backplane data bus, and the backplane data bus connects to inputs of another 81LS95, called driver B, whose eight outputs connect to the eight data pins on the LSI chip. The control circuit enables driver A so that data from the LSI chip can be put on the backplane bus by asserting EA low, and it enables driver B by asserting EB low so data on the backplane can be sent to the LSI chip. The control circuit has input R/W which is high if memory is being read and low if it is being written, negative logic CE that is asserted low if the LSI chip is being written into or read from, and a positive logic DACK. (DACK is direct memory access acknowledge. In direct memory access, as will be discussed in chapter 4, the LSI chip behaves like the microprocessor by supplying data to be written in memory, or by picking up data read from memory.) Design the control circuit so that data from the LSI chip is put on the backplane only when R/W is high CE is true, and when DACK is true and RW is low, and so that data from the backplane is sent to the LSI chip at least when R/W is low and CE is true, or when R/W is high and DACK is true. Otherwise, reduce your logic to a minimum.

20. Assume that a R/W signal is generated by a 74LS32 for Intel 2102 memories and the data from the microprocessor passes through more than one 74LS245 bidirectional bus driver to the data pins on the 2102. (a) Write an expression to determine the minimum interval T6809 during which the MC6809 has to maintain stable data if the R/W signal passes through a series of n 74LS32s and the data pases through a series of m 74LS245s to get to the 2102s, in terms of the set-up and hold times T2102 for the 2102, the delay times T7432 for the 74LS32, and the delay T74245 for the 74LS245. (b) Using the delays T7432 and T74245 and the set-up and hold time of the Intel 2102A-2 T2102 as [6, 11], [9, 18], and [−180, 0], for each n (number of 74LS32s) determine the maximum number m (of 74LS245s) that can be permitted to connect the MC6809 to the Intel 2102a-2s.

21. Write subroutines to implement interval arithmetic. (a) Describe an algorithm to multiply two intervals that always gets the correct interval result, and an algorithm that finds the inverse of an interval that detects when the result is not an interval (because it contains infinity). (b) Assume all intervals have minimum and maximum numbers, each of which are thirty-two-bits, as in:

FDB MININT,MINFR,MAXINT,MAXFR

where MININT is the integer part of the minimum, MINFR is the fractional part of the minimum, MAXINT is the integer part of the maximum, MAXFR is the fractional part of the maximum, MININT and MAXINT are two's complement numbers, and MINFR and MAXFR are unsigned fractions. Write four subroutines that can add ($C = A + B$), multiply

$(C = A \times B)$, negate $(C = -A)$, and invert $(C = 1/A)$ intervals in memory-to-memory operations, checking for all possible error conditions. Assume for each subroutine that X points to the source A, Y points to the source B, and U points to the destination C, and that a subroutine that already exists will invert a thirty-two-bit number, integer part in accumulator D, and fractional part in index register Y, leaving the result there.

3 Parallel Input/Output

The first two chapters were compact surveys of material that is really prerequisite to the study of interface design. That is why they were a little heavy with concepts and definitions. In the remainder of the book, we will have more expanded discussions and we will have more opportunities to study some interesting examples and work some challenging problems. The material in these chapters is not intended to replace the data sheets provided by the manufacturers nor do we intend simply to summarize them. If the reader wants the best description of a chip discussed at length in the book, data sheets such as are in *The Complete Motorola Microcomputer Data Library*, supplied by Motorola or others that are included in the appendixes for reference should be consulted. The topics are organized around concepts rather than around integrated circuits because we consider these more important in the long run. In the following chapters, we will concentrate on the principles and practices of designing interfaces with I/O LSI chips in general, and the Motorola chips compatible with the 6809 in particular.

Though this chapter is not the longest, it is the most important chapter in this book. The simple parallel input-output device is studied from both a hardware and software viewpoint. This device is most common among I/O devices and is a key building block of all the other I/O devices, so its importance to the design of interfaces should be obvious.

The first section considers some principles of parallel input/output architecture. The architecture is how input/output devices appear to the programmer. You have to consider the architectural alternatives in your design before you design either the hardware or the software. This section also shows how to build the simplest input and output devices. The second section introduces some very simple software that is used with input and output devices. While the software is simple, the memory cycle timing is often very important and just a little more intricate. We will study this aspect carefully. Also, microcomputers are often used to replace industrial controllers whose digital logic and relays have become obsolete. The software for such controllers is studied in the second section. The last section introduces the LSI parallel input-output chip. Some general observations are made, then the M6821 is introduced, and finally an application of M6821 to build a simple tester for integrated circuits is considered.

Upon finishing this chapter, the reader should be able to design hardware and write software for simple parallel input and output devices. An input device using a bus driver, an output device using a register, or a device using an M6821 should be easy to design and build. Programs to input data to a buffer, to output data from a buffer, or to control something using programmed or interpretive techniques, on the order of a hundred lines of code, should be easy to write and debug. Moreover, the reader will be prepared to study the devices introduced in later chapters, which use the parallel input/output device as a major building block.

3-1 Input/Output Architecture and Simple Input/Output Devices

We first consider the architecture of the parallel input-output device, that is, the way it appears to the programmer. One of the aspects introduced is whether I/O devices appear as words in primary memory, to be accessed by LDA and STA instructions, or as words in an architecturally different memory, to be accessed by different instructions. This is covered in the first subsection. The other aspect is whether the device can be read from or written in or both. One of the topics for a computer scientist's joke collection is the "write-only memory." Well, the write-only memory is a real possibility in an input/output device. To understand why you might use such a thing, the hardware design and its cost must be studied. We therefore introduce the hardware design of these devices. Moreover, the hardware design introduced here will be useful in the next section, which introduces the software used with these devices.

3-1.1 Isolated and Memory-Mapped I/O

There are two major ways in a microcomputer to access I/O, relative to the address space in primary memory. In *isolated I/O*, the devices are read from by means of *input instructions* such as IN 5. This kind of instruction would input a word from I/O device number 5 into an accumulator. Similarly, *output instructions* like OUT 3 would output a word from an accumulator to the third I/O device. The second way is called *memory-mapped I/O*. Here, the device is considered to be a word in memory, at some location such as $4000. A standard load instruction like LDA $4000 is then an input instruction, and the store instruction like STA $4000 is an output instruction. There is no need for a separate input or output instruction. Some machines like the M6809 have no I/O instructions and exclusively use memory mapped I/O. Other machines have input-output instructions and they can use either isolated I/O or memory mapped I/O.

Memory-mapped I/O uses the data and address buses just as memory uses them, as we discussed in the last chapter. The microprocessor thinks it is reading or writing data in memory, but the I/O devices are designed to supply the data read or to capture the data written at specific memory locations. As in the memory design in section 2-3.2, the basic hardware is enabled or clocked by an address decoder that decodes the address on the A bus. The decoder can be completely specified, built with decoder integrated circuits, or incompletely specified. Generally, though, it must enable or clock the device when a specific memory address is sent out and must not clock it when any other address used by the program is sent out. Isolated I/O is really quite similar in hardware to memory mapped I/O. To save pins, the device address is sent from the microprocessor on the same bus as the memory address, but some control signal is asserted when the address is an I/O address and not a memory address. The memory address decoders must be built to enable or clock the memory only when this variable is false, and the I/O address decoders must be built to enable the device only when this variable is true.

Each technique has some advantages. An input/output instruction, such as in the INTEL 8080, uses a one-byte op code and a one-byte device address, while almost all memory mapped I/O instructions have a tendency to be three bytes long. This extra length can be a serious problem if a program for a dedicated application uses a lot of I/O operations and must be fit into the smallest possible size memory to save cost. The 6809, however, has direct page addressing and index addressing that can be used to improve the static efficiency of I/O routines. The device address decoder is simpler, since it need consider only eight address bits and some control signals, rather than sixteen. More important, isolated I/O is not as susceptible to software errors as is memory-mapped I/O. In the latter case, especially if the microcomputer has a stack in memory, an error in a loop that has an instruction to push data onto the stack can fill memory with garbage in no time. In our personal experience, this happens all too often. If output registers send signals to turn on motors, say in a tape drive, putting garbage in them could produce interesting effects (spill tape, stretch and change density of tape). Memory mapped I/O is sometimes awkward when large memories, like the (65536,8) memories, occupy the addresses needed for memory mapped I/O registers. You have to design the address decoder so that the memory does not put data on the bus when the input device is read.

Nevertheless, memory-mapped I/O is gaining in popularity because most microcomputers have instructions that operate directly in memory, such as INC $4000 or ROL $4000. Indirect addressing can be used with memory mapped I/O if the program is in read-only memory. The program can be mass produced to be used in many different systems, in order to take advantage of the low cost of read-only memories, yet the different systems could have I/O devices at different addresses. The indirect address, in read-write memory, could be modified, while the program, in read-only memory, can be left alone. The use of these instructions operating directly on (readable) output registers in memory mapped I/O is very powerful and can shorten programs that would otherwise need to bring the word into the accumulator, operate on it, then output it, and the use of indirect addressing makes programs in read-only memory efficient and economically attractive.

We do have to worry about accidentally writing over the output registers when we use memory-mapped I/O. Memory mapped I/O can be protected, however, by a *lock*. The lock is an output register which is itself not locked, so the program can change it. The output of the lock is ANDed with address and other control signals to get the enable or clock signals for all other I/O registers. If the lock is F, no I/O devices can be read or written. Before reading an I/O device, the program has to store T in the lock, then store F in the lock after all I/O operations are complete. In dedicated microcomputers that execute fully debugged programs, a lock is not needed. In software development systems, a lock can drastically reduce the ill effects of memory-mapped I/O while providing most of its advantages.

3-1.2 Basic Input and Output Devices

Architecturally, a (one-word) parallel I/O device has an address in memory (or device number if isolated I/O is used) and a capability for reading and writing. With regard to the address, we consider whether we should use completely or incompletely specified addressing, and we consider where the device will be addressed by the program in memory. The former consideration was explained in section 2-3.2, when we studied the design of a memory. Consideration of the address assigned to the device may depend on the location of other memories and devices. For example, if several devices are addressed in consecutive locations, the PSHU instruction can load them from registers efficiently. In this section, we will also focus on the remaining consideration, which is the read and write capabilities of the device.

The basic input device is capable of sampling a signal when the microcomputer executes an input instruction (or an equivalent instruction in memory-mapped I/O) and reading the sample into the accumulator (or operating on it as if it were a memory word). Since most microcomputers use tristate bus drivers, the device has to put the sample of data onto the data bus during the bus cycle in which the microprocessor executes a read command with the address of this device.

A typical input device is shown in figure 3-1a as set up for memory-mapped I/O to input eight-bit data, which we will call SRC, whenever and LDA $4000 instruction or its equivalent is executed. The decoder is completely specified to decode fully all sixteen address bits for the address

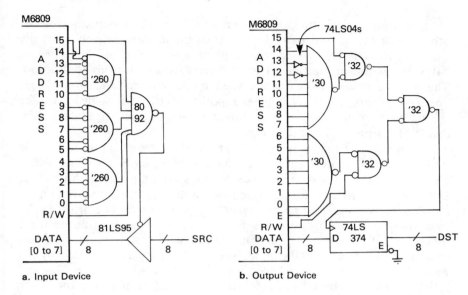

Figure 3-1. Logic Diagrams for Basic I/O Devices

$4000, and to check that R/W is high. Whereas a seventeen-input AND gate would be nice, the largest AND gate has thirteen inputs. To save inverters, negative logic input positive logic output AND gates (positive logic NOR gates) are useful. A gate in the 74LS260 is well suited to check that five inputs are low. Three of these can check the fifteen address bits that have to be low. Feeding these into a five-input positive logic input negative logic output AND gate, together with address bit fourteen and R/W, which must be high, completes the decoder. Half of an 8092 positive logic dual five-input NAND gate can be used. The actual input device, an octal bus driver like the 81LS95, is enabled with the output from the decoder.

In order to prevent the generation of the noise spike that result when two drivers drive a bus to different levels, an input device can be designed never to drive the bus in the first quarter of the memory cycle, as address and control lines are indeterminate at this time. The OR of the E and Q clocks is high for the last three quarters of the cycle, when the abovementioned signals are determinate. The output of this OR gate can be used in the decoder of an input device to prevent the generation of noise spikes. This insures that the drivers "break before make" in old-fashioned relay terminology. On the other hand, the hardware can be designed to tolerate the noise with the use of active terminators on the bus, the installation of 0.1 microfarad bypass capacitors directly across the bus driver integrated circuit power and ground pins, and the use of solid (up to 16-gauge copper wire) ground lines wherever possible.

Sometimes a single-bit input is required. This can be grouped with seven other single inputs and treated as a word input. Alternatively, a single tristate driver can be enabled to put the data on one of the data lines. A 74LS125 has four independent tristate drivers suitable for this application. The other data lines will be floating when this input is read and should be ignored by the program. Usually the sign position is used for single inputs like this because it can be sensed in a branch on sign instruction, like the BPL and BMI instructions of the M6809.

If a number of single inputs should be used, where each is to be a single bit in a word for convenience in software, a collection of them can be implemented in a *selector* or *multiplexer* that has a tristate output. An *n* input by one output selector is an *n*-position switch that can select one of *n* inputs to be output by means of an address. Coupled with a tristate driver in the same integrated circuit this makes an ideal one-bit wide input device for *n* inputs. A 74LS251 is a one-of-eight selector with tristate output. For instance, the three least significant address bits are used as an address by the multiplexer to choose one of eight inputs: the remaining thirteen bits and R/W are examined by a decoder for the correct address to enable the driver in the selector. The bits will appear as the sign bit of eight words in consecutive address locations in memory having the same high order thirteen bits.

The output device usually has to hold output data for an indefinite time, until the program changes it again. The basic output device is therefore a latch or register that is capable of clocking data from the data bus whenever the microcomputer executes an output instruction (or an equivalent instruction in memory mapped I/O). The D bus is connected to the D input of the register or latch, and the clock is connected to an address decoder so that the register is clocked when the microprocessor executes a write command at the address selected for this device.

Figure 3-1b shows a typical memory-mapped output device that will hold and output an eight-bit word of data written at memory location $4FFF, as in the STA $4FFF instruction. The data is constantly available as the signal, which we will call DST, to some external hardware. For example, each bit could be used to control a single traffic light, to turn it on if true and off if false. Two eight-input positive logic input negative logic output gates (74LS30s) check for the presence of highs required in the positive logic address bits fourteen and eleven to zero and clock E, and using 74LS04 inverters, lows on bits thirteen and twelve. These outputs and address bit fifteen and R/W (which must be low) feed a tree network of 74LS32 negative logic input and output AND gates. This develops the clock for a register with positive (rising edge triggered) clock input such as the 74LS374.

We emphasize the need to put the E clock signal into the decoder so that it asserts its output (low) only when the E clock is high. The M6809 guarantees that the data on the data bus is determinate at that time. The clock of a latch should not be asserted except at that time. Also, the edge that clocks data into a register must occur at the end of a memory cycle. The R/W signal (which may not even be needed in the decoder if the address is never used for a recall or fetch memory cycle) can rise in the beginning of the next memory cycle. At that time, the data is indeterminate. If you do not use the E clock signal in your decoder, you may be outputting garbage whenever you write in the device. (Decoders to LSI I/O devices, however, may not have this E input or they may fail to satisfy set-up and hold times of the device. The E signal is put on a pin of the LSI chip and ANDed with the chip select signals from the decoder inside the LSI chip.)

If a single-bit output is required, a flip-flop having one bit of the D bus connected to its D input can be used, of course. If this output will take data from some input bit that is in the sign position, it too should be connected to the most significant bit of the data bus, to avoid having to shift bits as they are moved.

If a number of single-bit outputs should be implemented, up to eight can be put in an *addressable latch* like the 74LS259. This addressable latch has eight D flip-flops internally connected to a decoder. The chip has a single D, an address, and an enable input, and Q outputs from each of the flip-flops. The D input to the chip is connected to all D inputs of the flip-flops and exactly one of them is clocked, as selected by an address, when the chip is enabled. The chip is used like the selector. The three least significant bits of the address bus are connected to the three address pins of the chip, the most significant bit of the data bus to the D input, and the other thirteen address lines and R/W are connected to a decoder to supply the enable signal to the addressable latch.

We have discussed the basic input device and the basic output device as separate modules. The basic input device is a "read-only memory." The program cannot write in it. In effect, some external system writes data into it and the microprocessor can only read it. Similarly, the basic output device is write-only. The microcomputer can only write data in it, and cannot read the data in it. It is a "write-only memory" as far as the program is concerned. Its data is read by the outside world.

An output device can be combined with an input device at the same address that inputs the data stored in the output register. This *readable output device* is more costly than the basic output device, which is read-only, but it is more flexible. Figure 3-2 shows a readable output device that can be read from or written in at location $7FFF. The device is actually a basic output device whose output is available to the outside world, and which is connected to a basic input device at the same memory address so it can be read. The decoder is constructed so that the basic output device is clocked when location $7FFF is written into, and the input device is enabled when loca-

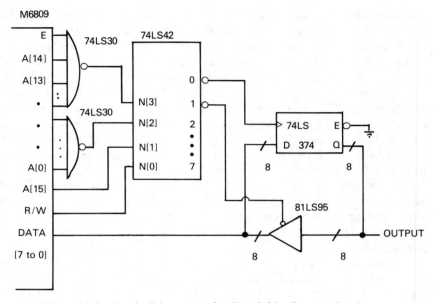

Figure 3-2. Logic Diagram of a Readable Output Register

tion $7FFF is read from. The 74LS30s check that the clock E is high, and that addresses fourteen to zero are high. These gates assert their outputs low when the address is correct. The rest of the decoding is done by a 74LS42, a standard "one of ten" decoder used in a nonstandard way. The input to the 74LS42 is a four-bit number N, and the Nth output is asserted low, the other outputs are negated high. (Note that the output of a decoder is a singulary number.) The two high bits of N are the outputs of the 74LS30s, and the two low bits are address bit fifteen and R/W. Output zero is asserted low when N is LLLL, and that occurs only when the device is being written into. Output one of the decoder is asserted low when N is LLLH, and that occurs only when the device is being read. So we connect output zero to the clock of the output register and output one to the enable of the tristate gate that forms the input device. In building address decoders a decoder integrated circuit is useful in place of gates if it replaces a number of gates so that fewer packages are used, but an address decoder does not have to use a decoder chip, and decoder chips can be used just to employ a few gates that happen to be in them.

Note that the R/W and E must be sensed low and high, respectively, by the decoder for it to assert the output latch clock or generate a clock edge for an output register so the output device will be clocked only when a word is being sent from the microprocessor and is valid on the data bus. The decoder should only enable the input bus driver if R/W is high, and can only drive the bus as long as the address is stable. To avoid having two bus drivers driving the data bus, however, the decoder could be disabled when the address and R/W are indeterminate, so it may be built to enable the input bus driver only when E is high or the OR of E and Q are high.

An interesting alternative to a readable output register is a *RAM shadow output register*. The output register is built like a basic output device, using a decoder and latch, but its address happens to be identical to the address of some word in random access memory (RAM). For example, if a RAM is addressed 0 to $3FF, then an output register at location $3FD is a RAM shadow output register. That is, the output device appears to be in the "shadow" of the RAM. Like a readable output register, the word that was last written in the I/O register can be read from that location. Whenever a word is written in the output register it is automatically saved in the corresponding RAM location. However, if the I/O register has a shorted output line or a bad I.C., the RAM shadow output technique would not report this error, while the readable output register would report the error.

A readable output register or a RAM shadow output register then behaves like a one-word read-write memory. This kind of output register is very useful in memory mapped I/O because it is essential for the operation of memory-to-memory instructions like INC $4000 or ROL $4000. These instructions will not work if the output device is the basic kind shown in figure 3-1b because they first read and then write the word in the register. An output register with read capability is useful when several programs that were written by different people at different times use the same register. One program can check to see if another wrote something in the register by reading it. This kind of output register is useful in software development systems because it can be examined when the program is being debugged. Nevertheless, the basic output register without read capability is often quite adequate. The word written there can also be separately stored in RAM whenever it is written, if it must be known by some other program. Keeping two copies of the word, one in the output register and the other in a RAM word, is usually less costly than building the extra hardware to make the output register readable. The RAM shadow output register automatically keeps a copy of the output word in RAM.

It is possible to wire some inputs of an input device to some output bits of an output device at the same address and to some external signals, so that when this input device is read, it reads the part of the output register to which it is connected. Those bits read from the output register are readable, so the device is a *partially readable output device*. For example, if bits six to zero of an input device are connected to bits six to zero of an output device that appears at the same address, but bit seven of the input device is connected to an external signal, it is possible to read bits six to zero and rewrite them, as is done by the INC ALPHA instruction, and also to input bit seven from the outside world, since it can be sensed in an instruction like BMI after the INC ALPHA instruction. Partially readable output devices are quite often used as control registers to send commands to external hardware and to read the status of that hardware together with the commands that have been sent earlier. We will see them in many LSI I/O devices.

Finally, we note that two completely different input and output devices can use the same address. When this location is read, the input device is enabled, and when this location is written, the output device is clocked. It is often cheaper to use the same memory address for two completely different devices like this because they can share their address decoder hardware. They share the decoder in the same way that the readable output register shares a single decoder for both input and output.

This section discussed the architecture of parallel input-output devices. If you design an I/O device, you have to consider these issues, and even if you use an LSI I/O chip, you have to be aware of these issues that were considered by the designers of the chip. The architecture is generally specified first, so the hardware and software can be developed simultaneously from that specification. In computers that have isolated I/O, we can use isolated I/O or memory mapped I/O. In development systems we use completely specified I/O, which could be used to debug erroneous programs, because an error that uses an illegal address is particularly hard to pin down even with a logic analyzer. We use incompletely specified addressing in small systems that execute fixed (error free) programs to save some logic in the decoder. A one-word I/O device can be a basic input, a basic output, a readable output, a RAM shadow output, or a partially readable output device. In general, you should use the simplest output device, unless a more complex one is required. Most output devices we have seen are simple, and most that you design will be simple output devices.

This section also showed how a basic input or output device or a readable output device can be realized in hardware, by way of explaining the rationale for the architectural alternatives. We will use these devices in the next setion to show how the software uses them.

3-2 Input/Output Software

Software for input and output devices can be very simple or quite complex. In this section, we look at some of the simpler software. The software to use a single input and a single output device to simulate (replace) a wire will be considered first. It provides an opportunity to examine microscopically what is happening in input and output instructions. We discuss input to a buffer and output from a buffer next. Programmed control of external mechanical and electrical systems is discussed next. We will discuss the control of a traffic light and introduce the idea of a delay loop used for timing. Then, a slightly more involved example will discuss a table-driven traffic light controller. Finally, a linked list interpreter, which can implement a sequential machine, will be discussed.

3-2.1 I/O Transfers and Buffered Input and Output

Three simple things that we do with I/O devices are moving data through a computer under the control of a computer, gathering data that is collected at an input, or supplying a stream of data to an output. Timing of these operations is often critical. We will consider the timing of input and output operations in terms of memory cycles, using the technique introduced in section 2-2.2. The logic analyzer can be used to examine the address and data bus on a memory cycle basis to see what actually happens, to confirm the timing. This is a very good experiment, which we recommend to really give you the feeling of instruction execution.

Suppose that a one-word input device is implemented to input data SRC in location $4000 and a one-word output device outputs data to DST in location $4FFF. See figure 3-1. The following program will simulate a (bundle of) wire from SRC to DST:

L LDA	$4000	F,F,F,N,D
STA	$4FFF	F,F,F,N,D
BRA	L	F,F,N

The timing of these instructions, shown in the comment field, can be determined using the technique discussed in section 2-2.2. The symbols F, N, and D are those used in table 2-1 to represent fetch, null, and recall or memorize cycles. The LDA instruction, for example, consists of the following memory cycles: Fetch, Fetch, Fetch, Null, Recall. In fact, if you looked at a logic analyzer, where L was location $100, location $FFFF had value $58, and the input device now read the value $34, the picture on the display giving the R/W signal (values R for read and W for write) and address and data (in hexadecimal) for one-loop execution will look this way:

R 0100	B6	LDA OP CODE
R 0101	40	HIGH ADDRESS
R 0102	00	LOW ADDRESS
R FFFF	58	NULL CYCLE
R 4000	34	READ INPUT

R 0103 B7	STA OP CODE
R 0104 4F	HIGH ADDRESS
R 0105 FF	LOW ADDRESS
R FFFF 58	NULL CYCLE
W 4FFF 34	WRITE OUTPUT
R 0106 20	BRA OP CODE
R 0107 F8	DISPLACEMENT
R FFFF 58	NULL CYCLE

The LDA instruction takes five memory cycles, in which data is read from $4000 in the fifth cycle. The STA instruction takes five memory cycles in which data is written into $4FFF in the last cycle. Finally, the BRA instruction takes three cycles. This loop takes thirteen cycles. If a cycle takes one microsecond, data at the input is sampled every thirteen microseconds and is output with a delay of five microseconds after it is sampled. Thus, it is not a perfect wire. But it is reasonably close.

The reader is not encouraged to build a microcomputer with these registers just to replace a wire. This example shows that data is in fact sampled and delayed by a microcomputer. It shows that input and output can be very simple. A simple pair of input/output devices like this could be used to monitor the data being moved through the computer, to check and modify it. Or the computer could have several input and output devices, and it could route data from one input to another output device under software control. This is the basic function of many microcomputers used in communications systems. Once a microcomputer is put in the path of a signal, its intelligence can be used to advantage.

A second application of input software is the sampling of inputs and storage of the samples in memory, to get a "movie" of what happened. An *input buffer* is an area of memory that is set aside to store the incoming words. It is like a stack buffer as discussed in section 1-2.1. Normally the first word read from the input port is put at the top (least address) word in the buffer, and successive words are put in successively higher locations. The following program will collect $100 words from the input SRC into a buffer located between $200 and $300.

```
      NAM    INBUF
      LDX    #$200 INITIALIZE POINTER
    L LDA    $4000 GET A WORD FROM THE INPUT DEVICE
      STA    ,X+ PUT IN BUFFER, MOVE POINTER
      CMPX   #$300 ALL WORDS IN?
      BNE    L NO, LOOP FOR ANOTHER WORD
      END
```

This basic routine can collect $100 successive samples from the input device. It could be used to collect data as in a "movie," or, if the input happened to be connected to a paper tape reader and the paper tape reader could be pulled so that a pattern of holes appeared each time the recall cycle of the LDA instruction were executed, the patterns could be copied into memory. This is the basis of secondary memory I/O devices and communications devices like UARTs (universal asynchronous receiver transmitters). A similar program can feed consecutive words from a buffer to an output device. One of the problems often faced here is timing. How fast can data be read? How fast will data be output? The timing study for the "wire" program can be used to answer these questions. The input to buffer program takes eighteen memory cycles to complete the loop. If the memory cycle time is one microsecond, data is sampled every eighteen microseconds. (A faster program is possible, but we leave that as an exercise for the reader—see problems 6 and 8.)

3-2.2 Programmed Logic Control

Microcomputers are often used for *Logic-timer* control. In this application, some mechanical or electrical equipment is controlled through simple logic involving inputs and memory variables, and by means of delay loops. Numeric control, which uses A/D and D/A converters, is discussed in chapter 5. A traffic light controller is a simple example, in which a light pattern is flashed on for a few seconds before the next light pattern is flashed on. Using LEDs instead of traffic lights, this controller makes for a simple and illuminating experiment to perform in the laboratory. Moreover, techniques used in this example extend to a broad class of controllers that are based on logic and timing, and little else.

In the following example, a *light pattern* is a collection of output variables that turns certain lights on and others off. See figure 3-3. Each bit of the output register LIGHTS turns on a pair of lights (through a power amplifier, discussed in chapter 5) if the bit is T. For example, if the north and south lights are paralleled and the east and west lights are similarly paralleled, six variables are needed; if they are the rightmost six bits of a word, then TFFFFF would turn on the red light in the north and south lanes, FTFFFF would turn on the yellow light, and FFTFFF the green light in the north and south lanes. FFFTFF, FFFFTF, and FFFFFT would similarly control the east and west lane lights. Then TFFFFT would turn on the red north and south lights and the green east and west lights. We will assume that the basic output register at location $4FFF (called LIGHTS in the program) is connected so its right six bits control the lights as described above. This register is constructed as in figure 3-1b in the previous section. Also, for further reference, TIME will be a binary number whose value is the number of half-seconds that a light pattern is to remain on. For exam-

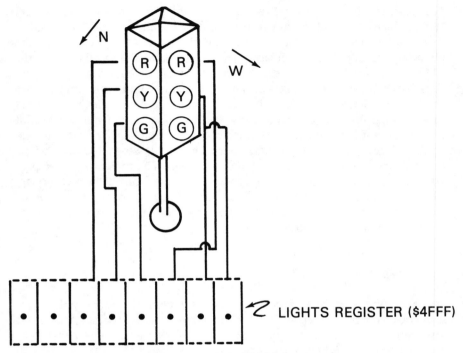

Figure 3-3. A Traffic Light

ple, the pair LIGHT = TFFFFT and TIME = 5 will put the red north and south and the green east and west lights on for two and a half seconds. Finally, a *sequence* will be several pairs of light patterns and associated times that describes how the traffic lights are controlled. In this example, the sequence is a *cycle*, a sequence that repeats itself forever. The input in this example will be a binary number N read from a basic input register that appears to be at location $4000.

We now wish to *program* the sequences by means of immediate operands. See the following program, for example.

```
        LDA    #%00100001    TURN ON RED N-S AND GREEN E-W
        STA    LIGHTS        PUT INTO OUTPUT REGISTER LIGHTS
        LDA    #5            SET OUTER LOOP COUNTER EQUAL 5
L1      LDX    #62500        SET INNER LOOP TO DELAY 1/2 SEC
L2      LEAX   -1,X          DECREMENT INDEX REGISTER X
        BNE    L2            LOOP FOR A HALF SECOND
```

```
DEC   A              DO THE INNER LOOP 5 TIMES
BNE   L1
```

In this technique as the program is executed it supplies immediate operands (as in line one) to the output register (as in line two) and immediate operands (as in line three) to control the duration of the light pattern. A loop like lines five and six or a pair of nested loops like lines four to eight is called a *delay loop*. It is used to match the time of the external action with the time needed to complete the instruction. Delay loops are extensively used in I/O interface programs. The delay loops use index register X to count out half a second of delay (in the inner loop in lines five and six). Index register X or Y can be used as counters because the instructions LEAX and LEAY set the Z condition code when the result is zero, but index register U may not be used because LEAU does not change the condition codes. Since the loop takes exactly eight memory cycles and a memory cycle is one microsecond in our examples, the loop must be cycled 62,500 times. The fourth line sets up the index register to be decremented that number of times in the inner loop. An outer loop is executed a number of times specified by the number in accumulator A in line three. Since each inner loop takes 0.5 seconds, the total delay will be about 2.5 seconds. Another segment of the program much like this one would be written to output another pattern for another period of time. The entire sequence could be programmed by writing segments like this one for each pattern.

We observe that the program has some undesirable features. The inner loop may take 0.5 seconds, but the set up instructions make the delay a few microseconds longer. While the average motorist will not be too upset about this error, if several traffic lights along a street have different programs in them, these miniscule errors could accumulate so that in a month or two the lights may be so far out of sequence as to stop the flow of traffic at every light. With a little effort, though, the delays can be trimmed so that each program segment is precisely timed. Writing such a program takes a fair amount of effort, but timing can be adjusted so that errors do not accumulate and traffic will flow smoothly without needless stopping at each light. The memory cycle, however, must also be adjusted to be precisely one microsecond in this example, since the timing is predicated on an accurate delay for each memory cycle. This can be achieved using a crystal controlled oscillator for the microcomputer clock, but the controllers will have to be resynchronized every few months because even a crystal has limited accuracy. Noting that the problem is the relative error between controllers, an easier solution would use some global clock to keep all the controllers synchronized. Though slow and not precisely accurate, the 60-Hz power line provides a universal clock to keep them in synchronization. The inner loop would wait for the rising edge of the power line signal, and the outer loop would count in sixtieths of a second, for instance.

3-2.3 Table and Linked-List Interpreters

A better way to program a control sequence than using immediate operands is described in the following paragraphs. This method makes it easier to write and modify the control sequences and to store them in a small microcomputer memory. These advantages are so great that the technique introduced in this section is usually recommended for most applications.

An *interpreter* is a program that reads values from a data structure such as a table, a bit or character string, list, or a linked-list structure to control something, like drill presses, traffic lights, or to execute high level languages like APL or LISP. You might like to scan section 1-3.1 to review data structures before looking at interpreters. Table and linked-list interpreters are particularly useful in interface applications. The table interpreter is described first, then the linked-list interpreter is introduced by modifying the table interpreter.

A light pattern cycle can be stored in a table. The table has two columns, one to store the pattern and the other to store the time, and it has one row for each pair. Consecutive rows are read from the table to the output register and to the delay loop. For example, a cycle could be described by table 3-1.

Table 3-1
A Traffic-Light Sequence

	LIGHT	TIME
	TFFFFT	5
	TFFFTF	2
	FFTTFF	7
	FTFTFF	2

Tables are stored in a computer as arrays. Recall from section 1-3.1 that arrays can be stored in row major order or column major order. We store the table above in row major order because the rows are accessed as a whole using autoincrement addressing. The table can be stored in the 6809 this way:

FCB	%100001
FCB	5
FCB	%100010
FCB	2
FCB	%001100
FCB	7

```
        FCB                     %010100
        FCB                        2
```

If the first word is at location 100, then the first row of the table is stored in location 100 and 101, location 100 containing 00100001 and location 101 containing 00000101. The next rows are stored in the same way below this one.

A table interpreter for this table is now shown:

```
        NAM     TRAF
L       LDY     #TBL    POINT TO FIRST ROW
L0      LDA     ,Y+     GET LIGHT PATTERN, MOVE
                        POINTER
        STA     LIGHTS  OUTPUT PATTERN
        LDA     ,Y+     GET DELAY (IN 1/2 SECS)
L1      LDX     #62500  SET UP LOOP FOR 1/2 SECOND
L2      LEAX    -1,X    DECREMENT INDEX REGISTER X
        BNE     L2      DELAY 1/2 SECONDS
        DEC A
        BNE     L1      EXECUTE INNER LOOP "DELAY"
                        TIMES
        CMPY    #TBL+8  AT END OF TABLE?
        BNE     L0      NO, GO TO NEXT ROW
        BRA     L       YES, REINITIALIZE
        END
```

The first line sets the index register to point to the first word in the table. The next two lines read the light pattern from the entry in the first column into the output register. The delay time is next read, then the delay loop is entered. Index register X is set up to count 62,500 inner loop cycles, as before, and the delay times, read from the table, is used to count out the number of times this loop is executed by the outer loop. Index register Y has already been incremented twice by autoincrement instructions LDA ,Y+, and is now pointing to the next row in the table and the program above is essentially repeated. This way, consecutive rows are read out to control the consecutive light patterns. After the last row is read out, however, the index register must be repositioned to point to the first row, to cycle the patterns. This is done in the last three lines by comparing the index register with the address of the word just beyond the end of the table and branching to line one to reload the index register when it reaches that point.

Linked-list interpreters strongly resemble sequential machines. We have learned that most engineers have little difficulty thinking about sequential machines, and that they can easily learn about linked-list interpreters by the way sequential machines are modeled by a linked-list interpreter. (Conversely, programmers find it easier to learn about sequential machines through their familiarity with linked-list structures and interpreters as in this example.) Linked list interpreters or sequential machines are powerful techniques that are used in sophisticated control systems, such as robot control systems. You should enjoy studying them as you dream about building your own robot.

A *Mealy sequential machine* is a common model for (small) digital systems. While the model is intuitive and is described below, if you want more information, consult almost any book on logic design, such as *Fundamentals of Logic Design* by C.H. Roth, published by West Publishing Co. (chapter 14). This model is conceptually simple and easy to implement in a microcomputer using a linked list interpreter. Briefly, a Mealy sequential machine is a set S of internal states, a set I of input states and a set O of output states. At any moment, the machine is in a *present* internal state and has an input state sent to it. As a function of this pair, it provides an *output* state and a *next* internal state. The next internal state becomes the present internal state in the next moment.

The Mealy sequential machine can be shown in graphical form or in a table. See figures 3-4a and 3-4b for these forms for the following example. In this example, the machine has internal states $S = (A, B, C)$, input states $I = (a, b)$ and output states $O = (0, 1)$. The graph shows internal states as nodes, and for each input state an arc from a node goes to the next internal state. Over the arc the pair input state/output state, is written. In the table each row describes an internal state and each column an input state. In the table the pair, next internal state/output state, is shown for each internal state and input state. In this example, if the machine were in internal state A and received input a, it would output 0 and go to state B; if it received input b, it would output 1 and go back to state A.

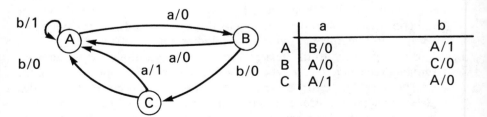

	a	b
A	B/0	A/1
B	A/0	C/0
C	A/1	A/0

a. Graphical Representation   b. Table Representation

Figure 3-4. Mealy Sequential Machine

Consider a simple example of the operation of a sequential machine. If the machine starts in internal state *A* and the input *a* arrives, it goes to state *B* and outputs *a* 0. In fact, if it starts in state *A* and receives the sequence *abbaba* of input states it will go through the sequence *BCABCA* of internal states and it will output the sequence 000001 of output states.

The table representation can be stored in a microcomputer in standard row-major order. The following assembler-language directives show how this can be done in the M6809:

A	FDB	B	NEXT STATE FOR PRESENT STATE A, INPUT a
	FCB	0	OUTPUT FOR PRESENT STATE A, INPUT a
	FDB	A	NEXT STATE FOR PRESENT STATE A, INPUT b
	FCB	1	OUTPUT FOR PRESENT STATE A, INPUT b
B	FDB	A	NEXT STATE FOR PRESENT STATE B, INPUT a
	FCB	0	OUTPUT FOR PRESENT STATE B, INPUT a
	FDB	C	NEXT STATE FOR PRESENT STATE B, INPUT b
	FCB	0	OUTPUT FOR PRESENT STATE B, INPUT b
C	FDB	A	NEXT STATE FOR PRESENT STATE C, INPUT a
	FCB	1	OUTPUT FOR PRESENT STATE C, INPUT a
	FDB	A	NEXT STATE FOR PRESENT STATE C, INPUT b
	FCB	0	OUTPUT FOR PRESENT STATE C, INPUT b

If this table is stored, beginning at location \$0100, then the row for state *A* will start at \$0100, for *B* at \$0106, and for *C* at \$010C. The first three words, at locations \$0100 to \$0102, would be:

FFFFFFFT

FFFFFTTF

FFFFFFFF

The interpreter for this table (or linked list structure) would read an input, presumably from an input register SRC at location $4000, and send the output to an output register DST at location $4FFF, as before. The input state a is the value $00 when read from the input register and b is $01. The internal state is associated with the row being read, and this is determined by the index register X. If the initial internal state is A, then the program implements this by initializing X to the address of the row associated with state A. The table is stored as shown above, and is interpreted by the following program:

```
        LDX     #A    POINT TO INITIAL STATE A
   L1   LDA     SRC   READ INPUT STATE
        BEQ     L2    IF INPUT IS "b"
        LEAX    3,X   MOVE OVER 3 WORDS
   L2   LDA     2,X   READ OUTPUT STATE
        STA     DST   INTO OUTPUT REGISTER
        LDX     ,X    PUT ADDRESS OF NEXT STATE IN X
        BRA     L1    REPEAT FOREVER
```

The first line initializes index register X to start the machine in state A. The input state is read and examined. If it is a (value 0), the third word of the table is output, and the first and second words give the address of the row associated with the next state. Line three branches to line five to read the output state, and line six outputs it. Line seven gets the address associated with the next state, so that when line one is reentered the same operation is repeated for that state. If the input is b (1), the LEAX instruction adds three to index register X so that lines five to seven pick up the output and next states from the sixth, and fourth and fifth words of the table, respectively.

The linked list structure has been introduced by comparison to a row of the table. The structure is accessed (read from or written in) by a program, an interpreter. The key idea is that the next row to be interpreted is not the next lower row, but a row specified by reading one of the columns of the table. For example, after interpreting the row for state A, if a b is entered, the row for A is interpreted again because the address read from words five and six of the table is the address of this same row. This view of a list is intuitively simple. More formally, a *linked list structure* is a collection of *blocks* having the same *template*. A block is a list like the row of the table and the template is like the column heading. Each block is composed of *fields* that conform to the template. Fields can be one bit to tens of bits wide. They may or may not correspond directly to memory words (bytes), but if they do, they are easier to use. In our example, the block (row) is composed of four fields, the first of which is a sixteen-bit field containing a next address, the second is an eight-bit output field, and the third and fourth fields are like these two. Addresses generally point to the first word of a block, as in our example, and are loaded into the index register to access data in the block. Fields are accessed by using the offset in indexed addressing. Another block is selected by reloading the index register to point to the first word of that block. Rather than describe it as a row of a table, we describe the block by showing the blocks graphically as arcs from address fields to the blocks they point to, as in figure 3-5. Note the simple and direct relationship between figure 3-5 and figure 3-4a. This intuitive relationship can be used to describe any linked-list structure, and the graph can be translated into the equivalent table and stored in the microprocessor memory without much effort.

Linked-list structures are especially useful in the control of sophisticated machines, robots, and so on. You can model some of the operations as a sequential machine first, then convert the sequential machine to a linked-list structure and write an interpreter for the table. You can also define the operations in terms of a linked list and its interpretive rules. Some of our hardware colleagues seem to prefer the sequential machine approach, but our software friends insist that the linked-list structure is much more intuitive. You may use whichever you prefer.

Interpreters are useful for logic-timer control. A table is a good way to represent a straight sequence of operations, such as the control for a drill

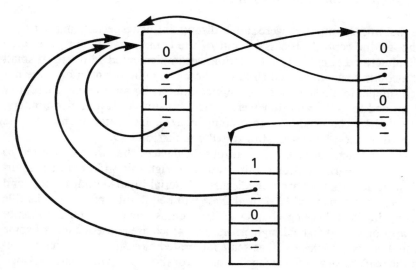

Figure 3-5. A Linked-List Structure

press that drills holes in a plate at points specified by rows in the table. A linked-list interpreter is more flexible, and can be used for sequences that change depending on inputs. Interpreters are useful in these ways for driving I/O devices. Their use, though, extends throughout computer applications, from data base management through operating systems, compilers, and artificial intelligence.

3-3 Programmable Parallel Input/Output Devices

Microcomputers often use LSI chips called *programmable parallel input-output devices* that are capable of being both inputs and outputs, selected under software control. The programming of the selection is—how shall we put it—different. We will offer some reasons why you have to program these devices in such an illogical manner in the first section, and introduce the programming ritual used to select the mode of operation of these devices. The M6821 is such a programmable chip that is in the same family as the M6809. We will introduce it in the second subsection, to show how rituals are written. An application is shown in the last subsection. We will design a tester for integrated circuits. This example will discuss top-down design and hardware details concerned with connecting the M6821 to the M6809 and the outside world.

3-3.1 Problems with LSI I/O and the Ritual

The first microcomputers were rather disappointing, especially in their I/O. Although the central processing unit of the computer was put on a large scale integrated circuit, the I/O section was implemented with tens of small and medium scale integrated circuits. These early microcomputers were not much smaller in physical size than minicomputers because so much circuitry was needed for I/O, and they were quite a bit slower than minicomputers. Motivated by the need for more compact I/O, integrated manufacturers began to develop large scale integrated circuits for I/O.

The first general class of input-output devices that were converted to large scale integrated circuit chips were the eight-bit wide parallel input-output devices that we are now discussing. Serial input-output devices and counters were converted later, and these will be the subject of considerable scrutiny in the following chapters. These chips have some characteristics that appear at first to be design errors, but which are consequences of some unusual characteristics of large scale integrated circuitry. In order to comfort the reader, we will review the rationale for these annoying characteristics.

The two key problems for large scale integrated circuit applications are volume production and pins. The cost of designing such a chip is on the order of a million dollars, but the chip has to sell for on the order of ten dollars. Therefore, these chips can only be designed if they can be sold in the hundred thousands, so they are often designed to be used in several similar applications to encompass a sufficient market to pay for the design. For example, the 74LS374 can be used as an output register, of course. On the connection of its outputs to the data bus, it can function as an input register. One chip can work as either an input device or an output device. Possibly twice as many chips will be sold if it can be used in both applications, than if it can only be used in one. To further extend the use of a chip, some pins can be added that determine how it functions. These *parameter* pins are normally connected to the positive supply or ground to input a T or F constantly to select a function. The INTEL 8212 is an excellent example of a chip with parameter pins: a mode pin MD is strapped to low to make the chip serve as an input device, and high to make it an output device. The CMOS 4034 is a readable output register that can serve s a shift register using a shift control pin. The Universal Asynchronous Receiver Transmitter (UART) discussed in chapter 7 is an example of parameterization taken to an extreme. The pins used for this are not cheap. They cannot be used for data input and output. More pins require a larger chip that takes more area on a printed circuit board. Not only is the larger chip more expensive, but the area on the printed circuit board is also costly, as some boards on the order of one square foot can cost a few hundred dollars just for the bare board.

An alternative to the use of parameter pins is to put these connections literally inside the chip itself, the parameters to be stored in a *control register*. This register looks rather like the data register in an I/O chip, in that an output instruction can load it with data; however, the values stored in it are used to set parameters that determine how the chip will function. For example, one bit in a control register may determine if the chip is to function as an input register or as an output register. This technique is a solution to the volume production problem and the pin problem: it permits the same chip to be used in various similar applications, but it does not require a large number of pins to select the specific function the chip performs.

A secondary and similar problem is that some LSI chips have too many registers and not enough pins. The address used to select the register is sometimes provided in part by bits that are stored in other registers inside the chip to avoid using other pins. This has the effect that several registers appear at the same location, to be read by an instruction like LDA $8000, for instance, but the register that is actually read depends on some bits in another register, and you have to store an appropriate word in that other register to be able to read the register that you want.

Moreover, it seems every solution creates some new problem. The control register has to be *initialized* to set the parameters when the microcomputer is powered on. This has to be done before the device is actually used. It can be done just before it is used, or right after power is turned on. Initializing the control register *configures* the device. The initialization routine is rather like an obscure *ritual* that is hard to explain and understand but relatively easy to do. The programmer has to determine exactly which bits in the control word have to be set to make the chip perform its specific function, and the correct sequence to set these bits. While the initialization ritual is efficiently done before the device is used, this technique is especially prone to software bugs like the kind that write garbage all over memory, including memory mapped control registers. Input registers become output registers, interrupts are mysteriously generated, and other marvelous happenings follow. Using some bits of a control register to select a register from a collection of registers is like a magician's *hat trick*—now you see it, now you don't. It is difficult to know when a program error has changed one of the hidden registers when you are analyzing an erroneous program. You have to check them too. The hat trick is one feature of LSI I/O chips that makes life difficult for programmers. Of course, if you cannot trust the program, the best thing to do is put a lock on the I/O device decoder to minimize all these calamities.

3-3.2 The M6821 Input-Output Registers

The M6821 is a large scale integrated circuit designed for parallel I/O that incorporates a control register to increase its flexibility. This chip is also called a *peripheral interface adapter* or PIA. We use the part name M6821 rather than the name PIA. The use of names like PIA reminds us of alchemy—oil of vitriol, eye of bat, and so on—so we just simply do not like them. Besides, Motorola produces two different chips, the M6820 and the M6821, both called PIAs. Over the life of this book there will probably be more chips like the PIA and they may also be named PIAs if that is Motorola's wish. So we prefer to use the part name like M6821 in this book, but you may wish to use either, and you ought to know both.

The chip has two almost identical input-output devices in it: each device has a data register that can be either an input register or an output register, or part input and part output register using a technique we discuss below. Each device has eight pins, *peripheral data* pins, to accept data from the outside world when the device is an input register, or to supply data to the outside world when it is an output device. Each device has hardware to generate interrupts. Its input-output circuitry is discussed now. The interrupt circuitry will be discussed in chapter 4 when the appropriate concepts have been introduced. The M6821 is fully described in *The Complete Motorola Microcomputer Data Library*.

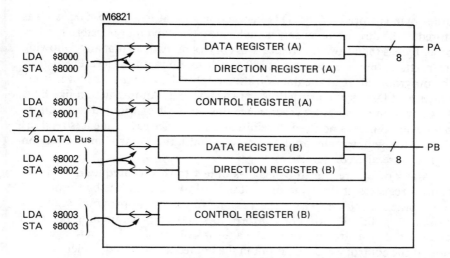

Figure 3-6. Simplified Block Diagram of the M6821

Each device in the M6821 has three eight-bit registers, *data*, *direction*, and *control*. See figure 3-6. The direction register determines, on a bit by bit basis, whether a data register bit is treated as an input bit or as an output bit. In the most common case, the direction bits are all T or all F, which makes the whole data register an eight-bit output register or an eight-bit input register, respectively. Both the devices in the 6821 are capable of being input, readable output, or partially readable output registers. These three registers in one device are accessed as just two words of memory using a "hat trick." A bit in the control register acts as a seventeenth address bit to select either the data or direction register. For example, these two words might be $8000 and $8001. If the program reads or writes in $8001, it always reads or writes data in the control register. If the program reads or writes in location $8000, it accesses the direction register if bit two of the control register is F, or it accesses the data register if that bit is T.

Suppose the device at $8000 and $8001 is to be an input device. The following ritual will be put in the reset routine to select this mode:

$$\text{CLR} \qquad \$8001$$
$$\text{LDD} \qquad \#\$0004$$
$$\text{STD} \qquad \$8000$$

The first instruction clears bit two in the control word so that when location $8000 is accessed, the direction register will be read from or written in. The next instruction puts zero into the high order and four into the low order bytes of the index register. The last instruction stores these two bytes in locations $8000 and $8001 respectively. Observe carefully that the high order byte is stored by the STD instruction first at location $8000, so it is stored in the direction register, to make the device an input register. The low order byte is then stored. It puts a T in control bit two, so that any following instructions that access location $8000 will see an input device. Thereafter, the program can read the data on the peripheral data pins whenever it executes an LDA $8000 instruction or its equivalent. An instruction like STA $8000 will do nothing, however, since this device is configured to be an input device. There is no need to reinitialize the device each time it is read, as the device will remain an input device until the control and direction registers are altered.

Many of our respected colleagues object to this technique to load two control registers at the same time. It is hard to read, so it is bad programming practice. Nevertheless, the reason we call these program segments "rituals" is that they do not conform to standard programming practices and rules. If you are going to make a mistake here, it will be in the generation of the control word that is put in the immediate operand, which is quite tricky to determine, rather than in the flow of the program segment. Thus, we have no objection to using tricks like using a sixteen-bit register to load two control registers in an initialization ritual. The other sixteen-bit registers, X, Y, or U, can be used in place of D if D has something in it, and PSHU can be used to initialize a set of control registers at one time. In fact, in the 6800, the index register X is the only register capable of recalling or memorizing two words at a time. (However, some I/O chips are not capable of loading two registers in consecutive memory cycles due to poor design, so you may have to load them one at a time using STA instructions.)

If the device is to be configured as a readable output, the following ritual is performed before the device is ever used:

```
CLR     $8001
LDD     #$FF04
STD     $8000
```

The first instruction clears bit two in the control register so that the STD instruction can put all Ts in the direction register to make the device an output device. The STD instruction also sets bit two so thereafter location $8000 is an output register. The instruction STA $8000 will store in the data register a word whose value will be available on the peripheral data pins to the outside world. The output register is also readable. An instruction LDA $8000 will read the word in the output register that was last stored there and is being output on the peripheral data pins. Also, an instruction like INC $8000 will read the current value, add one, and store the new value in the output register. Again, it is not necessary to execute the initialization ritual each time data is to be read or written in the data register: once the direction and control register are set up as above, the data register is treated as a readable output register.

Since each bit in the data register is selected for input or output by the corresponding bit in the direction register, it is possible to make the same device an input for some bits and an output for others (a partially readable output device). For example, if two output bits are needed and six input bits are needed, the following ritual will make the two low order bits outputs and the others inputs:

```
CLR     $8001
LDD     #$0304
STD     $8000
```

If a STA $800 instruction is executed, the two low order bits are stored in the output register, the other bits being discarded in the input bit positions. An LDA $8000 will read the two low order bits that were last stored there, and the other six bits from the corresponding peripheral data pins that input data from the outside world.

A *reset* pin is provided on most I/O chips, and this is connected to a similar pin on the M6809. When power is first turned on, or when this (negative logic) reset signal is asserted low (by a panic button reset switch) the M6809 is restarted in a manner discussed in chapter 4. In this restart program, we can often guarantee that all registers in all I/O chips are cleared, so it is unnecessary to execute a full initialization ritual. In particular, the direction registers (and the other registers) of the M6821 are cleared, so the device is (almost) configured as an input device. This is the safe way to configure an input-output device so that two outputs will not be connected to the same line, one driving it high while the other pulls it low. If the device is initially automatically configured as an input device until the programmer configures it, at least the gate outputs will not be stressed or destroyed. It is still necessary to change the control register of M6821s so that bit two is T, or you will read only the direction register when you think you are reading the input data register. To configure an M6821 as an input device after reset at location $8000, execute the instruction:

```
LDA     #$4
STA     $8001
```

We emphasize that this is one of the most common errors in using the M6821, that is, assuming that it is configured as an input device when power is applied or the machine is reset. You must change the control register before you can use the data register as an input. Otherwise, you will be reading the direction register.

The M6821 chip has two almost identical devices called the A and B devices. The B device behaves just as we discussed above: the A device has outputs like open collector outputs with pull-up resistors inside the chip, so that when a bit is configured as an output bit and is read by an LDA $8000 instruction, the data that is read is, in fact, the positive logic AND of the bit stored in the output register and the outputs of any gates driving this bus line. Usually, the A and B devices occupy four consecutive words in memory; for example the A data/direction register is at location $8000, the A control register is at $8001, the B data/direction register is at $8002 and the B control is at $8003; however, it is possible and often desirable to connect the address pins to the chip in a different manner. It is possible to put A and B data/direction registers at $8000 and $8002 respectively, and A and B control at $8002 and $8003, respectively. Then the data registers can be read or written using the LDD $8000 and STD $8000 instructions as if they were sixteen-bit data registers.

3-3.3 An Example: An IC Tester

In this section we consider a design problem to show how parallel I/O devices are built and programmed. Elements of top-down design are exemplified and the interconnection of the M6821 to an M6809 and the ritual to initialize the device are demonstrated.

We want to be able to test small and medium scale integrated circuits at the behavior level. That is, we want to be able to put an IC into a socket, then run a test program that will determine whether the IC provides the correct sequence of outputs for any sequence of inputs, but we are not testing the delays, the input and output electrical characteristics, or the set-up, hold, rise or fall times of signals. We want to be able to test standard fourteen- (and sixteen-) pin ICs in which positive five volts is applied to pin fourteen (sixteen) and pin seven (eight) is grounded. Such ICs comprise about 90 percent of the ones we use. Such a tester could be used to check ICs bought at bargain mail order houses.

In principle, there are two design strategies: top-down and bottom-up. In top-down design, you try to understand the problem thoroughly before you even start to think about the solution. This is not easy, because most microcomputer design problems are said to be *nasty*; that means that it is hard to state the problem without stating one of the solutions to the problem. In bottom-up design, one has a component or a system and he spends his efforts trying to find a problem that can use the solution that he already has. This is like a character on a late night TV show, Carnak the Magnificent. Carnak reads the answer to a question that is written inside an envelope, then he opens the envelope and reads the question. This is bottom-up design. We do it all the time. The answer is microcomputers, now what was the question? Now if you are an applications engineer for

Zilog, you are paid to find uses for a chip made by Zilog that are grudgingly acceptable to us purists. But if you are a design engineer, you have to design in a top-down manner! This philosophy of top-down design is so important that we will preach about it again in chapter 6.

We now approach the design of this IC tester in a top-down manner. We actually need fourteen input-output bits to supply signals to all the pins and to examine the outputs for all the pins except power and ground, but the pins are not standard from chip to chip. Pin one may be an input in one chip and an output in another chip. This indicates that the M6821 would be more suitable than the 74LS374/81LS95 type of output and input device, because a line to the M6821 can be made an input line or an output line under control of software, so it can be changed easily for different chips. Note this is not always the case, and a simpler I/O device (using 74LS374 or 81LS95 chips) may be indicated because it may be cheaper and use up less board space. (We are a bit guilty of bottom-up design here because we chose a problem in such a way that it would point to using the M6821, which we are studying at this time.)

In order to wire the M6821, we have to study its pin connections and those of the M6809 which must be connected to it. See figure 3-7. We digress for a moment in order to learn the interconnection rules for the M6821, but we will return shortly to the design problem when we know what lines are to be used.

The M6821 has ten pins to connect to the outside world for each device,

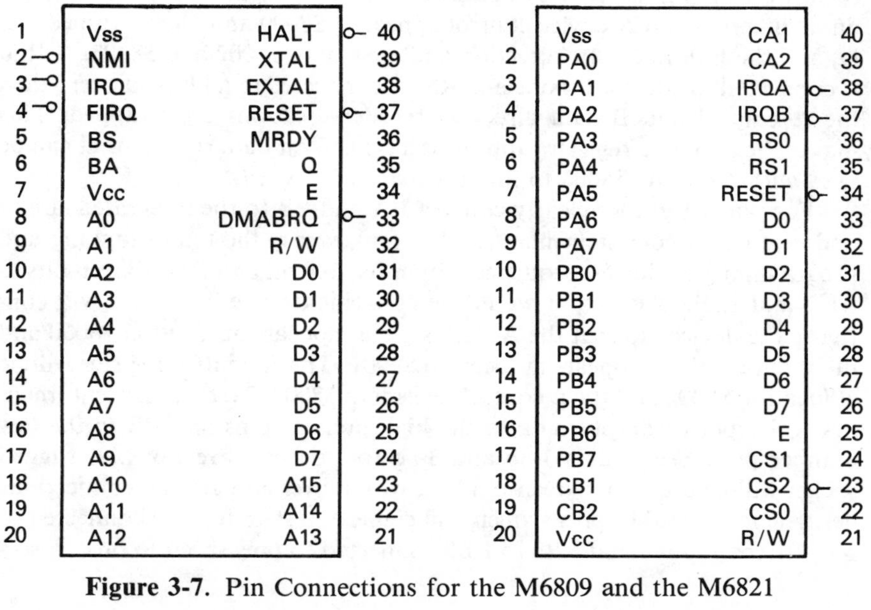

1	Vss	HALT	o– 40		1	Vss	CA1	40
2 –o	NMI	XTAL	39		2	PA0	CA2	39
3 –o	IRQ	EXTAL	38		3	PA1	IRQA	o– 38
4 –o	FIRQ	RESET	o– 37		4	PA2	IRQB	o– 37
5	BS	MRDY	36		5	PA3	RS0	36
6	BA	Q	35		6	PA4	RS1	35
7	Vcc	E	34		7	PA5	RESET	o– 34
8	A0	DMABRQ	o– 33		8	PA6	D0	33
9	A1	R/W	32		9	PA7	D1	32
10	A2	D0	31		10	PB0	D2	31
11	A3	D1	30		11	PB1	D3	30
12	A4	D2	29		12	PB2	D4	29
13	A5	D3	28		13	PB3	D5	28
14	A6	D4	27		14	PB4	D6	27
15	A7	D5	26		15	PB5	D7	26
16	A8	D6	25		16	PB6	E	25
17	A9	D7	24		17	PB7	CS1	24
18	A10	A15	23		18	CB1	CS2	o– 23
19	A11	A14	22		19	CB2	CS0	22
20	A12	A13	21		20	Vcc	R/W	21

Figure 3-7. Pin Connections for the M6809 and the M6821

A and B. Eight pins called PA0 to PA7 and PB0 to PB7 are the parallel input-output pin connections, and four pins called CA1, CA2, CB1, and CB2 are used in the interrupt circuitry, which is discussed in chapter 4. The remaining pins on the M6821 are connected to the M6809 on the 6821 in an almost methodical manner. The so-called enable pin E, which is actually a clock, is connected to the E clock or to a signal that is a slightly delayed E clock to account for skew in the data bus. This pin should never be held high or low for a long time on any LSI I/O chip because many of them use dynamic logic that is clocked by this signal. Although the M6821 does not use dynamic logic, its control is sequenced by shift registers that depend on the E signal to keep going. Never use it as part of the addressing mechanism to enable the chip. If you do not periodically clock this pin, signals (which are actually charges on capacitors) will become indeterminate inside an LSI I/O chip. This is always connected to the E pin, which is the 6809 clock. The data bus pins on the M6821 are connected to the data bus to the M6809, of course, and the R/W pin to the R/W line and RESET to the RESET bus line. IRQA and IRQB are used for interrupt signals, and are not connected in this example. The remaining address pins, CS0, CS1, CS2, and RS0 and RS1 are connected to the address decoder. For any register in the chip to be accessed, CS0, CS1, and CS2 have to be H, H, and L, respectively. CS2 is often used as the chip enable, since the decoder usually outputs the enable in negative logic. CS0 and CS1 can be used as positive logic enables, in lieu of putting these inputs into the decoder, in order to simplify the decoder. Finally, the RS1 and RS0 pins are normally connected to address bits one and zero. If RS0 is connected to address bit zero and RS1 to address one, then if the chip is selected by addresses $8000 through $8003, the A device data/direction and A device control appear at $8000 and $8001, respectively, and the B device data/direction and control at $8002 and $8003. If RS0 is connected to address bit one and RS1 is connected to address bit zero then the A control and B data direction register locations are swapped. This makes the two data registers appear as a sixteen-bit data register that can be used with the LDD $8000 to input a sixteen-bit word.

For our design, we clearly connect PA and PB to the integrated circuit under test in a consistent manner that makes easy the understanding and programming of the test sequences. In order to load and read sixteen bits, a STD and LDD instruction would be convenient. Therefore, we will configure the devices so that the A data register appears at location $8000 and the B data register appears at location $8001. The A control register will be at location $8002 and the B control register at $8003. To be consistent, then, PA will input or output data to the high number pins and PB to the low number pins. See figures 3-8b and 3-8c for socket corrections. A rugged socket will be used for sixteen-pin ICs, with power and ground connections permanently wired to pins sixteen and eight, and PA6 to PA0 connected to pins fifteen to nine and PB6 to PB0 connected to pins seven to one. A second rugged socket will be used for fourteen-pin ICs, with power and ground connections permanently wired to pins 14 and 7, PB0 to PB5 connected to pins 1 through 6, PB7 connected to pin 8, and PA0 to PA4 connected to pins 8 through 13. The user will plug a sixteen-pin IC into the sixteen-pin socket and not put anything in the fourteen-pin socket to test a sixteen-pin IC, or plug a fourteen-pin IC into the fourteen-pin socket and nothing into the sixteen-pin socket to test it. This configuration makes it possible to input or output data from the sixteen-bit X index register so that the rightmost bit corresponds to pin one, the next to pin two, and so on, to reduce the chances of programming errors, and also makes it impossible to connect an output register to power or ground, which may destroy the output circuitry.

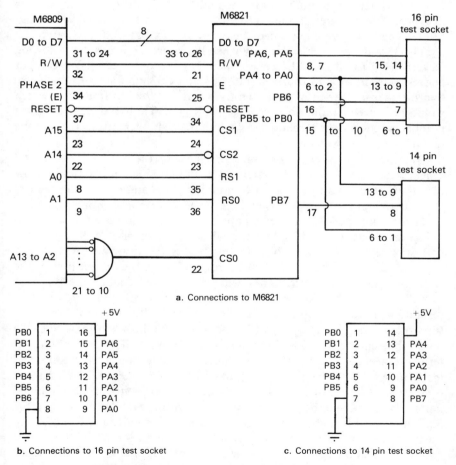

Figure 3-8. An Integrated Circuit Tester

We now consider the connections between the M6821 and the M6809. See figure 3-8a. It hardly has to be said, but V_{SS} (pin one) on the M6821 is grounded (remember: ground the SS), pin twenty is connected to positive five volts, and a 0.1 microfarad capacitor is connected between these two pins, as close as possible to the pins. It hardly has to be said, but we repeat it because we have mysteriously lost a good number of M6821s in the lab, and about the only way to burn out the chip is to apply power and ground backwards. As noted above, R/W (pin twenty-one) is connected to R/W on the M6809, E (pin twenty-five) is connected to the 6809 E pin (thirty-four), and RESET (pin thirty-four) to the RESET circuitry connected to the 6809 reset pin. The data bus is connected: D0 to D7 (pins thirty-three to twenty-six) are connected to the data bus. In order to configure the chip so the data registers can appear in locations $8000 and $8001, it is necessary to connect RS0 (pin thirty-six) to address bit one and RS1 (pin thirty-five) to address bit zero. The decoder should recognize any address between $8000 and $8003. This means that gates need be connected so that CS0, CS1, and CS2 are H, H, and L, respectively, only when the address bus has the following pattern: HLLLLLLLLLLLLLXX (where XX is a don't care). We can put address bits fifteen and fourteen into CS1 and CS2, and design some gates that output an H when bits thirteen to two are all low, to feed CS0, which would be a twelve-input positive logic NOR gate. Though there are a large number of good ways to build such a gate from simpler gates, we leave the rest of the design as an exercise.

We now turn to the programming aspect of the design. The general scheme will be as follows. A pattern of T and F values will be put into the direction registers: an F if the corresponding pin is an output from the test IC (and an input to the M6821) and a T if the corresponding pin is an input (output from the M6821). Then a pattern will be put in the data register, to set up the inputs to the IC under test wherever inputs are needed. The bits corresponding to the output pins are don't-cares. Then the data will be read from the I/O devices, and the bits corresponding to the output pins of the test chip will be examined. They will be compared against the bits that should be there, and these bits will come from the program. The bits corresponding to the input pins on the test chip are don't-cares here. To reduce the storage requirements, the test IC input bits and the bits compared to the output bits can be stored in the same sixteen-bit word. Two sixteen-bit patterns are needed, one for the direction register and one for the combined test chip input pattern/required output pattern. If pin i + 1 is an input pin on the test IC, bit i in the direction pattern is T and bit i in the combined pattern is the value to be put on the input pin of the test IC; otherwise, if the pin is an output from the test IC, bit i in the direction pattern is F and bit i in the combined pattern is the value that should be on the pin if the chip is good. A direction pattern will be set up once, just before the chip is inserted, and a sequence of combined patterns will be tested, one at a time, to check out the chip. Ideally, these sequences should be read from a table by a table driven interpreter. For simplicity in this example, however, we will show a programmed sequence, using immediate operands.

Tests for different chips will require different programs of course. A sample program to test the 74LS00 chip is now discussed. Other combinational logic chips can be tested in an almost identical manner. Chips with memory variables require initialization of these variables and more care in testing; also, a thorough test of any chip can require a lot of patterns. If a combinational chip has n inputs, then $2^{**}n$ patterns have to be tested; however, a simple test can be used to detect almost all the bad chips. For example, a quad two-input NAND gate like the 74LS00 contains four independent gates, which can be tested simultaneously. See *The TTL Data Book*. The truth table for one of the four gates in the 74LS00 is:

Table 3-2
Truth Table for the 74LS00

A	B	C
L	L	H
L	H	H
H	L	H
H	H	L

We will supply the two inputs, A and B, and check to see if the output is correct. This can be done for each gate simultaneously. The inputs A and B for one gate are on pins one and two and the output C is on pin three. These correspond to the rightmost bit positions, bits zero, one, and two, respectively, as they are output from the M6821. At the same time, the same pattern is applied to inputs A and B on pins four and five, and the output on pin six is checked, applied to inputs on pins ten and nine and checked on pin eight, and applied to pins thirteen and twelve and checked on pin eleven. All gates are checked for the correct behavior for the first row of the truth table at one time. The next three rows are checked in like manner, but such a test will not detect a possible short from one of the gates to another inside the chip. Nevertheless, the simpler test will be quite useful for our application.

```
        NAM              TST00
        CLRA                      CLEAR ACCUMULA-
                                  TOR D
        CLRB                      IN ORDER TO CLEAR
                                  THE CONTROL
                                  REGISTER
```

STD	$8002	IN ORDER TO ACCESS THE DIRECTION
LDD	#%1111101101011011	REGISTER TO MAKE PINS 3,6,8,11
STD	$8000	INPUTS TO CPU, PUT IN DIRECTION REGISTER
LDD	#$0404	CHANGE CONTROL TO ACCESS DATA
STD	$8002	
LDD	#%0000010010100100	TRY PATTERN FOR FIRST ROW
STD	$8000	OF TRUTH TABLE. PUT TO INPUT PINS
CMPD	$8000	CHECK RETURNED BITS, SHOULD BE 1
BNE	ERROR	IF NOT, BAD CHIP
LDD	#%0000110110101101	TRY PATTERN FOR SECOND ROW
STD	$8000	JUST AS IN THE PREVIOUS ROW
CMPD	$8000	CHECK RETURNED BITS, SHOULD BE 1
BNE	ERROR	IF NOT, BAD CHIP
LDD	#%0001011010110110	TRY PATTERN FOR THIRD ROW
STD	$8000	AS WE DID FOR OTHER PATTERNS
CMPD	$8000	CHECK RETURNED BITS, SHOULD BE 1
BNE	ERROR	IF NOT, BAD CHIP
LDD	#%0001101100011011	FINALLY, TRY LAST ROW OF TRUTH
STD	$8000	TABLE. THIS TIME, OUTPUT SHOULD
CMPD	$8000	BE A 0 FOR EACH GATE.
BEQ	OK	IF SO, CHIP IS GOOD.

ERROR   . . .   REPORT THE CHIP IS
                                    BAD

OK   . . .   REPORT THE CHIP IS
                                    GOOD

         END

The chip has outputs on pins three, six, eight, and eleven, and the other
pins are inputs. So XXXTTFTTFXFTTFTT should be put into the direction register. The don't cares (X) can be made outputs to simplify the comparison step. This is stored in the direction register in lines four and five in
the program. Lines eight to eleven test the first truth table entry for each
gate simultaneously, where all the inputs are low (and the program variables
are false). If the expected pattern is not read back, the program branches to
ERROR to report the chip is defective. In like manner, the other three truth
table entries are checked in the following rows. If all patterns are read and
verified, the program branches to OK to report that the chip tested is good.

3-4 Conclusions

The parallel input/output device is the most flexible and most common I/O
device. In designing a parallel I/O device, the first step is to decide on the
architecture of the device. Select the address and the input-output capability. The hardware can be implemented using simple TTL MSI chips, or an
LSI chip like the M6821. This chapter showed how to use the popular
81LS95 and 74LS34 medium scale integrated circuits to implement these
devices. This approach is really very simple, and is often desired because it
uses less board space and cheaper ICs than the other approach discussed,
using a large scale parallel I/O chip like the M6821. The M6821 was introduced and shown to be more flexible. This chip is often used in printed
circuit card microcomputers that are mass produced and intended for a
wide variety of applications. It can be configured by the appropriate ritual
for almost any parallel I/O device. It can also be used to implement two I/O
devices on one (large) chip rather than on (two) smaller chips. This can be
attractive if the devices are readable outputs because they take more (small)
chips to build both the input and output parts of the device, but RAM
shadow output registers can be used to the same advantage too. If the device
is changed from input to output under software control, the programmable
parallel output chip is better. Finally, we saw some details of how to connect the M6821 to the M6809 in hardware. This example showed the use of
top-down design and the need for it. The same approach to designing an
I/O system can be used to study such a system or an integrated circuit that is

already built, to understand why it was designed the way it was, and to infer what it is useful for.

We saw some I/O software that moved data through a microcomputer and moved data into a buffer, and some that implemented a traffic-light controller using the simple I/O devices. Timing is an important aspect of these programs, so we studied the timing of such program segments.

The interfacing of a microcomputer to almost any I/O system using parallel I/O devices has been shown to be simple and flexible. In the remaining chapters, these techniques are extended to analog interfacing, counters, and communications interfacing.

Problems

Note

Problems 1 and 14 are paragraph-correction problems. See the problems at the end of chapter 1 for guidelines. Guidelines for software problems are given in the problem section of chapter 1, and those for hardware in that of chapter 2.

1. *Memory mapped I/O is used on the M6809 and is popular on microcomputers that have isolated I/O because it is able to use instructions that operate on memory directly and because it is more reliable in the face of a runaway stack than is isolated I/O. In the event that a program error may write over I/O devices, however, a lock can be used to prevent the calamity. A basic input device is a tristate driver and a decoder; the decoder need only look at the address and the R/W line to see if the device is to be read. A basic output device may use a latch or a register, and a decoder. The decoder must check the address and must check the R/W signal—and that is all it has to check—to be sure the device is to be written in. A basic output device is a write-only register that cannot be read by the program. Therefore, the program should keep an extra copy of a word in such an output device if it wants to know what is in it. Such output devices are commonly used because they are cheaper than readable output devices. The selection of read-write capabilities is the architectural issue that has to be settled early in the design so the hardware and software design can progress from there.

2. A group of eight one-bit input devices is to be addressed at locations \$2C30 to \$2C37 so they will be read in the sign bit position. Show the logic diagram of a device to do this whose decoder is fully specified and whose input is a 74LS251 one-of-eight multiplexer with tristate output.

3. A group of eight one-bit output devices is to be addressed at locations \$73A8 to \$73AF so that they will write the sign bit of these words. Show the logic diagram of such a device whose decoder is fully specified and whose output latches are in the 74LS259 addressable latch. (Note that this group of output devices can have the same address as a read-write memory, so that when words are written in the memory, the sign bits appear in the outputs of the corresponding latch to be used in the outside world. This would implement eight one-bit wide RAM shadow output registers.)

4. An output system having sixteen output bits is addressed at location \$D3A1. If a number $2 \times n + 1$ is written into this location, the nth one-bit latch is set, and if a number $2 \times n$ is written into this location, the nth one-bit latch is cleared. Show a logic diagram of such a system of output latches whose address decoder is fully specified and whose latches are in

two 74LS259 addressable latches. (Note that this type of output is well suited to controlling solenoids and lights, since it is as easy to generate an immediate operand like $2 \times n + 1$ as it is to set an ordinary output register and there is less chance that another output will be accidentally changed when one is changed.)

5. Show the logic diagram of a partially readable output register which is addressed at location $8023. The seven least significant bits of the output are readable, but the most significant bit read comes from the outside world. The address decoder is to be specified completely, and it should use 74LS260 NOR gates and the 74LS139 dual one-of-four decoder. Use a 81LS95 for the input device and a 74LS374 for the output device. Show all chips and pin numbers.

6. Write all possible input buffer programs like INBUF (section 3-2.1) which are the fastest in execution, and give the rate at which words can be input to the buffer for the set of fastest programs, assuming a one-megahertz E clock. Consider using CMPX and DECA as do-loop control instructions and consider using different addressing modes. Do not use the stack pointer, as this is a dangerous practice, but use a do-loop.

7. A pair of input devices, at locations $6F39 and $6F3A, can be read by the LDD $6F39 instruction. They are connected to a sixteen-bit serial in parallel out shift register in order to input one-bit serial data shifted into the shift register into a buffer. (a) Show the logic diagram for this pair of devices using 74LS347s and a pair of eight-bit serial in parallel out shift registers using 74LS164s, using fully specified decoding for the address decoder. (b) Write a (fastest) program to store this data into a buffer using LDD and STD instructions. How many bits per second can it collect? (c) Suppose your program starts at location $1AB2: give a picture that would appear on a logic analyzer showing the R/W bit, and the address and data bus values in hexadecimal, for every memory cycle in one execution of the do-loop, assuming that $3D is input form device $6F39 and $2C is input from device $6F3A.

8. In order to output data as fast as possible, it can be pushed onto the stack pointed to by S before the output begins. Output can be done by pulling data from the stack, then "pushing" it using a PSHU instruction into a single output register. (a) Design an output register that will output a word stored between locations $8000 and $8007. Aside from ignoring the low order three bits, use completely specified decoding and use a 74LS374 register. (b) Write a program to output $100 words as fast as possible, using PULS A,B,DP,X,Y and PSHU A,B,DP,X,Y, where PSHU repetitively pushes the words into locations $8006 to $8000. Do not use a do-loop. (c) How many bits can be moved per second using this approach?

9. Suppose a one-bit input device using a 74LS125 inputs a signal A in the sign bit of location $8000. Measure the time from when A is low until

the time that it is high. (a) Show a logic diagram of the input device using incompletely specified decoding, assuming that the program uses only addresses zero to $1000, $8000 (for this device), and $F000 to $FFFF. (b) Write a program to measure this pulse width as accurately as you can, putting the width (binary number in microseconds) in accumulator D, assuming the E clock is one megahertz and the pulse width is shorter than sixty-five milliseconds.

10. Design a traffic light controller that uses the power line frequency to time the lights, and that uses immediate operands to control the lights. (a) Show a logic diagram of the I/O system. The input device, at location $4000, inputs a 60-hertz square wave signal in the sign positive of the word, using a 74LS125; and the output device, at location $4000, using a 74LS374, outputs a six-bit light pattern to control the lights as in figure 3-3. Use incompletely specified decoding, assuming the program will use only the addresses zero to $80, $8000 (for these devices), and $FF00 to $FFFF. (b) Show a program segment that tests the input so as to wait exactly one-half second. (c) Write a program using immediate operands to control the light patterns and using the program segment in (b) to time the lights to sequence the lights as in table 3-1.

11. Write a linked list interpreter to control the traffic light in figure 3-3 and linked lists to output: (a) the sequence in table 3-1; (b) a late night sequence in which the north-south lanes see a blinking red light, and the other lanes see a blinking yellow light which blink on for one second, and off for one second; (c) a fire truck emergency sequence in which the north-south lanes see red while the others see green for twenty seconds, then the east-west lanes see yellow for two seconds while north-south is still red, then the north-south lanes see green and the others see red for ten seconds, and then the sequence in table 3-1 is begun with the first line of the table.

12. Consider a vending machine controller. Its input register at location $8000 has value zero if no coins are put into the machine, one if a nickel, two if a dime, three if a quarter, and four if the coin return button is pressed. The output register, at location $8000, will dispense a bottle of pop if the number one is output, a nickel if two is output, a dime if three is output, and a quarter if four is output. This vending machine will dispense a bottle of pop if thirty cents have been entered, will return the amount entered if the coin return button is pressed, and otherwise will keep track of the remaining amount of money that has been entered. (a) Show the logical design of the I/O hardware, assuming incompletely specified decoding if the program uses only addresses zero to $80, $8000 (for these devices), and $FF00 to $FFFF. Use 74LS95 and 74LS374 chips. (b) Show a graphical sequential machine description of this controller. Internal states $S = [0, 5, 10, 15, 20, 25]$ will represent the fact that the total accumulated money is zero, five, ten, fifteen, twenty, and twenty-five cents. Input states $I = [B, N, D,$

Q, R] will represent the fact that no (blank) inputs are given; that a nickel, a dime, or a quarter is given, or the coin return button has been pressed. Output states $o = [b,p,n,d,q]$ will represent the fact that nothing (blank) is done, a bottle of pop, a nickel, a dime, or a quarter is to be returned, respectively. Assume the coin return button is pressed repetitively to return all the coins as the sequential machine steps through its internal states. (c) Show a program to implement this sequential machine by a linked list interpreter, and show the linked list. Assume the outputs have to be asserted for 0.1 seconds to activate the solenoids, and then the blank (0) output has to be written to release the solenoids that dispense the bottles and the money. Assume that you have to guard against responding to an input then checking that input again before it has been removed. (Hint: respond to an input only when it changes from that input back to the blank input.)

13. Show a linked list and a linked list interpreter that decodes the Huffmann code, using the coding tree given in figure 1-6. This linked list can be interpreted first as a sequential machine. Note that the zeroes and ones of the Huffmann code input are input states, the nodes except the leaf nodes of the tree are internal states, and the characters M, I, S, and P and the null output N are output states. The sequence of outputs, after the Ns are removed, should be the decoded outputs. (a) Show the sequential machine graphical representation and table representation. (b) Assume the input Huffmann coded string is stored in a buffer after location IN, most significant bit first, and the output character string, without the N (null) outputs, is stored in a buffer after location OUT. Show the linked list and the interpreter for the 6809.

14. *The key problems that lead to the rituals for LSI I/O chips are the need to compress the size of the I/O system using LSI, the need to produce as many copies of an LSI chip to spread the high design cost, and the need to keep the size of the chip below the size that is economically feasible. The ritual sets up control registers that fashion the LSI I/O device into a particular device that you might have built from MSI chips. Selection of the bits to store in the control register is analogous to picking the MSI chips from a catalog for a hardware design. Nevertheless, this creates serious problems for the programmer because it takes a long time to execute this ritual, and the registers hidden by a hat trick are difficult to watch if a programming error changes them.

15. Design a scanning monitor that uses a device of an M6821 as a partially readable output register. When you write into location $8000, the low order three bits are output to address a 74LS251 selector in order to examine one of eight inputs. When you read from location $8000, the low order three bits are the address you sent to the selector, and the most significant bit is the output of the selector. (a) Show a logic diagram of a partially readable output device using an M6821 so that the A device appears at loca-

tions $8000 and $8001, using incompletely specified decoding, assuming the program uses only the addresses zero to $3FFF, $8000 and $8001 (for this device), $8002 and $8003 for some other device that is not in the integrated circuit as the M6821 used for the scanning monitor, and $C000 to $FFFF. Show connections from the PA lines to the selector and all pins tied high or low. (b) Write a program ritual to initialize this device so the low order seven bits are outputs and the most significant bit is an input. (c) Write a program that continually scans the inputs, and jumps to location L*i* when the *i*th input is high. Use indirect addressing through the jump table:

TBL FDB L0-TBL,L1-TBL,L2-TBL,L3-TBL,...,L7-TBL

Note that the INC instruction can simultaneously change the input and sense the bit that was input; however, be careful to observe that the device is read before it is written by an INC $8000 instruction.

16. Show the logic diagram for the decoder in figure 3-8. Use SSI I.C.'s.

17. Write a program, similar to TST00 in section 3-3.3, to test a 74LS04 hex inverter in the tester in figure 3-8.

18. Write a program, similar to TST00 in section 3-3.3, to test a 74LS74 dual flip-flop in the tester in figure 3-8.

19. Write a table interpreter to test fourteen- or sixteen-pin integrated circuits using the tester in figure 3-8. The first row will define the inputs and oututs of the device and the remaining rows will define a sequence of tests on the device. The table will have a sixteen-bit row, bit zero outputting or testing pin one, and bit *i*, pin *i* + 1, and bit fifteen will be zero except for the last row of the table, where it is one. (a) Write a table in assembler language for a test on the 74LS00. (b) Write a table in assembler language for a test on the 74LS74.

20. Design a hardware breakpoint device. This device monitors the address bus of the M6809 to compare the address against a breakpoint address. The breakpoint address is written in output registers at locations $8000 and $8001, which are the A and B devices of an M6821. The address (when it is determinate) is compared with these two words by open collector exclusive nor gates (74LS266s) whose outputs are connected in a wire-AND bus. If they are equal, the outputs of the gates will be high, otherwise the outputs will be low. (The output can be used to generate an interrupt, discussed in the next chapter, to stop the program when the address is generated that matches the number in the output registers.) (a) Show a complete logic diagram of the M6809 and M6821 and a decoder that will implement this system, but do not show the memory that will be attached to the M6809. Show all connections and show actual 74LS gates and pins for your design. (b) Show a routine to set up the device so the output will be asserted high when the address $4F27 is present and determinate on the address bus.

21. Two microcomputers will send words to each other through a "window." The "window" appears as a programmable parallel I/O device at location $8000 in the first, and at location $4000 in the second microprocessor. To send a word, the first writes the word in location $8000 so the second can read that word at $4000; or the second writes a word in location $4000 so the first can read it at location $8000. This window is realized with a pair of M6821s, one in each microcomputer, whose PA ports are tied together. The device must be configured as an input device when not in use. (a) Write a program segment to output a word from the first microcomputer. (b) Assuming the first microcomputer has output a word, write a program segment to input that word into accumulator A of the second microcomputer.

22. One microcomputer is to be used to check out another microcomputer by reading from and writing into its I/O registers. The first microcomputer has an M6821 whose A device is connected to the D bus of the second computer, and the most significant bit of the B device is connected to the R/W line, and the first computer has another M6821 whose A device is connected to the high address and whose B device is connected to the low address bytes of the second microcomputer. The second microcomputer's microprocessor is removed from its socket so the first microcomputer can control its address and data bus. (a) Design the I/O device to be used in the first microcomputer to control the second microcomputer. The A and B devices of the M6821 that connects to the data bus and R/W signal are at locations $8000 and $8001, and the A and B data registers that connect to the address bus are at location $8002 and $8003. Show all connections between the M6809 in the first microcomputer and the two M6821s, and the completely specified decoder. (b) Show a program segment that will write a word $3C into location $4B28 of the second computer. (c) Show a program segment that will read the word at location $4B28 of the second microcomputer into accumulator A of the first microcomputer. (d) Show a program that will verify that an M6821 in the second microcomputer is functioning properly. Assume that M6821 is at locations $4B28 to $4B2B, the A device at the lower addresses, and that all outputs of the A device are connected to the input of the B device. Check that a T or F can be stored in the directon and readable output registers, and that either can be sent from one of the devices to the other. (This checks for open circuits and short circuits to power or ground.) Check that this can be done for each bit i, while the bits $i + 1$ and $i - 1$ have the opposite value. (This checks for short circuits between neighboring pins and lines.)

4 Interrupts and Alternatives

The computer has to be synchronized with a fast or slow I/O device. Two main synchronization requirements are for the inputting or outputting of data and for error conditions that arise in the I/O system. These require some appropriate action to be taken by the microcomputer program. This problem is to be studied in this chapter.

One of the most important problems in the design of I/O systems is timing. In section 3-2.1, we saw how data can be put into a buffer from an input device. We ignored, however, the problem of synchronizing with the source of the data so that we will get a word from it when it has a word to give us. I/O systems are often quite a bit slower, and are occasionally a bit faster, than the computer. A typewriter may type a fast thirty characters per second, but still the computer has to wait 33,333 memory cycles to send a character to be typed. That is, the computer may have to wait a long time between outputting successive characters to be typed. Behold the mighty computer, able to invert a matrix in a single bound, waiting patiently to complete some tedious I/O operation. On the other hand, some I/O systems like disks are so fast that a microcomputer may not take data from them fast enough. Recall that the time from when an I/O system requests service (such as to output a word) until it gets this service (such as having the word removed) is the latency. If the service is not completed within a maximum latency time, the data may be overwritten by new data and thus will be lost before the computer can store it.

Synchronization is the technique used to get the computer to supply data to an output device when the device needs data, or get data from an input device when the device has some data available, or to respond to an error if ever it occurs. Six techniques are used to match the slow I/O device to the fast microprocessor. Real-time synchronization is conceptually quite simple; in fact we have already written a real time program in the previous chapter to synchronize to a traffic light. Gadfly synchronization requires a bit more hardware, but has advantages in speed and software simplicity. Two kinds of interrupt synchronization, polled and vectored, are faster and require more hardware. Direct memory access and context switching are the fastest synchronization mechanisms. These synchronization techniques are discussed in this chapter.

The first section presents some principles relating to I/O synchronization as seen from the I/O device end. The next section shows approaches

191

including interrupts that are used for synchronization as seen from the microprocessor end. A section is devoted to the rich interrupt capabilities of the M6809, and the last section discusses approaches that require more processors and are more powerful than interrupts, including direct memory access (DMA). The M6844 direct memory access chip will be introduced in this section in order to make the concepts more concrete, but we emphasize again that these concepts can be extended to direct memory access chips made by other manufacturers.

This chapter should provide a fundamental understanding of I/O synchronization in general and of interrupt handling in particular. The reader should be able to connect a parallel input/output chip like the M6821 to recognize interrupts, to write programs to handle interrupts, and, using them, to input or output a buffer of data or report or correct an error.

4-1 Synchronization in Input/Output Devices

We first study the synchronization problem from the I/O device end. The first subsection introduces some general principles, including the busy/done states, and defines the terminology for the different approaches to synchronizing I/O devices to microcomputers. An example, a paper tape reader system, is introduced to be used in later sections in order to illustrate the different approaches. The use of address triggers and the need for a valid memory address signal are discussed. The second subsection introduces the interrupt mechanics of the M6821 integrated circuit. Again, the object of using this chip is to make the discussion more concrete, but the techniques can be used on other chips in the M6800 family, and on chips made by others.

4-1.1 Synchronization Principles of I/O Devices

An example of a paper tape reader will be used to illustrate the different approaches to I/O synchronization. The example will illustrate both the collection of data in a buffer and the recognition of and response to error conditions. An M6821 will be used so that data input from the paper tape can be read from location $8000. The associated control register is located at location $8001. Another control register at location $8003 will be used to signal an error condition. We need to use more of the control register than we used in the previous chapter, and we will consider that aspect in the next section to show concrete examples of interrupt techniques using the M6809.

Data from the data register can be read just as we did in the previous chapter and will be put into a buffer, as we now discuss. Recall from section

3-2.1 that a buffer is an area of memory reserved for input data. A paper tape reader will have a buffer into which words read from the tape can be written. The pattern of holes across a one-inch wide paper tape corresponds to a word of data: in each position a hole is a true value and the absence of a hole a false value. The values of such a pattern of holes under the paper tape head can be read at any time by an instruction like LDA $8000. The paper can be advanced by the computer when the next pattern is to be read. The first pattern is read and put into the first word of the buffer, the second pattern is put into the second word of the buffer, and so on, until all the patterns have been read and put in the buffer, as we did in the program called INBUF. When this happens, the buffer is said to be *full*, and some program that uses the data in the buffer may be started.

The paper tape reader may have an error condition, such as when the paper tape is to be read (before the buffer is full) but there is no paper tape under the reader. A response to an error condition may be to correct the error, which would have the microcomputer reload some paper tape into the reader and continue reading it, or just to report the error to someone who is attending the paper tape reader. The error could be reported by typing out a message on a "console typewriter" if one is available, or by turning on a light or sounding an alarm of some kind. In general, whenever one takes data from an input device or puts data into an output device, error conditions can occur, and the hardware and software that interfaces the microcomputer to the device must be able to correct the error or at least report the error so an attendant can correct it.

The various approaches to synchronize a computer with an I/O device to take data from it or send data to it use a simple but general model (a sequential machine) of the device. See figure 4-1. In this model, the device has three states: the *idle, busy, and done states*. The device is in the idle state when no program is using it. When a program begins to use the device, the program puts it in the busy state. If the device is in the idle state it is free to be used, and if in the busy state it is still busy doing its operation.

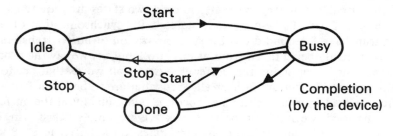

Figure 4-1. State Diagram for I/O Devices

When the device is through with its operation, it enters the done state. Often, the done state implies that the device has some data in an output register that must be read by the program. When the program reads the data, it puts the device into the idle state if it does not want to do any more operations, or into the busy state if it wants more operations done by the device. An error condition may also put the device into the done state and should provide some way for the program to distinguish between a successfully completed operation and an error condition. Note the program puts the device into the busy state or the idle state: this is called *starting* or *stopping* the device, respectively. The device enters the done state by itself. This is called *completing* the requested action. When the device is in the done state, the program can get the results of an operation or check to see if an error has occurred.

We continue our running example to illustrate the meaning of these states. The idle state indicates that the paper tape reader is not in use. The program starts the paper tape reader by putting it into the busy state. In the busy state, a motor pulls the paper tape forward until the next pattern is under the head. When the pattern is under or no paper is left under the tape reader, the reader enters the done state. The computer recognizes that when the reader is in the done state, data from the pattern should be read through the data register at location $8000 and put into the buffer in the next available location, or that an error condition might exist. Once this data is read, if the program intends to read the next pattern because more words are needed to fill the buffer, it puts the reader back into the busy state to restart it. If it does not want to read another pattern because the buffer is full, it puts the device into the idle state to stop it. If an error condition is signaled, the device is left in the done state so it will not be used until the error is fixed, and the error is corrected or reported. Note that there is a difference between the idle state and the done state. In the done state some data in the input register is ready to be read, and the I/O device is requesting the computer to read it, or an error has rendered the device unusable; in the idle state nothing is happening and nothing need be done. In some I/O systems which do not return values back to the computer, however, the done state is indistinguishable from the idle state, so only two states are required.

The main use of idle-busy-done states is for synchronization of one-word transfers. A second use is for synchronization of buffer transfers. If data is currently being taken from or put into a buffer, we say the process that is filling or emptying the buffer is *busy*. If all words that are to be loaded into the buffer are in it or all words that are to be taken from the buffer are read from it, we say the process is *done*. Finally, if the buffer is not being used, we say the process is *idle*. We are simply transferring the concepts of word transfer idle-busy-done states to the buffer level. Buffer process idle-busy-done states will appear in the discussion of direct memory access (DMA). They can also be implemented in purely software alternatives to DMA.

Finally, we introduce a technique that is widely used to start and stop devices. An *address trigger* is a mechanism wherein the address decoder itself provides a pulse that does something. Generating the particular address in the execution of an instruction will cause the address decoder to output a pulse that can be used to trigger a one-shot, clear or set a flip-flop, or be output from the computer. Figure 4-2 shows an example of a trigger on the address $7FFF. Figure 4-2a shows an address trigger in a block diagram by a dashed line. Note that the instruction LDA $7FFF does not load data from the one-shot, nor does STA $7FFF store anything from the accumulator into it. These instructions could simultaneously load or store data in another register even while the address triggers the one-shot, or they might load garbage into the accumulator, or store the accumulator into a nonexistent storage word (which does nothing). Also, any instruction that reads the location could be used instead of LDA (for example, LDB) or any that writes could be used instead of STA. Note that some instructions that operate on memory (for example, INC $7FFF) first read and then write in the location, so they can produce two pulses. Figure 4-2b shows how this is implemented in hardware. If an instruction like LDA $7FFF or STA $7FFF or equivalent is executed, the decoder will generate a pulse that causes the one-shot to "fire."

Two points about the hardware implementation must be stressed. First, the addresses are indeterminate during the first quarter of a memory cycle, so an address like $7FFF might be temporarily generated at that time even though the instruction does not use this address. Therefore, it is necessary to AND the E clock into the address decoder so its output will always be false during at least the first quarter of the cycle. Second, recall from section 2-2.2 that the microprocessor may be operating internally, not on memory, and may send some address on the address bus because it happens to generate it as an intermediate result. The M6809 puts out an address $FFFF and a request to read that word at such times. The M6800, however, has a signal called *valid memory address* (VMA) that is false when this kind of invalid address is generated, and true when the memory is actually being read from or written in. Also, when direct memory access is used, you have to generate such a signal, even with an M6809, because a memory cycle is needed when the M6809 releases control to the direct memory access chip, and when the direct memory access chip releases control to the M6809. It is also necessary to AND the VMA signal into the address decoder so that its output will be false when an invalid address is sent out. The M6800 will always generate a read command when VMA is false (except for the TST instruction, which will rewrite the same word with R/W low and VMA false), so no bad data is ever written, and your logic that generates VMA for direct

memory access can also be built so that a read command is generated
whenever neither the M6809 nor the direct memory access controller is driving the bus. So VMA is not needed in the decoders that control memory nor
in those that implement basic I/O devices. That is why we did not bring up
the issue before. Nevertheless, an invalid address can accidentally trigger
some action if an address trigger is used. In these cases, VMA must be true
for the address decoder to assert its output. Note these two signals in the
decoder in figure 4-2b.

A point about software should be emphasized. It is easy for a program
error, especially one that pushes data onto the stack, to generate addresses
that can trigger devices via an address trigger. Recall that an I/O lock can be
used to prevent such addresses from being decoded.

Finally, some variations of an address trigger are the *read address trigger*, which produces a pulse only when a memory read operation generates
the address, and a *write address trigger*, which generates a pulse only when
the address is recognized in a memory write operation. Obviously, to build a
read address trigger decoder, put the R/W signal into the AND gate in
figure 4-2b, and to build a write address trigger decoder, put the inverted
R/W signal into the decoder.

An address trigger can be used to start or stop a device. Suppose that
two flip-flops code the state of the device such that they are FF if the device
is idle, FT if it is busy, and TF if it is done. Then to start the device, the first
flip-flop must be cleared and the second must be set. An address trigger can
be connected to the clear input of the first flip-flop and to the set input of
the second. Any instruction that generates the address can start the device
by generating the trigger signal.

4-1.2 The M6821 Interrupt Mechanism

The interrupt mechanism in the M6821 can be used to illustrate various synchronization principles in concrete terms, so we introduce a little more of it

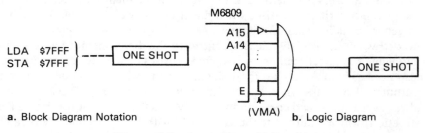

a. Block Diagram Notation   **b.** Logic Diagram

Figure 4-2. An Address Trigger

here. Recall that control bit two is used to determine whether the direction register or the data register can be accessed, if that bit is F or T, respectively. The use of the other control bits is now explored. Each of the two devices in the M6821 has a primary interrupt mechanism, and another mechanism that can be configured to be a secondary interrupt mechanism or an output bit.

The control register of either the A or B device governs a primary interrupt request mechanism as shown in figure 4-3a. The control register is partially readable. Bit seven of the control register is the read-only output of the D edge-triggered flip-flop IRQA1. Upon reading the control register, the sign bit will be this value. When it is set, we say *IRQA1 recognizes an interrupt*. A pin, CA1, and a control register bit, one, determine when IRQA1 is set. If bit one is false, IRQA1 is set on a high to low transition of the signal on the CA1 pin; if true, on the low to high transition of that signal. The IRQA1 bit is read-only—writing in the control regiser does not change it. However, because an interrupt usually requires reading the data from the data register, IRQA1 is cleared to false when the data register in that device is read. That is, an address trigger is used, so that reading the data register also clears the IRQA1 flip-flop. One of the common errors in using the M6821 is to try to clear the IRQA1 flip-flop by writing zero into the control register. (Similarly, reading the direction register will not clear IRQA1, so you have to set control bit two before you can read the data register to clear IRQA1.) Control register bit zero is ANDed with IRQA1, the output going in negative logic to the IRQA pin. This output can be sent through a negative logic wire-OR bus to the M6809 microprocessor IRQ pin (or other pins discussed in section 4-3). Alternatively, the IRQA pin can be left disconnected, or can even be connected to a light or an alarm if that is useful.

The primary interrupt mechanism is always available for use. A second part of the control logic can be used to implement another secondary interrupt mechanism or one of three different one-bit output mechanisms, depending on the values of control bits five to three. See figure 4-3b to 4-3e. If the other part is to be used as a second interrupt, then the user makes control bit five false. Then control bits six, four, and three function for this part exactly as control bits seven, one, and zero function for the device interrupt we discussed earlier. See figure 4-3b. That is, the IRQA2 flip-flop can always be read as bit six. It is set if bit four is false and the CA2 input has a high to low transition, or if bit four is true and CA2 has a low to high transition, and is cleared when the data register is read. Writing in the control register does not change the read-only bit, bit six, just as it does not change bit seven. The value of IRQA2 is ANDed with control bit three and ORed into the wire-OR bus through the same IRQA pin used by the IRQA1 flip-flop.

The logic connected to CA2 can use CA2 as an output if control bit five

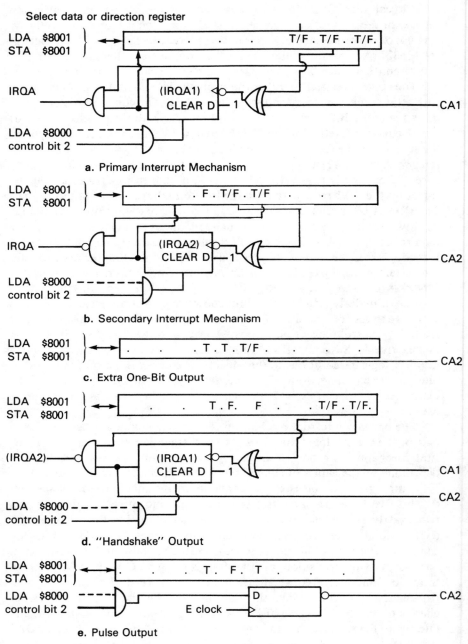

Figure 4-3. M6821 Device A Interrupt/Output Mechanisms

is T. Three modes are available. If control bit four is also a T, then control bit three is output in positive logic on the CA2 pin to give an extra output bit. This mode is simply called the *extra one-bit output* mode. See figure 4-3c. For example if control bits zero and one are supposed to be false and we want to access the data register, then storing $34 in the control register will output a low signal on the CA2 pin, and storing $3C in the control register will output a high on that pin. This extra output bit can be changed by the program, so it can control a motor in the I/O system, for instance. If control bits five to three are T, F, and F, CA2 is essentially the contents of the IRQA1 flip-flop. This mode is called *handshaking* because this is the same principle as that used in asynchronous communication called by that name. The external logic sets IRQA1 via CA1 and can read the value of this flip-flop to control a motor via CA2. For instance, the motor can advance the paper tape in our example, as long as this output is low. When the next pattern is aligned, a signal through the CA1 pin simultaneously requests IRQA1 to recognize an interrupt and turns the motor off. When the data register is read, IRQA1 is cleared and the motor is started to get the next pattern. If control bits five to three are T, F, and T, CA2 is normally high and drops for just one memory cycle when the data register is read. This mode is called *pulse* for obvious reasons. See figure 4-3e. This is an example of the address trigger available as an output to control an external part of the I/O system. This can be used to trigger an external one-shot to make a motor move one pattern ahead on the tape.

The two devices in an M6821 are almost identical. There are control pins for each: corresponding to CA1 and CA2, the control pins for the A device, are CB1 and CB2 for the B device. Separate interrupt signal outputs IRQA and IRQB are used for each device so they can be wired to different buses as discussed later, or one can be connected while the other is not. The logic associated with CA1 and CB1 is identical. The logic associated with CA2 is as discussed above, but the logic associated with CB2 is just a bit different. The logic for the B device is designed to make it more useful for output, while the A device is designed to be more useful for input. CB2 is pulsed with a negative signal when control bits five to three are T, F, and T, when the data register is written in, rather than read from as is CA2. (That is, replace read address trigger LDA $8000 with write address trigger STA $8000 in figures 4-3d and 4-3e for the B device.) CB2 is not quite the value of the IRQB1 flip-flop in the B device: it becomes high when IRQB1 is set, but it becomes low when the data register is written in; while the IRQB1 register is cleared when the data register is read from. (In the A device, CA2 is the positive logic output of IRQA1.) With these minor differences, which are easy to forget, the two devices in an M6821 are very flexible and can be used for almost any parallel input/output requirement.

4-2 Synchronization Alternatives

A microcomputer can synchronize with an I/O device in four ways, as
discussed in this section. Two ways, real-time and gadfly synchronization,
are simple but less efficient than the other two ways, polled and vectored interrupts. The first two ways are studied in the first subsection, and the last
two are studied in the next. Two alternatives, which require additional hardware for even more efficient synchronization, are introduced in section 4-4.

4-2.1 Real-Time and Gadfly Synchronization

Two very simple techniques can be used to synchronize to an I/O operation.
The real-time and gadfly techniques require the least amount of extra hardware, but are also the least efficient synchronization techniques. Nevertheless, they are often the most cost-effective techniques in microcomputer
systems, where there is no need to use such a cheap computer efficiently.
   Real-time synchronization uses the timing delays in the program to synchronize with the delays in the I/O system. While this is considered bad programming by almost all computer scientists, it is a practical alternative in
some primitive microcomputers that are dedicated to one application, such
as the traffic-light controller discussed in 3-2.2 or a microcomputer that is
dedicated to control a printer. The natural delay in executing useful programs can also be used to provide the required elapsed time. The traffic
light controller in section 3-2.2 used delay loops to time out the light pattern
that was displayed. The I/O device controlled by real-time synchronization
has idle, busy, and done states, but the computer has no way of reading
them in the real-time program technique. Instead, it starts operations and
keeps track of the time it expects the device to complete the operation.
Busy-done states can be associated, however, with the program segment being executed in synchronization with the device state. The device is started
and the time it takes to complete its busy state is matched by the time a program takes before it assumes the device is in the done state. While an exact
match in timing is occasionally needed, usually the microcomputer must
wait longer than the I/O device takes to complete its busy state. In fact, the
program is usually timed for the worst possible time to complete an I/O
operation. We consider a real-time program for our paper tape reader:

```
NAM        REAL
LDX        #BUFFER    ADDRESS OF FIRST WORD OF BUF-
                      FER TO X
LDA        #4         CONFIGURE M6821 FOR INPUT
```

```
        STA         $8001   AND DISABLE INTERRUPT
        LDA         #$80    SET UP TO COUNT INCOMING
                            WORDS
L1      LDB         $8000   READ A WORD FROM THE INPUT
                            REGISTER
        STB         ,X+     PUT IT INTO THE BUFFER
        LDB         #T      SET UP DELAY LOOP
L2      DEC B               COUNT OUT WAIT TIME
        BNE         L2      LOOP UNTIL TIME OUT
        DEC A               COUNT NUMBER OF WORDS TO BE
                            READ
        BNE         L1      REPEAT PROGRAM UNTIL ALL
                            WORDS READ
        END
```

Assume that $80 patterns read by the device are stored in consecutive words in a buffer and the first word of the buffer is called BUFFER. Also, assume that power has just been turned on, and the RESET line has just cleared all the registers in the M6821 that inputs the pattern at location $8000. Assume that a motor pulls paper through the reader at a constant rate and the paper tape reader requires exactly the same time to move the paper in order to read the next pattern as the microcomputer takes to execute the delay loop T times and to execute the other instructions in the outer loop one time. Finally, assume that the program executes its first LDA $8000 instruction exactly as the first pattern is able to be read from the tape. In the first four lines the pointer to store incoming words is set up, the M6821 is configured as an input device, and a counter to keep track of the number of words left to be input is initialized. The main loop reads in a word into the buffer, moves the pointer to be ready to read in the next word, waits the prescribed time, then repeats if more words are to be read.

Busy-done states can be recognized as the program segments are executed in synchronization with these states. The idle state is associated with the first four lines. Since we assume the paper holes are positioned to be read on the first execution of the LDB instruction, that instruction corresponds to a done state, as do the instructions that decrement A and branch to this instruction. The delay loop corresponds to the busy state. Although the significance of these states is not quite so important in real-time synchronization, their association with the program segments is useful in comparing this to other synchronization techniques.

Real-time synchronization uses the least amount of hardware of the approaches to the synchronization problem, but the effort of writing the program may be the greatest because of the difficulty of precisely tailoring the program to provide the required time delay. This approach is also sensitive to errors in the speed of the I/O system. If some mechanical components are not oiled, the I/O may be slower than that which the program is made to handle. The program is therefore often timed to handle the worst possible situation and is the slowest of the techniques for synchronizing to an I/O system.

The device interrupt can be used in *gadfly* synchronization. The technique is named after the great philosopher Socrates, who was called the "gadfly of Athens." In the Socratic method of teaching, one keeps asking the same question until one gets the answer one wants. Socrates kept pestering the local politicians like a pesky fly until they gave him the answer he wanted. (Regrettably, they gave him some poison to drink, too.) Similarly, the program continually bothers one or more devices to determine what they are doing. This bothering is usually implemented in a loop, called a *gadfly loop*, in which the microcomputer continually inputs the device state of one or more I/O systems until it detects the done state or an error condition in one of the systems. In this technique, the IRQA1 flip-flop may be used to indicate the done state. The I/O system sets the IRQA1 flip-flop by a signal sent through the CA1 pin of the M6821 when it determines that it is done with its operation. The program continuously tests the value of IRQA1, waiting for it to become true. The program may then decide to send it some more data or take some data from it, and restart it or leave it idle. Also, the IRQB1 flip-flop can be used to indicate an error. If the I/O system can detect an error, it can send an edge of a signal through a CB1 pin of an M6821 to set the flip-flop. The program can periodically test the flip-flop used in this way: if it sees the flip-flop set, it can jump to a program to handle the error condition.

We rework our example to show how the gadfly technique works. As before, BUFFER is the address of the first word in the buffer, which is to be filled with *N* words. We will assume that CA2 is used as an output to control the motor that pulls the tape forward: the motor advances the tape as long as CA2 is low. See figure 4-4. We will assume that CA1 is normally high, but drops low when a pattern is positioned to be read by the paper tape reader. We want the device to change from busy to done when CA1 falls. The "handshaking mode" of the M6821 would be ideal, because the motor is automatically stopped when the next pattern is ready to be read, and is restarted when the data is read from the input register so the next pattern will be positioned to be read. Finally, to detect an error such as there being no paper in the reader, we will assume that CB1 is normally high, becoming low when no paper is sensed. We want to jump to a program called ERROR if CB1 falls.

The program is very similar to that for the real-time technique, except that the control registers have to be initialized and a gadfly loop is used in place of the delay loop. The gadfly loop is put in front of the instruction that reads the word (while the delay loop was after it) because we want to check that the word is in place before we read it. This is necessary in a gadfly program. We will assume that all registers, including the direction registers, have been cleared by a RESET signal when the machine was turned on. In the initialization procedure the control register for device A should configure CA2 for output in the handshake mode and set IRQA1

```
        NAM     GADFLY
        LDA       #$24      SET UP CONTROL WORD
                            TO SET IRQA1 ON
        STA      $8001      FALLING EDGE OF CA1,
                            USE CA2 IN HANDSHAKE
        LDA        #4       SET UP CONTROL WORD
                            TO SET IRQB1 ON
        STA      $8003      FALLING EDGE OF CB1
        LDX     #BUFFER     INITIALIZE POINTER TO
                            BUFFER
        LDA       #$80      GET SIZE OF BUFFER TO
                            COUNT INPUT WORD
L1      LDB      $8003      CHECK FOR ERROR
        BMI      ERROR      REPORT ERROR IF FOUND
        LDB      $8001      CHECK FOR DONE STATE
        BPL        L1       LOOP UNTIL IRQA1 IS SET,
                            WHEN NEXT PATTERN
        LDB      $8000      CAN BE READ. THEN READ
                            PATTERN.
        STB        ,X+      PLACE WORD IN BUFFER
        DECA                COUNT OUT WORDS, TO
                            SEE WHEN BUFFER
        BNE        L1       IS FULL, IF NOT LOOP
                            AGAIN
        CLR      $8001      PUT DEVICE IN IDLE STATE


ERROR   LDA      $8002      CLEAR IRQB1
        END
```

when the CA1 input signal falls. This means bits five, four, and three should be T, F, and F, and bit one should be F. Also, when the program is reading data, bit two must be T or the direction register will be read instead. Bits seven and six cannot be written, so they are don't cares; and since the IRQA output is not connected, bit zero is also a don't care. The control word should thus be XXTFFTFX. Making don't care Xs into Fs for convenience, the hexadecimal number $24 should be written into control register A at location $8001. Note that when the machine is turned on, the CA2 is initially a high impedance input, so a pull-up resistor, shown in figure 4-4, makes the signal on CA2 high to prevent the motor from advancing the tape. When $24 is put into the control register, CA2 becomes an output, which is initially low, to advance the tape. Similarly, the other control register, at location $8003, should be loaded with $04 to configure the device for gadfly programming.

The gadfly program exhibits the idle, busy, and done states. The idle state is in effect if A device control bit five is false (as it is when power is turned on), since the CA2 line is configured as an input, and is pulled high to prevent the motor from pulling the tape. The busy state is in effect when control bit seven is false and control bits five to three are T, F, and F because the output on CA2 is low, advancing the paper tape, but the CA1 input has not fallen, which indicates the device has completed its action. The done state is indicated by control bit seven true and bits five to three T, F, and F, since this is caused by the completion of the action. Note that a start command is the writing of $24 into the control register, the completion signal is the falling edge of CA1, and the stop command is the clearing of the control register, as in the last step of the program segment. The gadfly synchronization technique monitors the busy/done states of the device to synchronize with it.

A few remarks about the LDA $8002 instruction at location ERROR are in order. An error condition will set the IRQB1 flip-flop and, testing this, the program will jump to location ERROR. If a message is sent to the attendant, who reloads the paper and restarts the program, the gadfly loop will promptly exit to ERROR again, even though there is paper in the reader. This will frustrate the attendant, because every time he reloads the paper he will get an error message. Poor soul. The IRQB1 flip-flop must be cleared somewhere in the program following ERROR, before the gadfly loop is reentered. The only way to clear IRQB1 is to read the associated data register. Hence the instruction LDA $8002. We are not interested in the data in the data register: it is garbage. We are doing this to generate an address trigger to clear the IRQB1 flip-flop. A final note is offered. Observe that the B device was initialized in lines three and four of the program, so that control bit two is T. Why bother? If this is not done, reading location $8002 in the error handling routine will read the direction register, which does not clear the IRQB1 flip-flop. This flip-flop is cleared only when the data register is read, and control bit two must be T to read the data register.

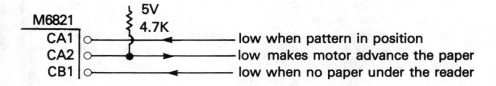

Figure 4-4. Connections to a Paper-Tape Reader

This discussion offers an opportunity to relate one of the best stories in computer design, which was confessed by a member of the design team at a EUROMICRO conference a couple of years ago. (This is a true story, but for obvious reasons we will not give any names.) Designing a computer, they wanted to make it faster. They had a lot of programs written for the computer, so they ran these programs and kept track of which instruction was executed most often. Make that instruction run faster, they reasoned, then the machine should run faster. They did find an instruction that occurred much more often than the others, they did manage to change the machine to make this instruction run quite a bit faster without slowing down the other instructions. But making this change, they did not get the machine to run any faster! Why? It should run faster! It turned out that the instruction was used in a gadfly loop, to wait for completion of I/O operations. The computer waited faster. The moral of the story: collecting statistics does not necessarily a better computer make. Another moral: computers spend a lot of time in gadfly loops.

4-2.2 Interrupts

In this section, we consider interrupt hardware and software. Interrupt software can be very tricky. Some companies actually have a policy never to use interrupts, but to use gadfly programs in their place. Nevertheless, with the background we have acquired from the last chapter and the previous sections, we should find interrupt software quite easy to use. At the other extreme, some designers insist on using interrupts just because they are readily available in microcomputers and I/O chips like the M6821. We advocate using interrupts where they are necessary and using simpler techniques when that is possible.

In this section, we will first consider a microcomputer that has just one interrupt. We will examine the IRQ line, and consider the sequence of actions that leads up to an interrupt. Then we will consider the paper tape reader example. Next, the multiple interrupt case will be studied, using two techniques called polling and vectored interrupts. These will be simple extensions to the single interrupt case and will be illustrated with an example having four potential interrupts.

Interrupt techniques can be used to let the I/O system interrupt the processor when it is done, so the processor can be doing useful work in the meantime until it is interrupted. Interrupts can also reduce latency time compared to a variation of a gadfly approach where the computer executes a subroutine, then checks the I/O device, then executes another subroutine, and then checks the devices, and so on; and that can be an important factor for fast I/O devices. Recall the basic idea of an interrupt from chapter 1. The basic idea of an interrupt is that a program P currently being executed can be stopped at any point, a device handler program D is executed to carry out some task requested by the device, and the program P is resumed. The device must have some logic to determine when it needs to have the processor execute the D program, and a wire to the microprocessor to inform it that the device needs service. P must execute the same way whether and whenever D is executed. Therefore, D must somehow save all the information that P needs to resume without error. Usually, all the registers used by D must be saved. This may be done automatically by hardware. Moreover, any memory words that might be used by D and P must be saved and restored. When D is finished, it must execute some instruction like a return from subroutine that resumes P exactly where it left off.

The sequence of actions that lead to an interrupt and that service it are outlined below. See figure 4-5. Seven steps are executed, in the following sequence:

1. The external hardware determines it needs service, either to move some data into it or out of it, or to report an error. When this happens, we say an *external interrupt is requested*.

2. The I/O chip such as the M6821 receives a signal, such as the rising edge of the CA1 signal. It sets a flip-flop such as IRQA1, which is an *interrupt request flip-flop*. When this happens, we say the IRQA1 flip-flop recognizes an interrupt (as we noted in section 4-1.2). If the I/O device

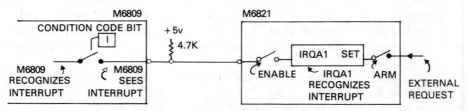

Figure 4-5. Interrupt Request Path

will recognize an interrupt when an external interrupt is requested, we say the device is *armed*, otherwise it is disarmed.

3. The I/O device asserts a (low) signal on a (wire-OR) bus line such as IRQ to the IRQ pin of the M6809. When this happens, we say *IRQA1 requests an interrupt*. When the IRQ pin on the M6809 is low, we say the *microprocessor sees an interrupt request*. If the I/O device asserts the IRQ signal (low) when it recognizes an interrupt, we say the *device is enabled*, otherwise we say it is disabled.

4. The microprocessor has a condition code flip-flop I, the *interrupt mask* flip-flop. When this bit is true, we say the *microprocessor is masked* (or the *microprocessor is disabled*), otherwise the *microprocessor is enabled*. If this bit is false when the IRQ input is low, we say the *microprocessor recognizes an interrupt*. (The I flip-flop can be controlled by the programmer to disable interrupts from being recognized when the program is unable to cope with them. This flip-flop is also controlled by hardware in the next step.)

5. The microcomputer is generally in the middle of an instruction, which it cannot stop. Therefore, if a microprocessor recognizes an interrupt, it will *honor an interrupt* at the end of the current instruction. When the M6809 honors an IRQ interrupt, it acts as if an SWI instruction were executed, saving the state of the machine on the stack and jumping indirectly through an address stored in high memory. However, whereas the SWI uses $FFFA and $FFFB as an indirect address, the IRQ interrupt uses $FFF8 and $FFF9. Importantly, the interrupt mask bit I is set in the condition code register after the former value of the condition codes is saved on the stack. (Some differences between the various interrupt handlers available for the M6809 are discussed in section 4-4.)

6. Beginning at the address specified by $FFF8 and $FFF9 is a routine that is called a *handler*. (When we consider multiple sources of interrupts, we will distinguish between the interrupt handler and the device handler, but for now we refer to it as a handler.) The handler is like a subroutine, in particular like an SWI "subroutine." It performs the work requested by the device. It may move a word between the device and a buffer, or it may report or fix up an error. One of the critically important functions of a handler that is easy to overlook is that it must remove the cause of the interrupt (by clearing the interrupt request flip-flop).

7. When the handler is completed, it executes an RTI instruction, which restores the state of the machine and resumes the program where it left off.

Some points about the interrupt sequence must be stressed. The M6809, like most computers, sets an interrupt mask as soon as it honors an interrupt. If it did not, the first instruction in the handler would be promptly interrupted—an infinite loop that will fill up the stack. Fortunately, the machine automatically sets the mask bit for you so this will not happen. And you do not even have to worry about clearing it, because step 7 above restores all the registers, including the condition code and its interrupt mask bit, to the values they had before the interrupt was honored. Since the mask bit was cleared then (or there never would have been an interrupt) it will be clear after the RTI instruction is executed. The programmer, however, can clear that bit using an ANDCC instruction if he needs to permit interrupts before the handler is finished. Note that the I/O device is generally still asserting IRQ (low) because it does not know what is going on inside the microprocessor. If the RTI is executed or the interrupt mask bit is otherwise cleared, this same device will promptly interrupt the processor again and again . . . to hang up the machine. Before the handler executes RTI or clears the mask, it *must* remove the source of the interrupt! (Please excuse our frustration, but this is so simple yet so much of a problem.)

A note is offered about enabling and arming interrupts. A disarmed interrupt is completely ignored. You disarm a device when you know it will externally request an interrupt but you have no intention of ever honoring it. A disabled interrupt is postponed, but not ignored. You disable an interrupt when you are not prepared to honor it right now, but will honor it later. Disarming takes place before the interrupt request flip-flop is set, so it completely inhibits that setting. Disabling takes place, in effect, after the interrupt request flip-flop is set, so it is still set if the device or the microcomputer is later enabled; however, the interrupt request flip-flop can be cleared just before the interrupt is enabled. This is sometimes necessary because we do not know the state of that flip-flop when we enable the interrupt, and we can get an interrupt right away before we are expecting it.

In the M6821, the primary interrupt IRQA1 is always armed, although external logic can be used to disarm it. The secondary interrupt IRQA2 is armed when control bit five is made false, which causes CA1 to become an input. The primary interrupt is enabled if control bit zero is true, and the secondary interrupt is enabled when control bit three is true and control bit five is false. Note that when the gadfly technique is used, you disable the interrupts (either by clearing control bits zero and three, or by setting mask bit I in the 6809).

We now consider the paper tape example, using a single interrupt for requesting that input data be put in the buffer. The hardware is the same as in earlier examples. The software is in three parts: initialization ritual, wait loop, and handler. The initialization routine is shown below:

```
LDX        #$200   INITIALIZE BUFFER
STX        POINT   SAVE IN GLOBAL VARIABLE
```

```
LDA        #$80    SET UP COUNTER
STA        COUNT   IN GLOBAL VARIABLE
LDX        #EXIT   SET UP RETURN ADDRESS
STX        RETAD   TO GO TO WHEN BUFFER IS FULL
LDD        #$25    SET UP DEVICE TO SET IRQA1 ON
STD        $8001   FALL OF CA1, ENABLE INTERRUPTS
LDA        $8000   CLEAR IRQA1, IN CASE IT WAS SET
ANDCC      $EF     CLEAR INTERRUPT MASK BIT
```

This initialization sets up global variables to hold the address where we are putting the data, and to keep track of the number of words yet to be brought in. The return address is set up so that when the buffer is full, we will go there. These are allocated by assembler directives like COUNT RMB 1, POINT RMB 2, and RETAD RMB 2 that appear in the program where page zero is allocated. The M6821 ritual configures it for this application. Note from figure 4-3 that control bit zero is to be true to enable the interrupt from IRQA1, but bit one should be false to set IRQA1 on the falling edge. Of course, bit two must be made true, and bit five is true so that the secondary interrupt is disarmed. The direction register is cleared to make all bits inputs. The IRQA1 flip-flop is now cleared, in case it was set before, so we will not get an interrupt after the next instruction. The M6809 interrupt mask is then cleared to allow interrupts.

The program is now free to execute some impressive routine that it was born to do, rather than loop in a delay or gadfly loop until the operation is complete. You will know that the buffer is full by testing the number in COUNT, which will become zero at that time. Note that COUNT is effectively the busy-done state of the process that fills the buffer: COUNT is zero when that process is done. It is sometimes difficult, however, to think of something to do while waiting for the buffer to fill; therefore, you may have to execute a *wait loop*. Such a wait loop is shown below:

```
L   BRA    L    LOOP HERE UNTIL HANDLER FINISHES
                 LOADING BUFFER
```

After the wait loop, you may have a program that does something with the data in the buffer. The address of this program is put into the location RETAD so the last few lines of the handler can jump there when the RTI instruction is executed. You know, when you leave the wait loop, that the buffer is indeed full and ready to be used. Nevertheless, wait loops are just as wasteful as delay or gadfly loops. If you do not get anything else done while interrupts are handling the input, you should consider using the cheaper real-time or gadfly synchronization mechanism.

The handler routine TPRDR for our example is shown below. The address, HNDLR, is put in locations $FFF8 and $FFF9 so that when the M6809 honors the interrupt, it will cause this handler to be executed.

```
            NAM    TPRDR
HNDLR   LDX    POINT   GET POINTER TO BUFFER
        LDA    $8000   GET PATTERN FROM PAPER
                       TAPE
        STA    ,X+     PUT IN BUFFER
        STX    POINT   SAVE FOR NEXT INPUT
        DEC    COUNT   COUNT OUT INCOMING
                       WORDS
        BNE    HNDLR1  IF BUFFER IS FULL, THEN
        CLR    $8001   PREVENT FURTHER INTER-
                       RUPTS
        LDX    RETADR  GET RETURN ADDRESS FROM
                       GLOBAL VARIABLE
        STX    10,S    PUT INTO PC WORDS SAVED
                       ON STACK
HNDLR1  RTI            RETURN TO WAIT LOOP OR
                       CONTINUE MAIN PROGRAM
        END
```

The handler looks very much like the INBUF program of section 3-2.1, except that we cannot assume that any registers can be used as local variables because, in principle, the handler can be "called" at any time. Therefore we store our variables as global variables on page zero. Nevertheless, some subtle points must be magnified. The instruction LDA $8000 not only perfoms the function of inputting the data from the input device, but also performs the critical function of clearing the interrupt request flip-flop. The RTI instruction likewise restores the registers, and clears the interrupt mask bit I. The three instructions above the RTI return the device to the idle state, and then insert the address of the routine we want to go to after the buffer is full into the words on the stack where the program counter is saved. When RTI restores the registers, it will put this address into the program counter to begin executing that program.

A logic analyzer can be used to see actually what happens when an interrupt is requested and honored. Suppose that wait loop is at location $100, the handler is at $180, and the stack pointer is $3FC. Suppose the word input to the device is $24. Suppose locations $FFF8, $FFF9, and $FFFF have values $02, $00, and $58, and registers U, Y, X, DP, B, A, and CC

have values $203, $405, $607, $8, $B, $A, $C. This image could appear on the
screen of a logic analyzer, where the first column is the external request
(R = request asserted), the second column is the IRQ line (I = interrupt request asserted low), the third column is the read/write signal (R = read, W =
write), and the next two columns are the address and data in hexadecimal:

—	—	R	0100	20	OP CODE BRA
—	—	R	0101	FE	DISPLACEMENT
—	—	R	FFFF	58	NULL CYCLE
—	—	R	0100	20	OP CODE BRA
R	—	R	0101	FE	DISPLACEMENT — EXTERNAL REQUEST ASSERTED
R	I	R	FFFF	58	NULL CYCLE — IRQ LINE DROPS LOW
R	I	R	0100	20	OP CODE BRA — CANT YET RECOGNIZE INTERRUPT
R	I	R	0101	FE	DISPLACEMENT — M6809 RECOGNIZES INTERRUPT
—	I	R	FFFF	58	NULL CYCLE — EXTERNAL REQUEST IS NEGATED
—	I	R	0100	20	
—	I	R	0100	20	
—	I	R	FFFF	58	NULL CYCLE — BEGIN HONORING INTERRUPT
—	I	W	03FB	00	PUSH LOW BYTE OF PC
—	I	W	03FA	01	PUSH HIGH BYTE OF PC
—	I	W	03F9	03	PUSH LOW BYTE OF U
—	I	W	03F8	02	PUSH HIGH BYTE OF U
—	I	W	03F7	05	PUSH LOW BYTE OF Y
—	I	W	03F6	04	PUSH HIGH BYTE OF Y
—	I	W	03F5	07	PUSH LOW BYTE OF X
—	I	W	03F4	06	PUSH HIGH BYTE OF X
—	I	W	03F3	08	PUSH DP REGISTER
—	I	W	03F2	0B	PUSH ACCUMULATOR B
—	I	W	03F1	0A	PUSH ACCUMULATOR A
—	I	W	03F0	0C	PUSH CONDITION CODES
—	I	R	FFFF	58	NULL CYCLE

—	I	R	FFF8	01	GET HIGH BYTE OF HANDLER AD-DRESS
—	I	R	FFF9	80	GET LOW BYTE OF HANDLER AD-DRESS
—	I	R	FFFF	58	NULL CYCLE
—	I	R	0180	B6	LDA OP CODE — FIRST INSTRUC-TION OF HANDLER
—	I	R	0181	80	HIGH BYTE OF DEVICE ADDRESS
—	I	R	0182	00	LOW BYTE OF DEVICE ADDRESS
—	I	R	FFFF	58	NULL CYCLE
—	I	R	8000	25	READ DATA FROM DEVICE, CLEAR IRQA1
—	—	R	0183	9E	LDX OP CODE

This output from the logic analyzer shows an external interrupt being asserted on a CA1 pin in the middle of the second execution of the BRA instruction. In general, the machine may have been in this wait loop for a long time before the request was asserted. It takes one microsecond for the M6821 to set IRQA1 and assert the IRQ bus line low. The M6809 sees the interrupt request, but in general it will complete one extra memory cycle before it will honor it. The external request can be removed at any time after it has set the IRQA1 flip-flop, but before it may need to request another interrupt, as the CA1 input is edge triggered. The interrupt is honored by pushing all the registers on the stack and getting the address of the handler. Extra null cycles appear because the M6809 is doing some internal housekeeping before and after the words are pushed on the stack, and after the handler address is obtained. The first instruction of the handler is executed, and this clears IRQA1, which removes the source of the interrupt.

This example shows that interrupts are really not that complicated. A few more techniques are needed to handle more than one interrupt on a line, but these are also quite simple, as we now show.

Since the IRQ line is a wire-OR bus line, any number of devices can be connected to it, so that if any of these devices require service, they can assert this signal (low). The processor can recognize an IRQ interrupt when this line is low, but it does not know which device asserted this IRQ line, so it does not know what to do. By reading the status registers of all the devices connected to the IRQ line that could cause it to become low, however, the processor can determine a device that needs service, can service it, and then clear the source of the interrupt in that device. Note that two or more devices could simultaneously request an interrupt, or one could request an interrupt while another is being serviced. Fortunately, it all works out. As the first interrupt is serviced, and the cause of that interrupt is cleared in that device, the other device still holds the IRQ line low. Thus, as soon the handler for the first interrupt is left, the processor immediately recognizes an IRQ interrupt again. It will then handle the second interrupt.

The handlers become a bit more complicated for multiple interrupts. The *IRQ interrupt handler* just finds out which device needs service. Each device has its own *device handler* that actually services the interrupt. In the previous case where there is but one interrupt source on a line, these two handlers merge into one (or else one can say the IRQ handler becomes trivial, or disappears). In this case, when the IRQ line is low and the IRQ handler is executed, it *polls* the devices to see which one caused the interrupt. The polling program checks each device, one at a time, in *priority* order, highest priority device first. Each M6821 device can be checked for an IRQ1 interrupt and the handler to service the interrupt can be executed. An example involving an assortment of four devices will be shown to demonstrate polling in an IRQ handler. The four devices are shown in figure 4-6.

Suppose there are three M6821s such that device A of one is at locations $8000 and $8001, device B is at $8002 and $8003, and that device A of another is at $8004 and $8005, and device A of a third is at $8008 and $8009, with the data/direction register having the lower address in each device. The IRQA and IRQB pins of the first M6821, and only the IRQA pins of the other two M6821s are connected to the IRQ bus line. (Note that we do not connect devices to the IRQ bus unless we intend to use them in an interrupt technique, nor do we poll devices that cannot cause an interrupt, or else we might do something we do not need to do, and miss doing something because the polling routine will always go this routine instead of the one that actually needs service.) Suppose, for simplicity, that the A and B devices of the first M6821 and the A device of the second M6821 have their control registers initialized to value 5, but the A device of the third is initialized to $D. Then the IRQA1 and IRQB1 flip-flops of the first device,

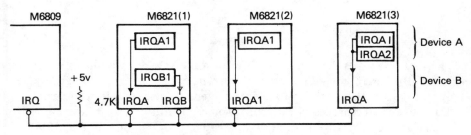

Figure 4-6. Multiple Interrupt Sources

and the IRQA1 flip-flop of the second M6821, and both the IRQA1 and IRQA2 flip-flops of the third M6821 can cause an IRQ interrupt if asserted.

```
              NAM   IRQHND
    IRQHND    LDA      $8001    GET STATE OF A DEVICE IN
                                M6821(1)

              EORA     #$81     INVERT IRQA AND ENABLE
              BITA     #$83     TEST BITS 7,1,0 FOR F
              BEQ   HNDLA1      GO TO DEVICE A(1) HANDLER
              LDA      $8003    GET STATE OF B DEVICE IN
                                M6821(1)

              EORA     #$81     INVERT IRQB AND ENABLE
              BITA     #$83     TEST BITS 7,1,0 FOR F
              BEQ   HNDLB1      GO TO DEVICE B(1) HANDLER
                                IF ALL F

              LDA      $8005    GET STATE OF A DEVICE IN
                                M6821(2)

              EORA     #$81     INVERT IRQA AND ENABLE
              BITA     #$83     TEST BITS 7,1,0 FOR F
              BEQ   HNDLA2      GO TO DEVICE A(2) HANDLER
              LDA      $8009    GET STATE OF A DEVICE IN
                                M6821(3)

              EORA     #$C9     INVERT IRQA1, IRQA2, AND
                                BOTH ENABLES

              BITA     #$83     TEST BITS 7,1,0 FOR F
              BEQ   HNDA13      GO TO HANDLER FOR IRQA1 IN
                                M6821(3)

              BITA     #$4A     TEST BITS 6,3, AND 1 FOR F
              BEQ   HNDA23      GO TO HANDLER FOR IRQA2 IN
                                M6821(3)

              END
```

The first line reads the control register of an M6821 at location $8000 and $8001. Bits seven and zero must be both true for an interrupt to be caused by this device. If bit seven is true but bit zero is false, the device interrupt did not cause the processor interrupt. Some other device must have caused it, so this one should be ignored. In order to test for two ones in the M6809, the easiest way is to complement all the bits and use BIT to test for zeros.

This simple test, however, makes maintenance a bit more difficult than a slightly more complex test. If the first M6821 is burned out, or is removed from the microprocessor, an attempt to read any word in the range $8000 to $8003 will probably read $FF. The IRQ device handler would read this word, so the test for Ts in bits zero and seven would pass and the device handler HNDLA1 would be executed. Unfortunately, since there is no chip here, attempts to remove the source of the interrupt will be futile, so the IRQ interrupt will be recognzied just as soon as the handler is executed, ad nauseam. To correct this troublesome problem, all that we have to do is check for an F in the control word too. Any F will do. Since we initialized the control register such that bit one is F, we check the word we read to verify that bits seven and zero are T and bit one is F, to execute the device handler. Note that an exclusive-OR instruction with an immediate operand, EORA #N, inverts those bits in the accumulator where the corresponding bit in the operand is T, and that a bit test instruction, BITA #N, sets condition code Z if all bits in accumulator A are F in those positions where the operand is T. Thus, the branch to the interrupt handler is taken if bits seven and zero are T and bit one is F. HNDLA1 may be a handler routine like TPRDR described earlier in this section. If this condition is not satisfied, the next device is tested and if it does not satisfy the test, the next is tested, then the next and the next until all are tested. Note that the IRQA2 interrupt source from the M6821(3) requires a slightly different procedure. Reading the control word at location $8009, we invert bits zero and seven to prepare to check the IRQA1 interrupt source, and simultaneously invert bits three and six to prepare to check the IRQA2 interrupt source. The IRQA1 source is checked as before. The IRQA2 source caused the interrupt if bits three and six are T, and bit one is F.

The polling technique described above checks the devices in priority order. The program should check the devices that need service fastest first. The A device at location $8000 and $8001 should be associated with the fastest I/O system, or the most critical one. Lower priority devices are handled after the higher priority device handlers clear the device interrupt that masks the lower priority interrupt, after the higher priority interrupt is fully handled. An alternative scheme is called a *round-robin* priority scheme. Here, the polling program is arranged as an infinite program loop. When the ith device in the priority order gets an interrupt and is serviced, the i-plus-first device assumes the highest priority, and whenever an interrupt occurs the polling program starts checking the i-plus-first device first. Polling in the same priority order is useful when some devices clearly need service faster than others; round-robin priority is more democratic and is especially useful if some device tends to hog the use of the computer by frequently requesting interrupts.

The previous example shows how multiple interrupts can be handled by means of connecting several devices to the IRQ line and polling them in the IRQ handler. The polling technique may take too much time for some devices that need service quickly. A *vectored interrupt* technique can be used to replace the interrupt handler software by a hardware device, so that the device handler is entered almost as soon as the device requests an interrupt. The basic idea is that each device puts its interrupt request signal on separate pins into a hardware module that performs the same function as the polling routine. If the ith interrupt request line is asserted (low) and all interrupt requests on lines zero to $i - 1$ are not asserted, the hardware supplies the address of the ith device handler instantaneously, as it interrupts the processor, to start the processor at the specified location.

Consider the following example. The three M6821 ICs in the previous example have four outputs. These can be fed to a *priority encoder* integrated circuit that generates the address used to get the two words that are the IRQ handler starting address. This chip has n outputs and $2**n$ inputs, which have a priority ordering. If only one input is asserted, say input i, then the binary number i is output. If more than one is asserted, the binary number is output corresponding to the one with the highest priority. See figure 4-7. The M6809 puts out a two-bit *bus state*, BA, BS, which is FT when and only when it is reading the indirect address for an interrupt (or SWI or RESET). If these two bits are FT, the normal memory can be disabled (by making a VMA signal that you use in all address decoders false), and the memory holding the interrupt addresses will be enabled. The low order four bits of the address indicate which interrupt is being read and will be eight and nine when an IRQ interrupt is being honored. These will be used as the low order bits of the PROM. Address bits five and four for the PROM that holds the indirect addresses of the handlers are supplied by this priority encoder instead of by the microprocessor. So if the microprocessor ever addresses this PROM, and this can only happen when it is getting the address of a handler of some kind, the priority encoder will determine address bits five and four, to select the two words used for the handler. If the A device at location $8000 and $8001 requests service, the first input is asserted to the priority encoder, which will output FT, so when the microprocessor thinks it is reading $FFF8 and $FFF9, it actually reads locations $18 and $19. These two locations of the PROM can contain the address of the first instruction of the device handler HNDLA1. If this device requests service, the processor immediately executes the handler, bypassing the polling routine and getting to business that much faster. Now, if that device does not want service, the B device at location $8002 and $8003 may request service. If so, it asserts the second input, which causes the output of the priority encoder to be TF, so the processor picks up words at locations $28 and $29 when it begins to service the IRQ interrupt. The address of the handler, HNDLB1, should be in those locations. The other requests are similarly made through separate inputs to the priority encoder, which selects a different device handler address from the PROM. Note that the two requests from the M6821(3) chip cannot be separated, since they are passed through the same pin on that chip, the IRQA pin, and are thus indistinguishable to the priority encoder. They can be distinguished by a small polling sequence, of course. Nevertheless, the vectored interrupt approach reduces latency because it eliminates a good part of the polling sequence. (Some problems exist with this simple example, such as a higher priority request changing the output of the encoder just as it finishes reading the first byte of the device address but before it reads the second. This problem can be solved by having all device handler starting addresses have the same high byte. Alternatively, an M6828 integrated circuit can be used; it incorporates a priority encoder and overcomes all the irregular problems.)

4-3 The Interrupt Mechanisms in the M6809

The M6809 incorporates a number of very useful interrupt mechanisms, including different interrupt bus lines and some useful special instructions, SYNC and CWAI. These features are discussed in this section.

The M6809 has four negative logic interrupt bus lines, including the IRQ line described in the last section, and the RESET line that behaves like an interrupt line. The others are the fast interrupt request (FIRQ) and nonmaskable interrupt (NMI) lines. In the following paragraphs we describe what happens in hardware when these lines request some service.

If RESET becomes low, processing stops. The RESET line normally clears all I/O registers when the processor is stopped. When the signal rises again, memory words at location $FFFE and $FFFF are read and become the high and low byte of the program counter. This starts the M6809 at the location specified by the contents of $FFFE and $FFFF. The program that is entered handles the reset operation, so we call it the *reset handler*. The reset handler configures many of the I/O devices that are not already configured as desired by the RESET signal, and that are not to be configured later as part of the program that uses the device. In earlier discussions, the rituals that were to be run just after power is applied are all put in the reset handler. The handler may also run diagnostic programs to check the microprocessor, memory, or I/O devices, clear all or part of memory, initialize some of the variables to be used in the following programs, and set up the stack pointer register. The handler then jumps to the applications program if the microcomputer runs a dedicated application, or to a program called a *monitor* which allows the attendant to load and examine memory and registers, and execute or debug programs. The locations $FFFE, $FFFF, the reset handler, and the monitor or the applications pro-

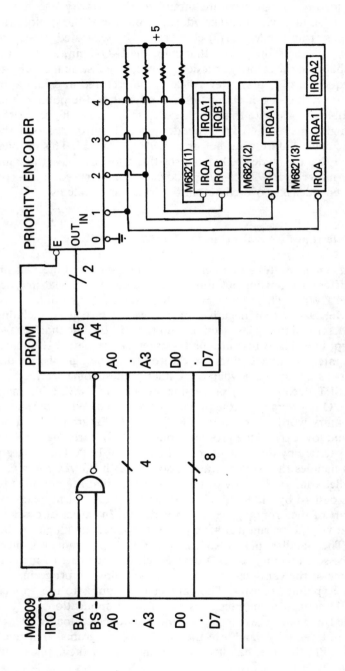

Figure 4-7. Vectored Interrupts

gram are normally in read only memory, for if we did not have these locations and programs in memory before the first instruction was executed, we
would have no way to start the machine. (You may laugh at this, but quite
often a machine proposed in a learned paper has this problem, that it cannot be started.)

If the NMI signal falls from high to low, we say *the processor recognizes
an NMI interrupt* and the following sequence of events occurs. (However,
NMI is not recognized in an M6809 until an instruction is executed that
loads the stack pointer register.) In the same way as the IRQ interrupt is
honored, an NMI interrupt is honored, except that the I interrupt mask is
not checked, and the address at $FFFC and $FFFD is used to jump to the *NMI
handler* because it is not masked by the I condition code. The NMI handler
will service this interrupt. One very important thing that it must do,
moreover, is to remove the cause of the low signal on the NMI line, or the
NMI signal will never fall again so no NMI interrupts will never be recognized again by the processor. The handler executes an RTI as its final instruction. This instruction pulls all the values saved on the stack, putting
them back in their respective registers, which resumes the program that was
interrupted so that it executes the same way as if no interrupt occurred.

Other devices can be connected to the NMI line and can be polled in the
NMI handler in a similar way. There are two additional considerations
when the NMI line is used. First, it is possible for a second interrupt to be
requested at the same time or just after another was requested on the NMI
line. The polling sequence will service one of them, and then return via an
RTI instruction, but the other device will still hold the NMI line down
because it has not been serviced. The microcomputer does not recognize this
interrupt because no falling edge of the NMI signal was noted, so it is not
serviced. Moreover, no other NMI interrupts can be serviced because the
line is being held low. To avoid this catastrophe, an input device should be
attached to the NMI line. Just before leaving an interrupt handler on an
NMI line, you should read the value of the NMI line from this input device.
If NMI is low, branch to the beginning of the NMI handler. If it is high, execute an RTI. (Note that device handlers for devices connected to the IRQ
line should end in an RTI instruction, and need not be polled after an NMI
interrupt is serviced.) The other consideration is that these interrupt requests cannot be disabled as a whole, as setting the I condition code disables
all the IRQ interrupts. Each interrupt on an NMI line has to be disabled individually if we want to disable all interrupts. These two considerations indicate that the IRQ line is easier to use for multiple interrupts, while the
NMI line is better used for an omnipresent interrupt such as would be requested when an attendant presses an ABORT button. Nevertheless, the

NMI line can be used to handle multiple interrupts with these two simple considerations.

The response to a signal on the FIRQ line is similar. Condition code bit six, called the *FIRQ interrupt mask* F, is used to prevent unwanted interrupts from signals on the FIRQ line. If the FIRQ signal is low, and F is false, then we say *the processor recognizes an FIRQ interrupt*. As when it recognized an IRQ interrupt, it is probably executing an instruction, so it completes the instruction and then saves the registers on the stack. It saves only the program counter and the condition code register, however, and not the index registers and the accumulators. That is why it is called the fast interrupt. It exhibits lower latency than the IRQ interrupt. We can return from such an interrupt by a PULS CC,PC instruction or by executing an RTI instruction which restores the registers, including the condition codes and the F bit, to their former values. After setting the I and F bit, the processor reads the words at locations $FFF6 and $FFF7 into the program counter to start executing a program. This program is called the *FIRQ handler*. It services the interrupt that was requested. Like the IRQ handler, it must remove the source of the interrupt before it clears the F bit (by executing RTI as its last instruction or by executing ANDCC $BF), or it will promptly be interrupted again, ad nauseam. Well, now, the RTI can be used to restore all twelve words into all the registers after an IRQ or an NMI handler, and can also be used to restore only three words into the program counter and condition code register after an FIRQ handler. How does it know how many registers to restore? The answer is the remaining condition code bit seven, called the *entire flag* E. E is set to true whenever all the registers are saved in a SWI instruction or on honoring an IRQ or NMI interrupt as the condition code and its E bit are pushed on the stack, but is cleared to false on honoring an FIRQ interrupt. RTI always pulls the top word from the stack. Examining the E bit, the instruction can now decide whether to pull just two more words into PC if E is false, or pull eleven more words into all the remaining registers if E is true.

We now rework our paper tape reader example, to use the interrupt technique. The request to put some data into the buffer will be handled by an IRQ interrupt and the error condition will be recognized by an NMI interrupt. This requires that the IRQA output of the M6821 be connected to the IRQ bus and the IRQB output be connected to the NMI bus line. Both wire-OR bus lines need pull-up resistors. Continuing our example, the program shown below will read the paper tape pattern whenever a new pattern appears, and will jump to the NMI handler whenever the reader runs out of paper.

```
        NAM                 INTERS
        ORG             0   LOW MEMORY IS RAM
```

```
POINT    RMB              2      ALLOCATE TWO WORDS
                                 FOR POINTER

COUNT    RMB              1      ALLOCATE ONE WORD TO
                                 COUNT WORDS

BUFFR    RMB            $80      ALLOCATE 128 WORDS FOR
                                 THE BUFFER

         ORG          $FC00      TOP 1K MEMORY IS ROM OR
                                 PROM

RSTHND   LDA          #$25       SET UP DEVICE A TO SET
                                 IRQA1 ON

         STA          $8001      FALL OF CA1, ALLOW IN-
                                 TERRUPT TO IRQA

         LDA          #$05       SET UP B DEVICE TO SET
                                 IRQB1 ON

         STA          $8003      FALL OF CB1, ALLOW IN-
                                 TERRUPT TO IRQB

         LDA          #$80       GET SIZE OF BUFFER
         STA          COUNT      SAVE IN WORD TO COUNT
                                 INPUTS

         LDX          #BUFFER    GET ADDRESS OF FIRST
                                 WORD IN BUFFER

         STX          POINT      SAVE IN WORDS FOR BUF-
                                 FER POINTER

         LDS          #$3FB      INITIALIZE STACK POINTER
         ANDCC        $EF        CLEAR INTERRUPT MASK
                                 FOR IRQ

         JMP          PROGRM     GO TO USEFUL PROGRAM
         •
         •
         •

PROGRM   BRA          PROGRM     WAIT LOOP TO REPLACE
                                 USEFUL PROGRAM
         •
         •
         •

IRQHND   LDA          $8000      GET DATA
         LDX          POINT      GET POINTER TO BUFFER
         STA          ,X+        PUT IN BUFFER
         STX          POINT      SAVE FOR NEXT INPUT
         DEC          COUNT      COUNT OUT INCOMING
                                 WORDS
```

```
              BNE        IRQHN1        IF BUFFER IS FULL, THEN
              CLR        $8001         PREVENT FURTHER
                                       INTERRUPTS
IRQHNI        RTI                      RETURN TO MAIN
                                       PROGRAM
NMIHND        LDA        $8003         CLEAR SOURCE OF INTER-
                                       RUPT (IRQB1)
               •                       REPORT ERROR TO ATTENDANT
               •
               •
              ORG        $FFF8
              FDB        IRQHND
              FDB        0             (SWI HANDLER ADDRESS
                                       GOES HERE)
              FDB        NMIHND
              FDB        RSTHND
              END
```

The first few lines have assembler directives that make room for pointer and counter variables and the buffer itself. They must be in read-write memory, and should be on page zero because they are global variables. The remaining lines are the program stored in read only memory. The reset handler, which begins at label RSTHND and has eleven instructions, initializes the registers and the variables needed by the program, initializes the stack pointer, clears the interrupt mask, and jumps to a user program called PROGRM to do something useful. (To avoid showing a useful program, we show a wait loop, but if you have to use a wait loop, you are better off using the gadfly mechanism for synchronization.) When power is first applied, or after the user presses a panic button to assert the RESET line low, the processor picks up the two words at locations $FFFE and $FFFF, which happen to be the address of this routine, to start executing it. Device A of the M6821 is initialized almost the same way as for the gadfly technique, but bit zero is also set so that when IRQA1 is asserted, it will assert the IRQA pin (low) which will send the interrupt request to the processor. Also, device B is similarly initialized as before, but bit zero is set to allow assertion of IRQB1 to send an interrupt request. The buffer pointer is initialized to the address of the first word of the buffer, and the counter is initialized to N, the number of words to be input. The stack pointer has to be initialized, or else you may be trying to save return addresses, registers, and local variables in nonexistent memory locations. Note that when power is turned on and RESET is asserted, the microcomputer sets the I and F condition codes, inhibiting IRQ and FIRQ interrupts. At the end of the RESET handler after the I/O devices have been configured as required, the I bit has to be cleared. If this is not done, IRQ interrupts cannot be recognized. If this is done sooner, an interrupt could be generated while an I/O device is being configured. Incidentally the main program can keep reading the value of COUNT to determine the busy-done state of the process that is filling the buffer; when the COUNT is zero the buffer is full and some routine that uses it could be started. The IRQ handler is "called up" in the same way as we showed the TPRDR handler in section 4-2.2 being "called up." If ever an error occurs, the IRQB1 flip-flop is asserted, which makes the NMI line drop, which causes the processor to recognize an NMI interrupt, which in turn causes the NMI handler to be executed. This informs the attendant that an error has occurred. Note that the source of the NMI interrupt is cleared by the NMI interrupt handler. The LDA $8002 instruction clears the IRQB1 flip-flop by means of an address trigger. If this is not done, then the NMI line will remain low, and the processor will not recognize any more NMI interrupts.

The M6809 has some instructions, CWAI and SYNC, that are used to manage interrupts. CWAI is an improved kind of wait loop, and SYNC is a fast gadfly loop. These are discussed now.

CWAI clears condition code bits (normally the I bit to enable IRQ interrupts or the F bit to enable FIRQ interrupts) and then waits for an interrupt, rather like the wait loop in section 4-3.2. However, CWAI is optimized to reduce latency time. As soon as CWAI is executed, it pushes all the registers on the stack as if an interrupt were honored. When an interrupt occurs, it does not have to save the registers. If you looked at a logic analyzer at the time an external interrupt was requested as we did for the single interrupt example in section 4-3.2, you would see null cycles before the interrupt was recognized by the M6809, then you would see the address being read from locations $FFF8 and $FFF9, then another null cycle, and the first instruction in the handler would be executed. CWAI can be used to reduce the latency to about four memory cycles.

SYNC can be used to synchronize to an external signal on the IRQ or FIRQ bus lines when the corresponding mask, I or F, is set. Setting the mask bits prevent the interrupts from being recognized and honored by the M6809. When the IRQ or FIRQ line is asserted low, the next instruction right after the SYNC instruction is executed. The registers are not saved on the stack and the IRQ or FIRQ interrupt handler is not executed. SYNC is, in effect, an optimized gadfly loop. (Some quirks associated with SYNC are: The SYNC instruction causes the address and data bus drivers in the M6809 to be disabled, so the buses will float. Negating VMA and making R/W high during SYNC are recommended. The SYNC instruction can be stopped by an NMI interrupt or a nonmasked IRQ or FIRQ interrupt, to enter the sequence to honor the interrupt and execute the handler. The next instruction following SYNC will be executed after the interrupt is handled. Finally, any interrupt request on the masked interrupt line can cause it to come out of SYNC, so a gadfly loop that examines one particular device will not exit if the wrong device requests an interrupt, but SYNC will do so. These quirks are easy enough to handle with some care, and the power and flexibility of the SYNC instruction is worth the effort.

4-4 Direct Memory Access and Context Switching

This final section discusses two techniques for I/O synchronization that are faster than interrupts. *Direct Memory Access* (DMA) is a well-known technique whereby an I/O device gets access to memory directly without having the microprocessor in between. By this direct path, the word input through a device can be stored in memory, or a word from memory can be output through a device, on request by the device. The second technique, *context switching*, is actually a more general type of DMA. The *context* of a processor is its set of accumulators and other registers (as Texas Instruments uses the term) and the instruction set of the processor. To switch context means logically to disconnect the existing set of registers, bringing in a new set to be used in their place, or to use a different instruction set. In DMA, as we soon see, both the instruction set and the registers are switched. A very primitive instruction is used to move the data from or to the I/O device and a new pair of registers is used to keep track of the placement in a buffer of the moved word. These two techniques are now studied.

The fastest way to input data to a buffer is direct memory access. This technique requires considerably more hardware and is considerably faster. It is the best technique for fast I/O, disks, which require the lowest latency. This technique can be used for input or output. It will be described below for the input operation and can be easily extended to the output operation. In DMA, a word is moved from the device to a memory in a *DMA transfer cycle*. Successive words moved this way are put into a buffer. Two DMA techniques are available for the M6800 microcomputer. If an I/O system wishes to input data, it *steals a memory cycle* to transfer one word or else it *halts the microprocessor* to transfer one or more words. First, the cycle steal technique is described, then the halt technique will be discussed.

In the cycle steal technique, the device requests to transfer a newly read word into memory. The microprocessor may be in the middle of an operation: it simply stops what it is doing for one memory cycle and *releases control* of the address and data bus to its memory by disabling the tristate drivers in it that drive these buses. The I/O system is then expected to use this memory cycle to transfer the word from its input register to a memory location. The cycle steal technique can transfer one word with latency time on the order of three microseconds (because of delays in handling the DMA request signals), but can transfer only one word before the processor resumes its operation. The processor is usually in the middle of an operation, with data stored in dynamic logic registers (as charges on capacitors), so if the processor does not keep moving, these temporary variables will become lost as the charge decays. In this mode the device can only steal a cycle, and then give the processor a cycle, and so on.

Another technique, the *halt DMA*, uses the principle that the interrupt technique uses: when a device wants to output a word to be stored in memory, it requests that the processor finish its current instruction, when all data is in user visible registers which are not dynamic, and then release control of the address and data bus so the I/O device can use them to store the word in memory. This technique permits the device to transmit as many words as it wants in successive memory cycles, because the microprocessor will not lose any data while the transfer is going on. It permits the greatest throughput, but the latency can be on the order of twenty microseconds because the instruction that was being executed when the request was made must be completed.

Intended for transferring buffers of data, DMA requires an *address register* to supply the memory address where the data is to be written. This address is incremented after the word is moved so the next input word will be written in the next location. Also, as a number of words are to be moved, a *counter* is needed to keep track of how many words are left to be moved. As each word is moved, this counter is decremented. Finally, DMA requires a busy/done mechanism, which can be tested by an interrupt mechanism or a gadfly loop, to inform the computer that the entire block of words has been entered. The DMA process, which fills the buffer, is busy if the buffer is being filled. The idle state indicates that no DMA activity is in progress; the busy state, that a word will be transferred whenever the device needs it to fill the buffer, and the done state, that all words in the buffer have been transferred. In order to use DMA, the program has to initialize the address register to the address where the first input word is to be stored, and the counter to the number of words to be moved. The interrupt handler has to be prepared to recognize the interrupt when all words are transferred, and to jump to an appropriate device handler to supply the operations needed when all words have been transferred, or a gadfly loop can be used to monitor the busy/done state of the DMA system. DMA requires extra hardware—an address register, a counter, and a busy/done mechanism—but permits data to be moved at a rate of one data word per memory cycle from an input device to memory.

Microcomputers implement direct memory access by means of a *direct memory access controller* (DMAC) chip. This, in conjunction with another I/O chip like the M6821, can implement a *DMA device*. Together the two chips can act like another microprocessor, the DMAC chip sending a read or write command on R/W and addresses on the address bus, and the other chip sending the data when the DMAC chip sends the address.

In order to show how direct memory access works, we will introduce a simplified M6844 direct memory access controller. The chip itself has four complete DMAC modules on it that can implement up to four separate DMA I/O systems, and each has a plethora of modes and features, which the reader is invited to study by reading the data sheet and the applications notes on the chip. See *The Complete Motorola Microcomputer Data Library* for details. Furthermore, to get all this flexibility the designers used and reused their forty pins to an extent that this chip is a great example of the fact that we are running out of pins to interconnect these large ICs. For our purposes, one of the simpler modes is just what we need to make concrete the discussion of DMA. This is all that we will discuss.

We will rework our good old paper tape reader example to show how DMA works. DMA should only be used when very low latency is required, such as for disk output or CRT output. It should never be used with a slow paper tape reader. Nevertheless, we will use it with the slow paper tape reader just to illustrate the technique using our running example. The computer for this example has some random access memory, a M6821 device A connected to a paper tape reader with data/direction register at $8000 and control register at $8001, and an M6844 which is described below. We introduce the M6844 first and discuss its registers and its signals to and from the I/O chip (M6821) and the microprocessor chip. Next we show all the chips and their interconnections to make a practical DMA system. Finally, we exhibit a simple program to read patterns from paper tape into a buffer which acomplishes the same ends as our previous examples.

On turning power on, the RESET signal clears all registers: this configures the M6844 for the mode which we will use, to use the halt mode to transfer a word at a time as it is input from the paper tape reader into a buffer, as in our previous examples, incrementing the address each time a word is put in the buffer. See figure 4-8. (Other modes can be selected by making some of the bits T in the registers shown in figure 4-8. For one of the problems at the end of this chapter, we note that the DMAC will request a read command if the least significant bit of $8030 is false, and will request a write command to memory if that bit is true.)

In order to transfer 128 words from the input device (the paper tape reader) to a buffer, the DMA controller is initialized in this way. The program loads the address of the first word of the buffer into the ADDRESS REGISTER, and the number, 128 of words to be moved into the COUNTER REGISTER. The DONE and BUSY flip-flops indicate the state of the DMA transfer: idle is FF, busy is FT, and done is TF. When reset, the M6844 is put into the idle state, of course. The program starts the DMA

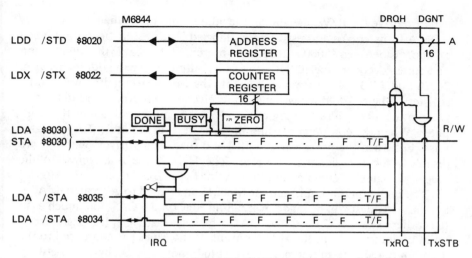

Figure 4-8. Simplified Block Diagram of the M6844

by setting the least significant bit of the register in location $8034, and the M6844 enters the busy state as transfers begin. After 128 words have been transferred, the controller enters the done state. This state indicates that the buffer is available to be used.

The DMA transfer takes place in the following manner. When in the busy state, if the I/O device asserts the TxRQ line, then the DRQH line is asserted by the DMAC. This line tells the microprocessor that it should halt to permit the DMA operation. When the processor finishes its instruction it asserts the DGNT line. This in turn causes the M6844 to assert the TxSTB line which indicates that the device should read out a word on the data bus at that time. Meanwhile, the M6844 controls the address bus and the R/W line. It sends out the address and instructs memory to write the data at the address. It then decrements the COUNTER REGISTER and increments the ADDRESS REGISTER. If the counter reaches zero, BUSY is cleared and DONE is set, as the DMA operation is completed and the done state is entered. Register $8030 exhibits the busy/done state. It can be checked in a gadfly loop. The least significant bit of the register at location $8035 is ANDed with the done signal, and this result is available in the most significant bit of this same register, as well as being sent out the IRQ pin (in negative logic). This signal can be used to request an interrupt.

The M6844 can be connected to an M6809, an M6821, and some random access memory, as shown in figure 4-9. Just as any other I/O chip, the M6844 has data bus connections and register select address lines, a R/W, and a chip enable so the processor can write or read the registers. It can also drive the R/W line and all the address bus lines when it commands a DMA transfer. An address decoder, labeled "A," asserts its output when an address between $8000 and $8003 is presented, to enable the M6821, and an address decoder labeled "B" asserts its output when an address between $8020 and $803F is presented, to enable the M6844 to read or write in its registers. The M6809 has two lines to receive requests from the M6844 and issue grants. The (negative logic) HALT line is a request to halt the computer. When the computer is using the bus, the bus available (BA) signal is false, but when the processor is halted and the tristate drivers within it are disabled, the BA signal is asserted. The HALT line is attached to the (negative logic) DRQH pin, and the BA line to the DGNT pin of the M6844.

The interrupt mechanism in the M6821 can be used to generate DMA requests. A request will be made by a falling edge on the CA1 line, much as in the earlier examples. This sets IRQA1, which asserts IRQA (low) as if to request an interrupt. But the IRQA output of the M6821 is connected to the TxRQ input. Some minor points are noted about the D flip-flop between them. The TxRQ input has an interval around the rising edge of the E clock where an indeterminate signal will actually cause it (and the M6800, if it is used in place of the M6809) to freeze up completely. It is necessary to maintain a stable signal at this time. Therefore a D edge-triggered flip-flop, clocked on the rising edge of the Q clock, is used. Moreover, an inversion of the logic levels is needed, and this can be obtained by taking the negative logic Q output from the flip-flop.) Asserting TxRQ will assert DRQH and HALT. When the processor completes its current instruction, it asserts BA which is DGNT, and this asserts TxSTB. In the two cycles, one before and one after the DMA cycle, VMA must be made false. This is done by the circuit shown on top of figure 4-9. TxSTB is asserted in the memory cycle when the M6844 puts the address on the address bus and sends a write command on the R/W line. A trick is played on the M6821. When TxSTB is asserted, it is forced to read out the data in the device A data register. Note that reading the data register also clears IRQA, which negates IRQ (TxRG), which negates DRQH (HALT), which effectively cancels the request until another is made by a falling signal on the CA1 line.

We now study the trick played on the M6821. Since this chip also has to be written in and read from in the usual way so the processor can initialize its control registers, this trick is played by some gates, which normally let the address decoder respond to processor addresses, but when TxSTB is asserted, they switch the register select, chip select, and R/W lines to make the chip read the data register.

Finally, we look at a program to move words from the paper tape reader to a buffer.

```
NAM     DMASET
LDA          #$25   CONFIGURE M6821 TO ASSERT IRQA
```

```
        STA        $8001    ON FALL OF CA1, USE CA2 IN HAND-
                            SHAKE
        LDX        #BUFFER  GET ADDRESS OF FIRST WORD IN
                            BUFFER
        STX        $8020    PUT IN M6844 ADDRESS REGISTER
        LDX        #$80     GET SIZE OF BUFFER
        STX        $8022    PUT IN COUNTER REGISTER
        INC        $8034    PUT M6844 INTO BUSY STATE
   L    LDA        $8030    EXAMINE STATE
        BPL        L        LOOP UNTIL DONE
        END
```

The program is quite simple because the hardware in the M6844 is doing most of the work. The first two lines configure the M6821 as usual, to let the device inform the M6821 when a new word is input by dropping CA1. The next four lines set up the address and count registers. Notice how similar this is to our previous examples. Then the least significant bit of the register at location $8034 is set by incrementing that word, to start the DMA operation. Next a gadfly loop is executed to wait for the done state. When this loop is left, the buffer is full and ready to be used.

This sequence of events happens when a DMA request is made:

1. As in an interrupt request, an external request is recognized by the IRQA1 flip-flop, which requests an "interrupt" by asserting IRQA low. This makes TxRQ high.
2. If TxRQ is high and the least significant bit of location $8034 is high and the DMA controller is in the busy state, then it asserts DRQH low. This asserts the M6809 HALT signal low.
3. If the HALT is asserted in the M6809, then at the end of the current instruction, the M6809 disables its tristate drivers on the R/W line and address and data bus lines, and asserts the bus available signal BA. This asserts the M6844 grant signal DGNT.
4. If the DGNT signal is asserted and the M6844 is busy, it asserts TxSTB low. This signal in the M6821 address decoder causes the M6821 to receive the signals that would be appropriate for reading data register A onto the data bus.
5. When the M6821 reads the data register, an address trigger clears IRQA1. This negates TxRQ, which negates HALT, which permits the M6809 to resume execution of the next instruction.

An interrupt could be used to indicate that the buffer is full, if the processor can do some useful work while the buffer is being filled. The IRQ output of the M6844 is connected to the IRQ bus, and the least significant

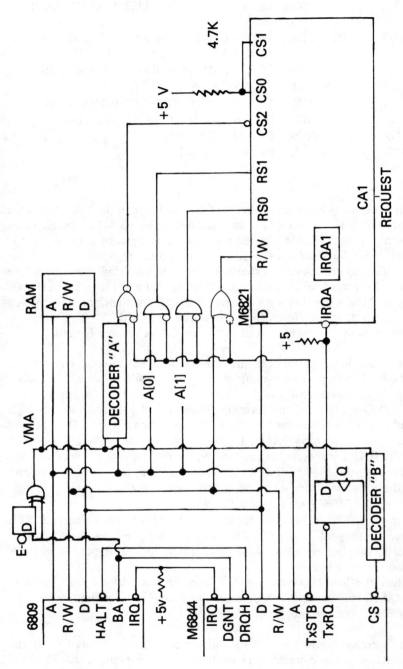

Figure 4-9. Interconnections for DMA

bit of location $8035 is set. When the M6844 is done, it will generate an interrupt. The IRQ handler should check word $8035 in exactly the same way it checked word $8001 in the example of a polling IRQ handler; it should branch to the M6844 device handler if bits zero and seven are H and bit one is L.

An interesting variation to DMA that is uniquely attractive using inexpensive microprocessors is to use two or more microprocessors on the same address and data bus. This is our sixth alternative for I/O synchronization. One microprocessor runs the main program. When a device requests service, it causes that one to stop, as if a DMA request were being honored, and another microprocessor to start. When the first stops, it releases control over the address and data buses common to all the microprocessors and to memory and I/O so the second can use them. The second microprocessor can execute the device handler. Not only is the second microprocessor started more quickly because the registers in the first are saved merely by freezing them in place rather than saving them on a stack, but also the registers in the second could already contain the values needed by the device handler so they do not need to be initialized. Whereas DMA using a DMA chip is restricted to just inputting a word into a buffer, or outputting a word from a buffer, in context switching, the second microprocessor can execute any software routine when it obtains control of the bus from the first microprocessor.

In the following example, a processor can read the word, i, from the input register and then increment the ith word in memory, to collect statistics on the occurrence of the value i. This processor is turned on when a new number i is presented at an input port, $0 > i > 256$, and we will assume that at most 256 occurrences of any i will ever be counted.

Suppose that two M6809s are connected to the same address and data buses, an M6821 is connected to be addressed at location $8000 to $8003, and its IRQA output is connected as shown in figure 4-10. Note that when power is applied, IRQA is high. This causes the top processor to run, while the bottom one thinks a DMA is going on because its HALT line is low. (Note also the need for an edge-triggered flip-flop to prevent the HALT lines from changing around the time when the E clock rises if an M6800 is used in place of an M6809. The same problem occurred in the DMA system, and is handled in the same way here.)

We will first consider the response to an input i, and then we will study the technique used to initialize the second processor to respond in that way. Assume that the index register X of the M6809(2) points to the beginning of the buffer, and that the M6821 is configured to work in the handshake mode. When the CA1 line drops, the bottom processor executes the following program. It reads i from the data register, and increments the ith word in the buffer. This collects statistics on the occurrence of different numbers

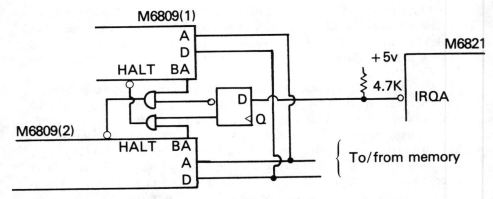

Figure 4-10. Connections for Context Switching

that appear on the input register when an interrupt is requested. It is easy to do with context switching, while ordinary DMA cannot do this operation, and it is quite a bit faster than ordinary interrupt synchronization because not only are the registers not saved but also they remain in the second M6809 so they do not have to be initialized.

```
        NAM     STATS
L       LDA     $8000   GET I FROM M6821
        INC     A,X     INCREMENT BUFFER (I)
        BRA     L       LOOP
        END
```

Curiously, the second processor will read the data in the first line, which will clear IRQA1, which will turn off the second processor and turn on the first one. When the next input is obtained, however, the second processor will resume its operation, incrementing the buffer word corresponding to the previous input, then reading the current input and halting. Even so, this shows how the context is switched, and how this permits a synchronization method almost as fast as DMA, yet almost as flexible as the interrupt mode.

In order to get the second processor to act this way, it must be initialized when the power is applied. In order to initialize both processors, the following reset handler can be used:

```
LDX     #BUFFER   IN (2), SET X TO POINT TO BUFFER
TST     $8001     CHECK IF YOU ARE (2)
BMI     L         IF SO, GO TO PROGRAM STATS
LDA     #$05      OTHERWISE YOU ARE (1) SO PERFORM
```

```
STA        $8001   STANDARD RESET HANDLER FUNCTIONS
LDS        #STKP   SETTING UP STACK ETC.
 •                 THEN GO TO MAIN PROGRAM
 •
 •
```

When power is applied, the main processor M6809(1) executes the routine first. Loading its X register does not hurt, since it will be loaded again before it will be used. Then, the M6821 control register is tested. At this time, since the RESET line has just cleared it, it will be zero. Hence the branch is not taken, and the control register is initialized for handshaking so that IRQA becomes a high output. The main program is entered after the reset handler is executed. One of the things done here is to make a copy of the program for processor M6809(2) in RAM, so it will be there when some data arrives. When the first number i is presented, IRQA becomes low, which requests the M6809(1) to halt. After it has completed its current instruction, the M6809(2) is allowed to proceed. It has not yet gone through its reset sequence, so it must do that first. In executing the reset handler, it will load the X register as required. Testing the M6821 control register, it will then enter the program described earlier.

Finally, any set of microcomputers having DMA capability can be used in this manner: the one operating the main program need not be the same as the one handling a device. This permits one to put a new microprocessor in his old microcomputer. The old microprocessor is turned on to run programs that are left over from earlier days, but the new microprocessor is turned on to execute the new and better programs for the new microprocessor. This is a alternative to simulation or emulation in microprogramming. It is better because the best machine to emulate itself is usually itself—and putting two microprocessors in the same microcomputer hardly affects the cost of the whole system.

Though this technique is rather new, it offers an alternative for microcomputers because the added cost for a microprocessor is so small and because the speed and flexibility are between true DMA and vectored interrupt, a quality that is often just what is required.

4-5 Conclusions

We have discussed six alternatives to solve the synchronization problem. Each has some advantages and some disadvantages.

Real-time synchronization uses the least hardware and is practical if an inexpensive microcomputer has nothing to do but time out an I/O operation; however, it can be difficult to program. Gadfly programs are easier to write, but require that the hardware provide an indication of the done state. Nevertheless, a computer cannot do anything else when it is in a gadfly loop, so this is as inefficient as real-time synchronization.

The interrupt-polling technique and the vectored interrupt technique require more hardware to request service from the processor. They are useful when the device needs service in shorter time; however, the tendency to use them just because they are available should be avoided. Vectored interrupt requires an extra chip to provide the address of the device handler, which is a significant cost. Although interrupt polling only requires a bus line from device to processor, if the gadfly approach is exclusively used, this line invites the mayhem of an unrecognizable interrupt if a software error rewrites the control register in the device. The interrupt technique can be used side by side with the gadfly technique. When the gadfly technique is used, the interrupts are all disabled by the setting of the I condition code, as in the ORCC instruction, or by clearing control bit zero in the M6821 device. Then the program can loop as it tests the device without fear of being pulled out by an interrupt. Commonly, gadfly is used for careful, individual stepping of an I/O system, and interrupt is useful for automatic and rapid feeding of the data.

The DMA technique is useful for fast devices that require low latency. This technique has the lowest latency and the greatest throughput, but can only store data in a buffer or read data from a buffer. A variation of it, context switching, is almost as fast as DMA and is almost as flexible as the interrupt technique.

With these various techniques, the designer has the opportunity to pick one that suits his application. This chapter has shown how simple and flexible these techniques are.

Problems

Note

Problems 1, 7, 11, and 21 are paragraph-correction problems. Refer to the guidelines in the problem section of chapter 1 for these problems. Guidelines for software problems are also given at the end of chapter 1, and those for hardware problems at the end of chapter 2.

1. *Synchronization is used to coordinate a computer to an input/output device. The device has busy, completion, and done states. It is in the busy state when data can be given to it, or taken from it. The device puts itself into the done state when it has completed its action that was requested by the computer. A paper tape punch, by analogy to the paper tape reader, is in the idle state when it is not in use, in the busy state when it is punching a pattern that corresponds to the word that was output just before the done state was entered, and in the done state when the pattern has been punched. The busy state and the idle states are indistinguishable in an output device like this one unless error conditions are to be recognized (in the idle state). An address trigger will generate a pulse whenever an address is generated. Its output should never be asserted if valid memory address (VMA) is false, nor when the E clock is high. Address triggers are often used to start a device or to indicate completion by the device.

2. Design an address trigger that asserts its output (low) whenever the location $3FOA is read from, and only at that time. (a) Show the logic diagram. (b) Indicate the timing of the output (as on an oscilloscope trace) if an instruction INC $3FOA is executed. Show the signal for the complete execution of the instruction, and show timing marks indicating the beginning of each memory cycle (which is one microsecond per memory cycle).

3. A 74LS74 dual D flip-flop is to store the busy-done states of a device. Show a logic diagram, including address triggers, that will start the device if address $5A31 is presented, stop it if address $4D21 is presented, and enter the done state if an input signal CMPLT rises from low to high. Assume that idle is FF, busy is TF, and done is coded as FT. (Hint: use CMPLT to clock the 74LS74 flip-flops as a shift register to change the state from busy to done.)

4. Show the initialization ritual to configure an M6821 at locations $8000 (data/direction) and $8001 (control) so the data register is an input register for the following cases: (a) IRQA1 is set when CA1 rises, CA2 outputs a low signal, and IRQA is never asserted. (b) IRQA1 is set when CA1 rises, IRQA2 is set when CA2 falls, and IRQA is asserted only when IRQA1 is set. (c) IRQA1 is set when CA1 falls, IRQA2 is set when CA2 rises, and

IRQA is asserted when either IRQA1 or IRQA2 is set. (d) IRQA1 is set when CA1 rises, CA2 pulses low when location $8000 is read, and IRQA is asserted when IRQA1 is set. (e) IRQA1 is set when CA1 falls, CA2 falls when CA1 falls and rises when $8000 is read, and IRQA is never asserted.

5. Note that the M6821 sets its IRQA1 input on a rising edge or a falling edge of the CA1 input, rather than on a level. Design an input device using the A device in an M6821 that will cause an interrupt on a high level, and another that will cause an interrupt on a low level signal. For each case, show the logic diagram and an initialization ritual that will set IRQA1 if that high or low level signal appears. Be careful to satisfy the set-up and hold times of the IRQA1 flip-flop.

6. Suppose IRQB is connected to a pull-up resistor and channel one of a dual-trace oscilloscope, while CB2 is connected to channel two. Show an oscilloscope trace of the signals that will appear after CB1 causes IRQB1 to be set, assuming the B device is configured as an output device in the handshake mode, as the following program segment is executed (Be accurate to within a memory cycle, and show each instruction execution interval next to your traces.):

```
LDX     POINT
LDA     ,X+
STA     $8002
LDA     $8002
STX     POINT
```

7.* The real-time synchronization technique uses the microcomputer E clock as a timing reference and the program counter as a kind of frequency divider to time the duration of external actions. This technique uses the least amount of hardware because the program itself contains segments that keep account of the busy-done state of the device. It is easy to program, and to change a program without upsetting the synchronization because program segments execute in the same time regardless of the instructions in the segment. But for no good reason, computer scientists abhor real-time synchronization, so it should never be used, even on a microcomputer dedicated to a single control function. Real-time synchronization cannot be used to synchronize error conditions, because we cannot predict the time until the next error. That is why the program REAL (section 4-2.1) did not include an error handler. Gadfly synchronization requires the hardware to keep track of the state of a device, and the program watches the outputs from this hardware. It is therefore possible to use feedback from the device so that an I/O operation can be completed as soon as possible. Nevertheless, real-time synchronization is always faster than gadfly synchronization because the former is always timed for the minimum time to complete an action in the device.

8. Write a program to punch $80 words from the buffer at location OUTBUF onto paper tape, the first word (at lowest address) punched first on the tape. Assume $8002 is the data/direction register and $8003 is the control register of a B device of an M6821, with PB connected to the hardware that punches a pattern of holes and CB2 connected to a motor that advances the paper. Use real-time synchronization, assuming the E clock rate is one megahertz and the hole punches have to be pulsed high for ten milliseconds to punch a hole, and the CB2 has to then be low for ninety milliseconds to advance the paper.

9. Write a program to output eight signals through an eight-bit output register, outputting an entire $80-word buffer each time a rising edge signal appears on a signal TM. The buffer will be read out one word at a time, outputting the next word every 100 microseconds. Use real-time synchronization to output the steady stream of words after the gadfly loop finds the edge of TM. Assume the B device at locations $8002 and $8003 is used, and that the rising edge signal on the CB1 input is sensed by the gadfly loop. (This routine could be used to turn on incandescent lamps controlled by a triac, as discussed in the next chapter.)

10. Write an SWI2 handler to input a word from location $8000 or output a word to location $8002 of an M6821, depending on the argument in the argument list below the SWI2 instruction. The sequence:

<pre>
                    SWI2
                    FCB   0
</pre>

will input a word, putting it into accumulator A so it can be used by the calling routine after the "call," and

<pre>
                    SWI2
                    FCB   1
</pre>

will output the word that was in accumulator A. Use a transfer vector, as described in section 1-2.2 in the discussion of SWI "subroutines" to execute the appropriate routine, and use a gadfly loop before inputting or outputting the word to check if the device is not busy. Since SWI2 does not alter the interrupt mask bits, you must do so by an ORCC instruction to use a gadfly loop safely. (This type of SWI handler is commonly used to call all the I/O "subroutines" from a high level language program.)

11.* Interrupts permit the computer to perform some useful function while waiting for a device to become busy, or for an error condition to arise. Interrupts are always faster than a simple gadfly loop because they save the state of the machine and restore it, while the gadfly technique has to loop a long time. When an external device requests an interrupt, if the device is enabled, the interrupt request flip-flop is set. Then, if the device is not disabled, the IRQ output is asserted (high). This signal could be used to light a lamp to signal an error, or it can be connected to the M6809 IRQ pin. When this signal is seen low by the M6809, it immediately honors the interrupt, saving the values in all output registers on the stack, and jumping directly to a handler routine. The handler may have just an RTS instruction to return to the program that was originally running. Vectored interrupts use external hardware to eliminate the polling routine in the device handler, so that the interrupt handler can be executed immediately. Interrupts, and vectored interrupts in particular, should be used whenever the latency requirement is critically small or something useful can be done while waiting for an interrupt, otherwise, real-time or gadfly synchronization should be used.

12. Complete the remainder of the output from a logic analyzer that would appear the first time the interrupt handler TPRDR is executed, as it was shown in section 4-2.2 below the program TPRDR. Show what happens in each memory cycle until the main program is resumed and one BRA instruction is executed in it.

13. At the end of chapter 3, you may have worked a problem to build an address comparator that checks for breakpoints. In this problem, you can design the rest of the system. The CA2 output will be compared against the R/W signal so that you can distinguish between a write into a location and a read from it. The signal CMP is high when the address matches the two words in the data registers and R/W matches the CA2 output; this signal is put into the CA1 input. Write a program to interrupt when the machine writes a word to location $0025, and jump to a monitor program (do not write the interrupt handler, which is the monitor program).

14. The interrupt handler IRQHND at the end of section 4-2.2 could use a general subroutine CHK21 to check for interrupts in one of the devices of an M6821. It would be called thus:

```
BSR   CHK21
FDB   LOC21
FDB   ADDR1
FDB   ADDR2
```

and it would jump to a device handler at location ADDRA if IRQA1 (or IRQB1) of the device whose data/direction register is at location LOC21 requested an interrupt, and to ADDR2 if IRQA2 (or IRQB2) requested an interrupt but IRQA1 (or IRQB1) did not. (Note that this subroutine checks only the A device or the B device, but must be executed twice to check both devices.) Write this subroutine, and then rewrite the handler IRQHND using this subroutine. Then compare the program length and execution time for both versions, assuming that the lowest priority interrupt handler is to be executed and that the E clock rate is one megahertz.

15. Write a round-robin IRQ handler that replaces the handler IRQHND at the end of section 4-2.2.

16. Assume that the IRQ handler in the IRQHND program (section 4-2.2) is now an NMI handler, and that the program at location HNDLA1 is to do the same thing for a paper tape reader as the program segment TPRDR. Write the NMI handler and the device handler HNDLA1.

17. Show the logic diagram of an M6809, an M6821, and a (32,8) ROM to implement vectored interrupts. If IRQA1 is asserted, the interrupt handler at addresses eight and nine of this ROM is to be executed, but if IRQA2 is asserted, the handler at addresses $18 and $19 are to be executed. All other handler addresses are duplicated, so for instance the RESET handler address is in $E, $F as well as $1E,$1F. Show all connections between the M6809, the M6821, and the ROM, and implement all other functions using positive logic two-input NAND gates.

18. Rewrite the program INTERS in section 4-3 so that input words are handled using gadfly synchronization, but errors are recognized by an interrupt. Show the entire program, including the RESET handler.

19. Rewrite the program INTERS in section 4-3 so that input words are handled using the FIRQ line and handler, while errors are handled by the IRQ line and handler. Show the entire program, including the RESET handler. (Hint: you will have to save and restore any registers you use.)

20. Rewrite the gadfly and interrupt synchronization programs to use the special CWAI and SYNC instructions. (a) Write a gadfly synchronization routine that does the same thing as the program GADFLY (section 4-2.1) but use the SYNC instruction in place of the gadfly loop. Compute the maximum rate at which words can be input using the original program, and using the modified program. (b) Write an interrupt synchronization program for a single IRQ interrupt, such as the TPDRD, using the CWAI instruction. Show the initialization ritual and the CWAI instruction in place of the wait loop as well as the IRQ handler. Compute the latency from when the external interrupt is requested until the word is picked up from the input register for the original program and for the program that uses the CWAI instruction.

21.* Direct memory access is a synchronization technique that uses an extra processor that is able to move words from a device to memory or vice versa. When an output device is able to output another word, it will assert a request to the DMA chip, which checks its busy-done state, and if it is done it requests that the M6809 stop and release control of R/W and of the address and data bus. The M6809 will send a signal to the DMA chip when it has released control, the DMA chip will output on the data bus and will send a signal to the I/O device to put a signal on the R/W line and an address on the address bus. The device must also negate the line to the DMA chip when it receives the word to be output. A DMA chip itself is an I/O device, whose busy state corresponds to the fact that a buffer full of data has been moved. The busy state then is an interrupt request. Either gadfly or interrupt synchronization can be used to start a program when the buffer has been moved.

22. Show the block diagram (similar to figure 4-9, but ignoring negative logic) of a DMA system using an M6844 controller and an M6821 whose B device will be used to output words, punching them on paper tape. Show also the initialization ritual like DMASET that will cause the words in the buffer BUFFER to be punched on tape.

23. Show the block diagram (similar to figure 4-10) and the reset handler that can set up an M6809 and an M6800 on the same data and address bus to implement context switching. Then show a program segment that will call a "subroutine" in the M6800 from the M6809, and a program segment that will call a "subroutine" in the M6809 from the M6800. In both cases, the calling routine simply turns on the other processor at an address SUB (stored as a global variable) and turns itself off, so that when it is turned back on it merely executes the next instruction. The other processor will load the address of SUB into its program counter and execute the program there as a conventional subroutine. The subroutine will execute an RTS instruction, which is supposed to jump to a program segment to turn on the other processor. Finally, to maintain order, the value in the M6800 stack pointer when the M6800 is started or stopped should be one minus the value in the M6809 stack pointer when the M6809 is stopped or started. Use a global variable STKPNT to transfer the stack pointer between processors.

5

Analog Interfacing

Analog circuits are commonly used to interconnect the I/O device to the "outside world." This chapter will focus on such circuits as are commonly used in microcomputer I/O systems. In it we will assume the reader has only a basic knowledge of physics, including mechanics and basic electrical properties. While many of our readers have far more, some, who have been working as programmers, may not. This chapter especially aims to provide them with adequate background to study I/O systems.

Before different analog components are discussed, some basic notions of analog signals should be reviewed. In an *analog* signal, voltage or current levels convey information by real number values, like 3.1263 volts, rather than by H or L values. In *sinusoidal alternating current* (AC), signal voltage or current has the form $A \times \sin(P + 2 \times \text{pi} \times F \times t)$ as a function of time t, where the amplitude A, the phase P and the frequency F can carry information. One of the most useful techniques in analog system analysis is to decompose any *periodic* (that is, repetitive) waveform into a sum of sinusoidal signals and to determine how the system transmits each component signal. The *bandwidth* of the system is the range of frequencies that it transmits faithfully (not decreasing the signal by a factor of 0.707 of what it should be).

Two kinds of analog signals are important. These correspond to AM and FM radio signals. In this chapter, we consider analog signals, where the amplitude carries the value whether the signal is a direct current or an alternating current signal, as AM radio signals carry the sound. In the next chapter, we consider analog signals where the frequency or phase carries the value of the signal, as FM radio signals carry the sound. Amplitude analog signals are more pervasive in interface design. It is hard to find examples of interface hardware that do not have some analog circuitry (and we had to search long and hard to find some decent problems for chapter 3 that did not have analog circuits in them). It is even hard to discuss frequency analog circuits without first discussing amplitude analog circuits. So we discuss amplitude analog circuits in this chapter and frequency analog circuits in chapter 6.

Analog signals are converted to digital signals by *analog-to-digital converters* (A-to-D converters), and digital signals are converted to analog by *digital-to-analog converters* (D-to-A converters) such that the digital signal, usually a binary or binary coded decimal number, corresponds in numerical value to the analog signal level. Analog signals are also converted to a single digital bit (H or L) by a *comparator*, and digital signals control analog signals by means of *analog switches*. The frequency of an AC signal can be converted to or from a voltage by a *voltage-to-frequency converter* (V-to-F converter) or by a *frequency-to-voltage converter* (F-to-V converters). Finally, analog signals are generated by *transducers* that change other measurements into voltages or currents, such as temperature-to voltage-transducers, which are amplified and modified by *operational amplifiers* (OP AMPs).

A basic theme of this chapter is that many functions can be done using digital hardware or using analog hardware or using software. The smart designer has to chose among the alternatives to pick the best technique to implement a particular function. Thus, the designer should know a little about analog circuitry. On one hand, a basic understanding of the operation and use of analog devices is essential in making intelligent hardware-software tradeoffs and is quite useful even for programmers who write code to interface to such devices, so we want to include the required material in this chapter. On the other hand, one can devote an entire year's study to these devices in order to use them well. We have to refrain from that much detail. Therefore we will aim at the level of detail that one should have to make good hardware-software tradeoffs in the design of microprocessor-analog systems and encourage those who seek more detail to read some of the many excellent books that are devoted to the topic of analog signal processing.

In the following sections, we will discuss conversion of physical quantities to voltages and from voltages, the basics of operational amplifiers, their use in signal conditioning and keyboard/display systems, digital-to-analog conversion, analog-to-digital conversion, and data acquisition systems. Much of the material is hardware oriented, and is qualitative; however, we do discuss in some detail the use of the CA3140 operational amplifier and the 4066 and 4051 analog switches to make the discussion concrete. Some practical construction information will be introduced as well. The reader might wish to try out some of the examples to gain a firm understanding of the principles being discussed.

This chapter should provide sufficient background on the analog part of a typical microcomputer I/O system. The reader should be aware of the capabilities and limitations of analog components used in I/O, and he should be able to write programs that can accommodate them.

5-1 Input and Output Transducers

A *transducer* changes a physical quantity, like temperature, to or from another quantity, often a voltage. Such a transducer enables a microcomputer that can measure or produce a voltage or an AC wave to measure or control other physical quantities. Each physical property will be discussed in turn—position, radiant energy, temperature, and pressure—and for each we will examine the transducers that change electrical signals into these properties and then those that change these properties into electrical signals.

About 90 percent of the physical quantities measured are positional. The position may be linear (distance) or angular (degrees of a circle or number of rotations of a shaft). Of course, linear position can be converted to angular position by a rack and pinion gear arrangement. Also, recall that position, speed, and acceleration are related by differential equations: if one can be measured at several precise times the others can be determined.

A microcomputer controls position by means of *solenoids* or *motors*. A *solenoid* is an electromagnet with an iron plunger. As current through the electromagnet is increased, an increased force pulls the plunger into its middle. The solenoid usually acts against a spring. When current is not applied to the solenoid, the spring pulls the plunger from the middle of the solenoid, and when current is applied, the plunger is pulled into the solenoid. Solenoids are designed to be operated with either direct current or alternating current and are usually specified for a maximum voltage (which implies a maximum current) that can be applied and for the pulling force that is produced when this maximum voltage (current) is applied. A solenoid is an inductor which causes problems in microcomputers. When current is suddenly changed in an inductor a large, sharp voltage spike is generated, which radiates noise to the microcomputor causing errors. A *direct current motor* has a pair of input terminals and a rotating shaft. The (angular) speed of the shaft is proportional to the voltage applied to the terminals (when the motor is running without being loaded), and the (angular) force or torque is proportional to the current. Direct current motors are also inductors, causing electrical noise. A *stepping motor* looks like a motor, but actually works like a collection of solenoids. When one of the solenoids gets current, it pulls the shaft into a given (angular) position. When another solenoid gets current, it pulls the shaft into another position. By spacing these solenoids evenly around the stepping motor, and by giving each solenoid its current in order, the shaft can be rotated a precise amount each time the next solenoid is given its current. Hence the term stepping motor. The *universal motor* can be given either direct current or alternating current power. Most home appliances use these inexpensive motors. Their speed, however, is very much dependent on the force required to turn the load that the motor is running. *Shaded pole motors* require alternating current, and their shaft speed is proportional to the frequency of the AC power rather than to its voltage. The torque is proportional to the current. These inexpensive motors often appear in electric clocks, timers, and fans. *Induction motors* are AC motors of usually greater power and their speed is proportional to frequency like the shaded pole motor. Finally, the *hysteresis synchronous motor* is an AC motor whose speed is accurately synchronized to the frequency of the AC power. These are used to control the speed of hi-fi turntables and tape decks.

In inexpensive systems, linear position or angular position is usually converted into a resistance, which determines a voltage level in a voltage divider circuit, or which determines a frequency of some kind of RC oscillator. A *potentiometer* converts angular position to resistance. A *slide potentiometer* converts linear position to resistance. See figure 5-1a. Both transducers are inexpensive but are prone to inaccuracy as the wiper arm in the potentiometer wears down the resistor or as a coat of dirt or oil builds up on the resistor. Also, these transducers are sensitive to vibration. Overall accuracy is limited to about 3 percent. Minute position displacements can be measured by piezo-electric crystals, such as in commercial *strain gauges*—a crystal phono cartridge uses the same mechanism. See figure 5-1b. The angular position of a disk can be converted directly into a digital signal by a *shaft encoder*, which uses a mechanical wiper or photodetector to read a track on the disk, the track being layed out so that the wiper or detector reads a digital word corresponding to the angle of rotation of the disk. See figure 5-1c. Also, a pair of wipers or detectors can sense the teeth of a gear or gear-like disk to count the teeth as the gear turns. See figure 5-1d. Two wipers are needed to determine both the motion and the direction of motion of the teeth. Finally, the most accurate and reliable position transducer is the *linear variable displacement transformer*. See figure 5-1e. In this device, a transformer having a primary winding and two secondary windings has a movable slug. As the slug moves, the two secondary windings of the transformer get more or less alternating current from the primary winding, and the relative phase of the sine waves output from the windings changes. Either the voltage level of the resultant sine wave, or the relative phase difference between the sine waves, may be used to sense the position of the slug. The linear variable displacement transformer is the most accurate device for measuring linear distances because it is not affected by dirt, wear, or vibration as are other devices, but it is the most expensive. Angular position can be measured by a *control transformer* using the same kind of technique. See figure 5-1f. This device has a primary coil in a rotor that can be turned by a shaft, and secondary windings in the housing that surrounds the rotor and is held stationary. The angular position of the rotor of such a device determines the amplitude and phase of a sine wave that is picked up by the secondaries of the transformer.

Velocity and acceleration can be determined by measuring position by means of one of the transducers above and differentiating the values in software or by means of an electrical circuit that differentiates the voltage. A *direct current tachometer* is a direct current generator. This is an inverse of

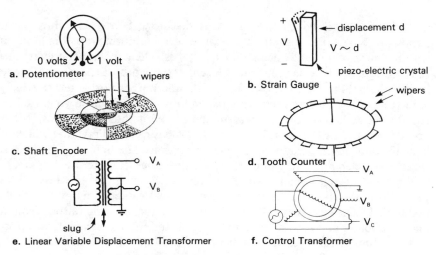

a. Potentiometer

0 volts   1 volt

wipers

b. Strain Gauge

+
V
−

displacement d

V ~ d

piezo-electric crystal

c. Shaft Encoder

d. Tooth Counter

wipers

e. Linear Variable Displacement Transformer

V_A
V_B

slug

f. Control Transformer

V_A
V_B
V_C

Figure 5-1. Position Transducers

a DC motor: its output voltage is porportional to the rotational speed of the shaft. An AC *tachometer* is an AC motor run as a generator: its output frequency is proportional to the (angular) speed of its shaft. Finally, acceleration can also be measured by producing a force F as a mass m is accelerated at rate a ($F = m \times a$), letting the force act against a spring, then measuring the displacement of the spring. This type of device, an *accelerometer*, can convert the acceleration into a position using mechanical techniques in order to measure acceleration at the output of the transducer. This is an alternative to measuring position and then using software to differentiate the values to determine acceleration. Conversely, an accelerometer can be used to measure acceleration, which can be integrated by a software program to derive velocity or integrated twice to get position. This is the basis of an inertial guidance system. This example shows that functions can be obtained by means of mechancial or electrical hardware, or by software methods, or by a combination of all three.

Radiant energy, light and infra red, can be produced or controlled by a microprocessor using lamps, *light emitting diodes* (LEDs), and *liquid crystal displays* (LCDs). The terms used for light and infrared radiant energy are those defined for radio waves. In a continuous wave (CW) or pulse coded mode (PCM), the radiant energy is either on (high) or off (low). In an amplitude modulated mode (AM), the amplitude of the radiation varies with a signal that carries analog information. In a frequency modulated mode (FM), the frequency varies with an analog signal. The common incandescent lamp is lit by applying a voltage across its terminals. The radiant energy is mostly uniformly distributed over the light spectrum, and includes infrared energy too. Gas discharge lamps and fluorescent lamps work in similar fashion, but require current limiting resistors in series with the lamp and usually need higher voltages. Their radiant energy is confined to specific wavelengths which are determined by the material in the lamp. While these are sometimes used with microprocessors, their relatively high voltage and current requirements, and the electrical noise generated by gas discharge lamps and fluorescent lamps, limit their usefulness. More popular are the LEDs and LCDs. An LED is basically a diode that will emit light if about ten milliamperes is sent through it. The light is generated in specific wavelengths: red and infrared are the easiest to generate, but green, yellow, and orange are also widely available. Passing current through an LED drops about 1.7 to 2.3 volts across the LED, depending on the diode material. LEDs are often used in displays to indicate some output from a microcomputer and are also used in communications systems to carry information. Inexpensive LEDs can be pulse modulated at better than ten-kilohertz frequencies, and special ones can work at frequencies on the order of a gigahertz. An LCD is electrically a capacitor that is clear if the (rms) voltage across it is less than about a volt, and is opaque if above about two volts. The voltage across an LCD must be AC, however, because DC will polarize and destroy the material in the LCD. Usually, one terminal has a square wave signal. If the other terminal has a square wave signal in phase with the first, the display is clear, and if it has a square wave signal out of phase with the first, the display is opaque. LCDs consume very little power, and are therefore very well suited to microcomputers.

Radiant energy is often measured in industrial control systems. A *photodetector* converts the amplitude to a voltage or resistance, for a given bandwidth of the very high frequency sine wave carrier. Often this bandwidth covers part of the visible spectrum and/or part of the infrared spectrum. The *photomultiplier* can measure energy down to the photon, the smallest unit of radiation, and has an amplification of about one million; however, it requires a regulated high voltage power supply. The *photodiode* is a semiconductor photodetector able to handle signals carried on the amplitude of the radiant energy on the order of ten megaHertz. The current through the diode is linearly proportional to the radiation if the voltage drop across it is kept small. This is done by external circuitry. It is inefficient, however: a unit of radiant energy produces 0.001 units of electrical energy. A photodiode might be used in a communication linkage to carry a signal on a light beam because of its high bandwidth and ease of use with integrated circuits. If the diode is built into a transistor, a *phototransistor* is made that relates about one unit of electrical energy to one unit of radiant energy, but the signal carried on the amplitude is reproduced up to about 100 kilohertz. Finally, a *photoresistor* is a device whose resistance varies as the intensity of the light shone upon it. While this device is also temperature sensitive, has poor frequency response, and is quite nonlinear, it can be used to isolate a triac as we discuss later.

Photodiodes, phototransistors, photoresistors, and other detectors are often used with LEDs or lamps to sense the position of objects, or to isolate an external system from the microcomputer. Photodetectors are commonly used with an LED light source to detect the presence or absence of an object between the light source and the photodetector. A shaft encoder or tooth counter can use this kind of sensor in place of a mechanical contact to sense the pattern on the disc under the contacts. Similar techniques place an LED and a phototransistor inside an integrated circuit package, called an *opto-isolator*, to isolate the circuitry driving the LED from the circuitry connected to the detector so that they can be kilovolts apart, and so that electrical noise in the driver circuitry is not transmitted to the detector circuitry.

Temperature is controlled by means of heaters or air conditioners. To control the temperature of a small component, such as a crystal, the component is put in an *oven*, which has a resistive heater and is fairly well insulated. As more current is passed through the heater, it produces more heat; as less current is passed, the natural loss of heat through the insulated walls brings down the temperature. The temperature of a large room or building is controlled by means of a furnace or air conditioner, of course. Since these usually require AC power at high currents and voltages, the microcomputer has to control a large AC current. An interesting problem in controlling air conditioners is due to the back pressure built up in them. If the air conditioner has just been running, is then turned off, and is quickly turned on, the motor in it will stall because it cannot overcome the back pressure in it. So if a controller turns an air conditioner off, it must not turn it on again for an interval of time long enough for the back pressure to drop off.

Temperature is often sensed in a microprocessor system. Very high temperatures are measured indirectly by measuring the infrared radiation they emit. Temperatures in the range from -250 degrees centigrade to $+1000$ degrees centigrade can be measured by a *thermocouple*, which is a pair of dissimilar metals (iron and constantan, for instance), where the voltage developed between the metals is on the order of 0.04 millivolts times the temperature. Note that such a low level signal requires careful handling and amplification before it can be used in a microprocessor system. The most popular technique for measuring temperatures around room temperature is to put a constant current through a diode (or the diode in the emitter junction of a bipolar transistor) and measure the voltage across it. The output voltage is typically 2.2 millivolts times the temperature in degrees Kelvin. This voltage level requires some amplification before conversion to digital values are feasible. Provided the current through the diode is held constant (by a constant current source), the transducer is accurate to within 0.1 degrees Kelvin. While a common diode or transistor can be used, a number of integrated circuits have been offered that combine a transistor and constant current source and amplifier. One of these (AD590) has just two pins and regulates the current through it to be one microampere times the temperature in Kelvin. Converting to and transmitting a current has the advantage that voltage drops in wires where the sensor is a long distance from the microprocessor or from switches that may have unknown resistance do not affect the current. The current is converted to a voltage simply by passing it through a resistor. Finally, temperature can be sensed by a temperature sensitive resistor called a *thermistor*. Thermistors are quite nonlinear and have poor frequency responses, but relatively large changes in their resistance result from small changes in temperature.

A microcomputer usually produces pressure as an indirect result of some other activity. For instance, by controlling the position of a valve, it can control the flow of liquid into a system, which changes the pressure in it. Pressure is also sometimes measured. Usually, the pressure positions a diaphram, and the position of the diaphram is measured. While this can be implemented with separate components, a complete system using a National Semiconductor chip in the LX3700 series of chips can measure absolute pressure or relative pressure to within one percent accuracy. These marvelous devices contain the diaphram, strain gauge position sensor, and compensation circuits for temperature and output amplifier on a hybrid integrated circuit. Weight is normally measured by the pressure that gravity generates. The device, called a *load cell*, is essentially a piston. Objects are weighed by putting them on top of the piston, and the pressure of the fluid inside the piston is measured.

Other properties are sometimes measured. These include chemical composition and concentration, the *p*H of liquids, and so on. A discussion of these transducers, however, goes beyond the scope of this introductory survey.

5-2 Basic Analog Processing Components

Basic analog devices include power amplifiers, operational amplifiers, analog switchers, and the timer module. These will be discussed in this section. The first subsection discusses transistors and SCRs, the next discusses OP AMPs and analog switches in general, and the last discusses practical OP AMPs and analog switches.

5-2.1 Transistors and Silicon-Controlled Rectifiers

In order to convert a voltage or current to some other property like position or temperature an amplifier is needed to provide enough power to run a motor or a heater. We briefly survey the common power amplifier devices that are often used with microcomputers. These include power transistors, Darlington transistors, and VFETs for control of direct current devices (motors, heaters, and the like), and SCRs and triacs for control of alternating current devices.

The *(bipolar) transistor* is a device with terminals called the collector, base, and emitter. See figure 5-2a. The collector current I_c is a constant (called the *beta*) times the base current I_b. The *power transistor* can be obtained in various capacities, able to handle up to a hundred amperes, and up to a thousand volts. These are most commonly used for control of direct current devices. A *Darlington transistor* has a pair of simple transistors connected internally so that it appears as a single transistor having very high beta. See figure 5-2b. Power Darlington transistors require less base current I_b to drive a given load, so they are often used with microprocessor I/O chips that have limited current output. *Field effect transistors* (FETs) can be used in place of the more conventional (bipolar) transistor. In an FET, the current flowing from drain to source is proportional to the voltage from gate to source. See figure 5-2c. A *vertical field effect transistor* (VFET) is faster than a standard FET and can withstand larger voltages (about 200 volts) between drain and source. The VFET is therefore a superb output amplifier that is most compatible with microcomputers. Suffice it to say for this survey, a power transistor, a Darlington, or a VFET is usually required to drive a direct current device like a motor or heater or lamp.

An alternating current device like an AC motor uses a *silicon controlled rectifier* (SCR) or a *triac* to amplify the voltage or control signal output from a microcomputer. The SCR has anode, cathode, and gate terminals, as in figure 5-2d. When sufficient current I_g (about fifty milliamperes) flows into the gate through the anode, the device looks like a diode, passing positive current from anode to cathode but inhibiting flow from cathode to

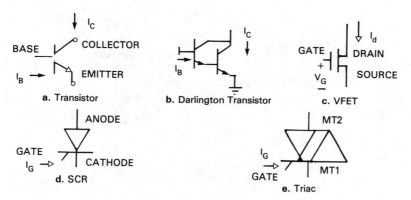

Figure 5-2. Power-Output Devices

anode. That is why it is called a controlled rectifier, since rectifier is an older name for a diode. The SCR has memory, moreover: once turned on, it remains on regardless of the current through the gate, until the current through the anode tries to reverse itself and is thus turned off. The gate controls only half a cycle, since the SCR is always turned off for the half cycle when current tries to go from cathode to anode but cannot do so, and it is turned on only when the gate is given enough current during which time the current will then flow from anode to cathode. To correct this defficiency, a pair of SCRs are effectively connected "back to back" to form a triac. (See figure 5-2e). The power current flows through main terminal 1 (MT1) and main terminal 2 (MT2) under the control of the current through the gate and MT1. If the gate current is higher than about fifty milliamperes, either into or out of the gate, MT1 appears shorted to MT2, and the short circuit remains regardless of the current through the gate until the current through MT1 and MT2 passes through zero. Otherwise, MT1 and MT2 appear disconnected. SCRs and triacs handle currents from half an ampere up to 1000 amperes, and can control voltages beyond 800 volts.

SCRs and triacs control motors, heaters, and the like by controlling the percentage of a cycle, or the number of cycles, during which full power is applied to them. The types of control are discussed below in terms of triacs, but these also apply to SCRs.

In *on-off* control, or *"bang-bang"* control, the triac applies either full power or no power to the motor. To do this, either full current or no current is applied to the gate. A simple variation of this technique applies gate current from MT2 through a resistor so that if the resistance is low when voltage on MT2 begins to build up current flows through the resistor to turn on the triac. See figure 5-3a. As soon as the triac is turned on, however, the

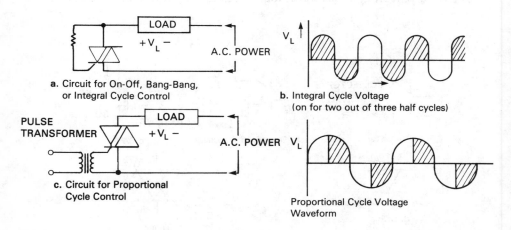

a. Circuit for On-Off, Bang-Bang, or Integral Cycle Control

b. Integral Cycle Voltage (on for two out of three half cycles)

c. Circuit for Proportional Cycle Control

Proportional Cycle Voltage Waveform

Figure 5-3. Triac Control Techniques

voltage on MT2 disappears. Thus, the current through the resistor stops as soon as it has done its work. This reduces the power dissipated in the resistor. If the resistance is large, no current flows through the gate, so the triac is off. The resistor can be a photoresistor coupled to an incandescent lamp or an LED in an optocoupler. When the LED or lamp is lit, the photoresistor has a low resistance, which turns the triac on. Otherwise the resistance is high and the triac is off. This configuration is particularly suited to on-off control of large AC loads by means of triacs.

A close cousin to on-off control is *integral cycle control*. Here, the triac is turned on for *n* out of every *m* half cycles. See figure 5-3b. The gate current has to be turned on at the beginning of each half cycle when the triac is supposed to be on. A final variation is called *proportional cycle control*. A pulse generator of some kind is commonly used to send a current pulse through the gate at a precise time in each half cycle. See figure 5-3c. For a fraction *F* of each half cycle, the triac is turned on. See figure 5-3d. Full power is applied to the device for the last *F*th of the cycle. Roughly speaking, the device gets power proportional to the fraction *F*. A pulse transformer is often used to isolate the controller from the high voltages in the triac circuitry. See figure 5-3c. The controller provides a short (five-microsecond) voltage pulse across the primary winding (shown on the left) of the transformer, which provides a current pulse to the triac to turn it on. The controller has to provide this pulse at the same time in each half cycle. The earlier the pulse, the more current flows through the triac, and the more power goes to the load.

On-off control is used where the microprocessor simply turns a device on or off. A traffic light would be thus controlled. Bang-bang control is commonly used in heating systems. You set your thermostat to seventy degrees. If the temperature is below seventy degrees, the heater is turned on fully, if above seventy degrees, the heater is completely off. Integral cycle control is useful in electric ranges, for instance, to provide some control over the amount of heating. Finally, variable duty cycle control is common in controlling lighting and power tools, since the other types of control would cause the light to flicker perceptibly or the tool to chatter. This type of control, however, generates a lot of electrical noise whenever the triac is turned on fully in the middle of a half cycle. This kind of noise interferes with the microcomputer and any communications linkages to and from it, so variable duty cycle control is normally used only when the other forms generate too much flicker or chatter.

5-2.2 Basic Linear Integrated Circuits

The basic module that is used to process analog signals is the operational amplifier, or OP AMP. It is used in several important configurations, which we will discuss below. We will then discuss the analog switch, which allows convenient microprocessor control of analog signals, and we will consider several important applications of this switch.

The OP AMP has two inputs labeled " + " and " − " and an output. See figure 5-4. The output voltage signal V_o is related to the signals V_+ on the " + " input and V_- on the " − " input by the expression

$$V_o = A \times (V_+ - V_-)$$

where A is a rather large number, such as 100,000. The OP AMP is in the *linear mode* if the output voltage is within the range of the positive and negative supply voltages, otherwise it is in the *saturated mode* of operation. Clearly, to be in the linear mode, V_+ has to be quite near V_-.

The first use of the OP AMP is as an *inverting amplifier*. Here, the " + " input is essentially connected to ground, so V_+ is zero, and *feedback* is used to force V_- to zero volts so that the OP AMP is in the linear mode. In figure 5-4a, if V_{in} increases by one volt, the V_- will increase by a small amount, so that the output V_o will decrease 100,000 times this amount, which is large enough to force V_- back to zero. In fact, V_o will have to be

$$V_o = -(R_f/R_i) \times V_{in}$$

in order to force V_- to zero. The *amplification* of this circuit, the ratio V_o/V_{in}, is exactly R_f/R_i, which can be selected by the designer as needed. In a slight modification to this circuit, one or more inputs having signals V_{in1}, V_{in2}, . . . , can be connected by means of resistors R_{in1}, R_{in2}, . . . , as in figure 5-4 b. The output voltage is then

$$V_o = -(((R_f/R_{in1}) \times V_{in1}) + (R_f/R_{in2}) \times V_{in2}) + ...)$$

in a circuit called a *summing amplifier*.

Another classical use of an OP AMP is for the integration of a signal. The relation of the current i through a capacitor to the voltage v across it is

$$i = C \, dv/dt$$

where C is the capacitance. In figure 5-4c, if V_{in} increases by one volt, then V_o will have to change by one volt per second so the current through the capacitor can offset the current through R_i to force V_- to zero. Generally, the relationship is

$$V_o = V_{ci} - \int_0^t (1/R_i \times C) V_i \, dv/dt$$

where V_{ci} is the voltage across the capacitor at the time we began integrating the input signal.

In the three applications described above, the voltage V_- is forced to zero. V_- is called a *virtual ground*. Of course, it cannot be connected to ground or no current would be available for the OP AMP V_- input. Nevertheless, complex circuits such as amplifiers, integrators, differentiators, and active filters, are analyzed using circuit analysis techniques which assume that V_- is effectively grounded.

A different use of the OP AMP puts the incoming signal on the " + " input, and uses feedback to try to force V_- to the same voltage as V_+. The *voltage follower*, shown in figure 5-4d, does this by connecting V_- to V_o. The noninverting amplifier uses the same principle, as shown if figure 5-4e, and satisfies the relationship

$$V_o = (1 + (R_f/R_i)) \times V_{in}$$

and the output voltage has the same polarity as the input voltage. Combining the ideas underlying the summing amplifier with those of the noninverting amplifier, we have the *differential amplifier* shown in figure 5-4f. One or more inputs such as V_{in1} are connected via resistors like R_{in1} to the " + " input of the OP AMP, and one or more inputs such as V_{in2} are connected via resistors such as R_{in2} to the " − " input of the OP AMP. The output is then

$$V_o = K_1 \times V_{in1} - K_2 \times V_{in2}$$

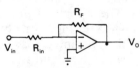

a. Inverting Amplifier

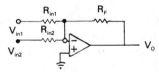

b. Summing Amplifier

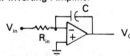

c. Integrator

d. Voltage Follower

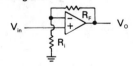

e. Noninverting Amplifier

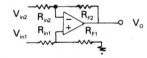

f. Differential Amplifier

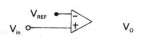

g. Comparator

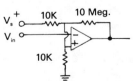

h. Comparator with Hysteresis

Figure 5-4. Operational Amplifier Circuits

where

$$K_1 = (R_{f1}/R_{in1} + R_{f1}) \times (1 + R_{f2}/R_{in2})$$

and

$$K_2 = R_{f2}/R_{in2}$$

In this circuit, if more than one input V_{in} is connected to the "+" OP AMP input via a resistor R_{in}, the term V_{in1} appears to be adding its contribution to V_o: and if an input such as V_{in2} is connected to the "−" input, it subtracts its contribution to V_o.

A final application for the OP AMP is to depend on the finite output range it has using the saturation mode of operation. The comparator has the connections shown in figure 5-4g. Here, the output is a high logical signal, H, if V_{in} is greater than V_{ref}; otherwise, it is L. The comparator can be reversed so that V_{ref} is on the "+" input and V_{in} is on the "−" input. Then V_o is high if V_{in} is less than V_{ref}. Using this variation, the comparator can be made insensitive to small changes in V_{in} due to noise: by connecting the output to V_+ as shown in figure 5-4h, the effective V_{ref} can be changed so it is higher when the output is H than when the output is L, so that the output remains H or L even when the input varies a bit. Suppose, for instance, that the input is low and the output is high. The input must exceed the higher reference before the output goes low. The output remains low until the input drops below the lower reference. When the input finally drops below the lower reference and the output goes high, the input has to exceed the higher reference again, before the output can go low, and so on. This mechanism is called *hysteresis* and is the basis of the *Schmitt trigger* gate used to ignore noise in digital systems.

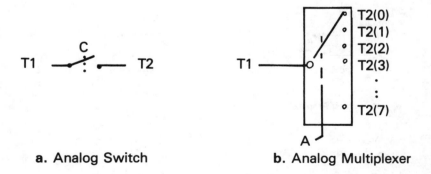

a. Analog Switch   b. Analog Multiplexer

Figure 5-5. General Analog Switches

The analog switch is implemented with field-effect transistors and has a control C, and two terminals T1 and T2. See figure 5-5a. If C is high, T1 is connected to T2 and the switch is said to be *on*; otherwise they are disconnected and the switch is *off*. Some number (eight) of such switches can be connected at the T1 terminal, and a decoder with (three-bit) address A can be on a chip. The Ath switch can be turned on by the decoder, the others being turned off. This chip then behaves like a(n) (eight-position) rotary switch that is controlled by the address input. See figure 5-5b. This kind of chip is an *analog multiplexer*. Single analog switches and analog multiplexers are valuable as ways to control analog signals from a microcomputer.

The final important device is the *timer*. A timer outputs a periodic signal whose period is proportional to the value of a resistor and a capacitor connected to it. (Often, the period can be adjusted by a control voltage, but the voltage-to-frequency converter is generally better.) The timer allows resistor-based transducers to generate AC signals where the information is carried by the frequency (period). Such signals are easy to handle and measure, as we will see in the next chapter.

5-2.3 Practical Linear Integrated Circuits

We now consider an operational amplifier, the CA3140, which is particularly suitable for microprocessors. This device has CMOS inputs, which use almost no current, and has bipolar transistor outputs that can supply plenty of current. Its characteristics are listed in table 5-1, and will be discussed below.

In this book, V_{s+} is the positive supply voltage and V_{s-} is the negative supply voltage. The first two entries in table 5-1 indicate that the total supply voltage may not be greater than thirty-six volts, nor less than four volts. Two very common connections are the *dual supply* where V_{s+} is exactly the negative of V_{s-} (for example, $V_{s+} = +15$ volts, $V_{s-} = -15$ volts) and the *single supply* where either V_{s+} or V_{s-} is zero (for example, $V_{s+} = 5$ volts, $V_{s-} = 0$ volts). A plus or minus fifteen-volt dual supply is useful when almost maximum output voltage range is needed, and a single positive five-volt supply is useful when the only power supply is the one supplying five volts to the logic part of the system. A good OP AMP for microcomputer applications should be capable of operating in either of the above cases. Clearly, both connections are within the specifications listed in the first two rows of table 5-1 for the CA3140. To make the information in the table more concrete, we will consider its significance for a single-ended positive five-volt supply application. The reader is invited to consider the significance of these parameters for a plus or minus five to fifteen-volt dual supply application.

Table 5-1
Characteristics for the CA3140

Characteristic	Value
Maximum $(V_{s+} - V_{s-})$	36 V
Minimum $(V_{s+} - V_{s-})$	4V
Maximum $(V_+$ or $V_-)$	$V_{s+} + 8$
Minimum $(V_+$ or $V_-)$	$V_{s-} - 0.5$
Max common mode input	$V_{s+} - 2.5$
Min common mode input	$V_{s-} - 0.5$
Input resistance	1 T Ω
Input capacitance	4 pF
Input current	2 pA
Input offset voltage	5 mV
Input offset current	0.1 pA
Output resistance	60 Ω
Maximum output voltage	$V_{s+} - 3$ V
Minimum output voltage	$V_{s-} + 0.13$ V
Maximum sourcing current	10 mA
Maximum sinking current	1 mA
Amplification	100,000
Slew rate	7 V/μ s
Gain bandwidth product	3.7 MHz
Transient response	80 ns
Supply current	1.6 mA
Device dissipation	8 mW

The next four entries indicate the range of input voltages. The maximum and minimum values of V_+ and V_- should not be exceeded or the OP AMP may be destroyed. For example, if V_{s+} is five volts and V_{s-} is zero volts, then neither input should have a voltage higher than 13 volts, nor lower than -0.5 volts. The full range of voltages can be used in the saturated mode of operation. This OP AMP has adequate capabilities using a positive five-volt single supply for comparator applications; however, if the linear mode of operation is used, the input voltages should be kept within the maximum and minimum *common mode* voltages. For our previous example, using the same supply voltages, the inputs should be kept within 2.5 volts and -0.5 volts for operation in the linear mode. Note that inputs above 2.5 volts will pull the OP AMP out of the linear mode, and this can be a problem for voltage followers, noninverting amplifiers, or differential amplifiers. However, since the common mode voltage range includes both positive and negative voltages around zero volts, inverting amplifiers, summers and integrators can be built using a single positive five-volt supply. This is a very attractive feature of a modern OP AMP like the CA3140.

The next five lines of the table show the input characteristics that may cause errors. The " + " and " − " inputs appear to be a resistor, a capacitor, and a current source, all in parallel. The equivalent input resistance, one teraohm, is very high. This high input resistance means that a voltage follower or noninverting amplifier can have such high input resistance, which is especially important for measuring the minute currents output from some transducers like pH probes and photodetectors. Moreover, it means that quite large resistors (100,000-ohm) and quite small capacitors (0.01-microfarad) can be used in the circuits discussed earlier without the OP AMP loading down the circuit. Especially when the rest of the system is so miniaturized, larger capacitors are ungainly and costly. The input capacitance, four picofarads, is very low, but can become significant at high frequencies. The current source can cause some error, but is quite high in this OP AMP, and the error can often be ignored. The " + " and " − " inputs have some current flowing from them, which is less than two picoamperes according to the table. If the " + " input is just grounded but the " − " input is connected by a megaohm resistor to ground, this input current causes two microvolts extra, which is multiplied by the amplification (100,000) to produce an error of 0.2 millivolts in V_o. The error due to input current can be minimized by making equal the resistances that connect the " + " and " − " inputs to ground. In figure 5-4a, a resistance equal to R_{in} in parallel with R_f can be connected between the " + " input and ground, just to cancel the effect of the input current of the output voltage; however, this particular OP AMP has such low input current that the error is usually not significant, and the " + " input is connected directly to ground.

The offset voltage is the net voltage that might be effectively applied to either the " + " or the " − " inputs, even when they are grounded. The offset current is the current that can be effectively applied to either input, even when they are disconnected. These offsets have to be counterbalanced to get zero output voltage when no input signal is applied. An *offset adjustment* is available on OP AMPs like the 3140 to cancel the offset voltage and current.

The next five entries describe the output of the OP AMP. The output resistance is the effective resistance in series with the output of the amplifier considered as a perfect voltage source. In this case, it is sixty ohms. A high output resistance limits the OP AMPs ability to apply full power to low resistance loads, such as speakers. The effective output resistance of an amplifier is substantially decreased by feedback, however. The output voltage can swing over a range from 2 volts to 0.13 volts if the power supply V_{s+} is 5 volts and V_{s-} is 0 volts. This means that for linear operation the amplifier can support about a 1.8-volt peak-to-peak output signal, but this signal has to be centered around 1.07 volts. Note that the output range is a serious limitation for a comparator whose output drives a digital input because a high signal is usually any voltage above 2.7 volts. An external (10,000-ohm) pull-up resistor, from the output to positive five volts, can be used such that whenever the OP AMP is not pulling the output low, the output is pulled up to nearly five volts. The output can source (supply) ten milliamperes, and can sink (absorb) one milliampere to the next stage. It can supply quite a bit of current to a transistor or a sensitive gate triac because these devices require current from the output of the OP AMP. However, this OP AMP's limited ability to sink but 1 milliampere, restricts its use to low power (CMOS, LSTTL, microprocessor NMOS) digital inputs, and it cannot sink 1.6 milliamperes reliably as is required to input signals to conventional TTL gates.

Recall that the bandwidth of an amplifier is the range of frequencies over which the gain is at least $1/\sqrt{2}$ times the maximum gain. If the bandwidth of an amplifier is 100,000 hertz, then any small signal sine wave whose frequency is between direct current and 100,000 hertz will be correctly amplified. Moreover, any complex periodic waveform can be decomposed into a sum of sine waves. In order correctly to amplify the waveform, all the component sine waves have to be amplified correctly. (The phase delays also have to be matched for all components.) Generally, a square wave of frequency F will be reproduced fairly accurately if the amplifier bandwidth is at least ten times F.

For most OP AMPs, the bandwidth decreases as the gain increases, so the product is constant. In the 3140, this constant is 3.7 megahertz. That means that if the circuit amplification factor is 1, the bandwidth is 3.7 megahertz. For an OP AMP shown in figure 5-1a with an amplification factor of 10, the bandwidth is 370,000 hertz. The bandwidth is an important limitation on the OP AMP's ability to amplify small high frequency signals. The slew rate is the maximum rate at which the output can change (due to a sudden change on the input). The slew rate usually limits the effective bandwidth of large signals, less than it limits the available bandwidth of small signals, because the output cannot change fast enough. This OP AMP has a very good slew rate: the output can change at a rate of seven volts in one microsecond. The transient response is the time delay between a sudden change in the input and the corresponding change in the output. A related parameter, the *settling time* is the time it takes for the output to reach the desired voltage. It is not specified in the table because it depends on the external component configuration and on what we mean by reaching the desired voltage. The transient response and settling time can be of concern to a programmer if he has to compensate for such delays. In circuits where a digital device interfaces with an OP AMP, the slew rate and transient response may be the limiting factor on the use of the OP AMP.

Finally, the power requirements of the device are given. It dissipates about eight milliwatts when operated using a single five-volt supply, taking 1.6 milliamps from the power supply under normal conditions. It takes about 6 milliamperes and dissipates about 180 milliwatts when operated from dual plus or minus fifteen-volt supplies. This parameter determines how big the power supply has to be to supply this device, and it can be significant when little power is available.

Figure 5-6 shows the pin connections for a CA3140, and illustrates some practical considerations in using it for a dual supply voltage follower. To avoid noise input and unwanted oscillation, 0.1-microfarad capacitors, called *bypass capacitors*, are connected between the V_{s+} pin and ground, and between the V_{s-} pin and ground. The connection should be made as close to the pin as possible. Wherever practical, every OP AMP should be bypassed in this manner. The 10,000-ohm potentiometer between pins one and five is used to counterbalance the voltage offset. The inputs (to the whole circuit, not the OP AMP) are connected momentarily to ground, and this potentiometer is adjusted to output zero volts. Although the voltage follower needs no resistors (as in figure 5-1d), resistors are put in the feedback loop and in the input to prevent excessive currents from flowing when the OP AMP is driven out of its linear mode of operation. Since the inputs have very high resistance in normal operation, these resistors have no effect in that mode. They should be put in if the OP AMP can enter a saturation mode of operation. Note that if the power to this OP AMP is off, and a signal is applied to the input, excessive current can flow unless these resistances are put in because that operation will be in the saturated mode.

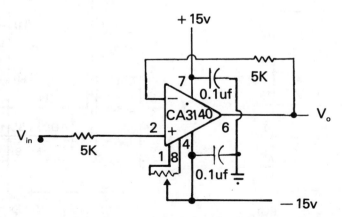

Figure 5-6. A Practical Voltage Follower

Some other considerations are offered. When handling devices with such high input resistances, tools, soldering irons, and hands should be connected via a large (15,000,000-ohm) resistance to ground. Such a device should never be inserted or removed from a socket when power is on, and signals should not be applied to inputs (unless a series resistor is used as in the voltage follower described above) when power is off. Especially if high (1-megaohm) resistances are used, keep them clean, keep the leads short, and separate the components on the input of an OP AMP as far as possible from the output circuitry. A sheet of metal connected to ground provides some isolation from electrical noise, and all components and wires should be close to this *ground plane*. The ground reference points for such high gain OP AMPs should be connected at one single point, running separate wires from this point to each "ground" point, to avoid so called *ground loops*. If this advice is ignored, the OP AMP may become an oscillator because the minute voltages developed across the small but finite resistance of a ground wire could be fed back into an input of the OP AMP.

We now turn to some practical aspects of using CMOS analog switches. The analog switch is almost perfect, its bandwidth is about forty megahertz, when closed it is almost a short circuit, and when open it is almost an open circuit. We now focus on the meaning of "almost." Look at figure 5-7, wherein the 4066 and the 4051 are shown.

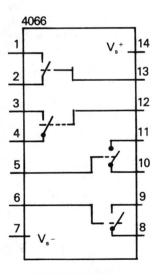

a. A QUAD CMOS Switch

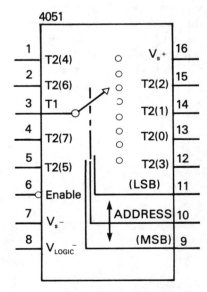

b. A CMOS Analog Multiplexer

Figure 5-7. Analog Switches

We consider the problem of supplying control signals that are compatible with the voltage levels on the terminals of the switch. The maximum V_{s+} $- V_{s-}$ voltage across the 4066 is fifteen volts. Sometimes, a dual ± 7.5-volt supply is used. If so, the control signals on pins five, six, twelve, and thirteen have to be around -7.5 volts to be considered low, to open the corresponding switch, and close to $+7.5$ volts to be considered high, to close the switch. Control signals from a microcomputer are normally in the range of zero to five volts, and have to be translated to control the switch. The 4051 has some level translation ability, however. The logic signals to address the switches and to enable them are referenced to V_{s+} and pin eight, so a high signal is close to V_{s+} and a low signal is close to the voltage level on pin eight. The analog levels on the terminals of the switch can be between V_{s+} and V_{s-}, which is on pin seven. Commonly, V_{s+} is positive five volts, pin eight is grounded and V_{s-} is negative five volts, to use directly control signals from a microcomputer, yet provide some range of analog voltages on the terminals.

When a switch is closed, it appears as a small resistance: about 80 ohms for the 4066 or about 120 ohms for the 4051. This resistance is not exactly linear, varying over a range of two to one. The resistance is more linear if $V_{s+} - V_{s-}$ is as large as possible. However, if it is used with external resistances on the order of 10,000 ohms in series with the switch, less than 0.5 percent distortion is introduced by the nonlinear resistance of the 4066, even for $V_{s+} - V_{s-} = 5$ volts.

When the switch is off, each terminal appears to be a small current source, about 100 nanoamperes for the 4066 and about 500 nanoamperes per analog switch in the 4051. This small current increases substantially with temperature and can be a serious source of error if the associated circuitry has very high resistance. To minimize it, we sometimes see a *heat sink* (a metal attachment to a transistor or integrated circuit to dissipate the heat) on an analog switch, and the switch is sometimes placed away from heat producing components. Finally, a substantial amount of unwanted current flows from the power supply to the terminals if the voltage from a terminal to V_{s-} is greater than 0.6 volts and positive current flows from pin three of the 4051, or from pins two, three, nine, or ten in the 4066. One should insure that positive current flows into these pins, or that the voltage drop across the switch is never more than 0.6 volts. In summary, the 4066 has a bit better performance, lower "on" resistance and lower "off" current, and may be used individually, but the 4051 incorporates eight switches into one chip and translates the control signal level from zero to five volts to control signals between plus and minus volts.

Finally, we discuss the timer module. The ubiquitous 555 is the most popular and least expensive timer. See figure 5-8a for the circuit that generates repetitive signals. Figure 5-8b shows a graph that gives the period of the signal as a function of the resistance, which is the value $R_1 + 2 \times R_2$ in figure 5-8a, and the capacitance, which is the value of C1.

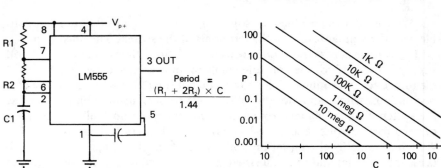

a. Basic Oscillator   b. Period Graph (approximate)

Figure 5-8. The 555 Timer

5-3 Signal Conditioning Using OP AMPs and Analog Switches

OP AMPs and analog switches are often used with microcomputers to condition analog signals before converting them to digital signals, to control analog signals used for other purposes, or to clean up or modify analog signals generated by D-to-A converters. The four main aspects of conditioning a signal are the filtering of frequency components, the selection of inputs, the amplification of or scaling of input levels, and the nonlinear modification of signal voltages. These are now considered in turn.

5-3.1 Filters

Recall that any periodic waveform can be considered as a sum of sine waves. Frequency filtering is commonly done when the signal of interest is accompanied by unwanted noise and most of the noise is at frequencies other than the frequencies of the sine wave components of the signal. If the signal frequencies are low and the noise frequencies are high, a *low-pass filter* is used. See the amplitude versus frequency characteristic of a low-pass filter in figure 5-9a and the circuit diagram in figure 5-9b. Intuitively, capacitor C_1 tends to integrate the signal, smoothing out the high frequency components, and capacitor C_2 further shorts out the high frequency components to ground. Some D-to-A conversion techniques generate high frequency noise, so a low pass filter is commonly used to remove the noise from the signal. If the signal frequencies are higher than the noise frequencies, a *high-pass filter* is used to reject the noise and pass the signal. See figure 5-9c for the amplification characteristics and 5-9d for a high-pass filter circuit. Intuitively, the capacitors pass the high frequency components, bypassing the low frequency components through the resistors. A signal from a light pen on a CRT gets a short pulse every time the electron beam inside the CRT writes over the dot in front of the light pen. The signal has high frequency components, while the noise, mostly a steady level due to ambient light, is lower in frequency. A high-pass filter passes the signal and rejects the noise. Finally, a *bandpass filter* can reject both higher and lower frequency components, passing only components whose frequencies are between the lower and upper limits of the band, and a *notch filter* rejects frequencies within the upper and lower limits of a band. See figures 5-9e through 5-9h for the amplification characteristics and circuit diagrams of these filters.

Compound filters can be used to reject various frequencies and emphasize other frequency components. Two techniques can be used: in one, the output from one filter feeds the input to the next filter to *cascade* them in a chain configuration, and in the other, the signal is fed to both filters and the outputs are added by a summing amplifier in a *parallel* configuration. For instance, a bandpass filter can be made from a low-pass filter that rejects components whose frequency is above the band, cascaded into a high-pass filter, that rejects components whose frequency is below the

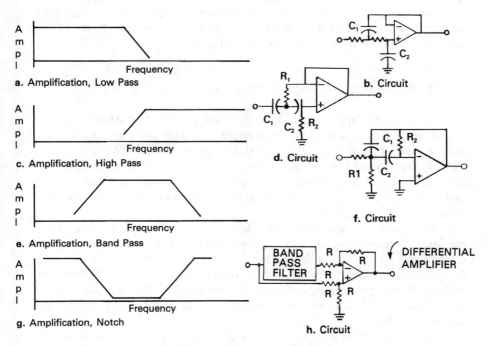

Figure 5-9. Some Filters

band. A notch filter can be made by summing the outputs of a parallel high-pass and low-pass filter. Compound filters can be used to attenuate more sharply the signals whose frequencies are above the low-pass band or below the high-pass band. The best way to cascade n low-pass filters to attenuate more sharply high frequency components to get a $2 \times n$ th order filter is a nice mathematical study, and three types of filters have been shown mathematically optimal in one sense or another. The *Butterworth* filter has the flattest amplification versus frequency curve in the low frequency band where we pass the signal in a low-pass filter; however, the phase delays are quite different for different components. A square wave comes out with a few notches and humps. The *Bessel* filter has the most linear relationship between frequency and phase delay, and is especially useful for processing signals whose information is carried in part by the phase of its components, and by pulse edges and shapes. The *Chebyshev* filter is characterized by a designer-specified irregularity in the amplification versus frequency curve in the low frequency band, and maximum rejection just outside this band, in a low-pass filter. All these filters look alike, but differ in the precise values of the components. These precise values can be obtained from tables, using simple transformations on the values in the tables, or by means of commonly available computer programs. Finally, while the above discussion concentrated on low-pass filters, the same terms and concepts apply to high-pass filters. And high-pass filters can be cascaded with low-pass filters to get bandpass filters or paralleled to get notch filters.

5-3.2 Selection of Inputs and Control of Gain

The selection of inputs and distribution of outputs is normally accomplished by means of analog switches under the control of a microcomputer parallel output port. The individual analog switches of a 4066 can be controlled, each by a bit from an output port, to obtain maximum flexibility over the system being controlled. Alternatively, the 4051 can select from one of eight inputs, or distribute to one of eight outputs, using three bits from a parallel output port.

Microcomputers are appearing in almost every electronic product. They are useful in a stereo system, for example, because the listener can program a selection of music for a day or more. The microcomputer acts as a very flexible "alarm clock." Analog switches can be used to control the selection and conditioning of analog signals in the preamplifier. We show an example of the use of 4051 switches for selection of inputs to a stereo preamplifier. See figure 5-10.

This preamplifier has four sources (FM radio, phono, tape, and auxilliary) and each source has two channels (for example, phono A and phono

B). All signals are no larger than 1.5 volts peak-to-peak and are as close to that range as possible. The four bits from the output port control the two switches such that the high order two bits are the high order bits of the addresses of both switches, but the lowest order bit is the low bit of the address of one of the switches, and the next lowest bit is the low address bit of the other switch. The two high order bits select the source: FF selects the tuner, FT selects the phono, TF selects the tape input, and TT selects the auxilliary input. The two low order bits select the mode: FF puts the A channel into both speakers, FT puts the A input channel into the A speaker and B input channel into the B speaker (stereo), TF puts the A input into the B speaker and the B input into the A speaker (reverse stereo), and TT puts the B input into both speakers. To select the phono inputs in the stereo mode, the program would put the value $5 into the output register.

We note some fine points of the hardware circuit in figure 5-10. Using a single positive five-volt supply for both the analog switches and the OP AMP makes level conversion of the control signals unnecessary. In order to achieve this, the direct current component of the analog signal has to be *biased* by adding a constant to it. The OP AMP has its " + " input connected to a voltage midway between the limits of the input and output voltage of the CA3140 to keep it in its linear mode of operation. The inputs are connected through capacitors to shift the input signal so it is between 0.2 volts and 2.5 volts.

The analog signal often has to be conditioned by amplifying or scaling down its magnitude. This is often required because A-to-D converters require a voltage range as large as possible without exceeding the range of the converter to get maximum accuracy, and D-to-A converters produce an out-

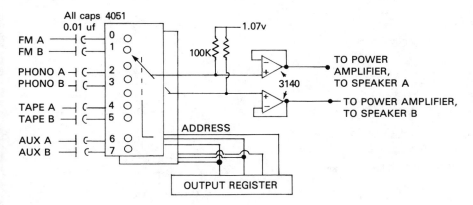

Figure 5-10. Selecting Inputs for a Stereo Preamplifier

put in a fixed range which may have to be amplified or reduced before it is sent out of the system. Two techniques for scaling down a signal are discussed first, then a technique for amplifying a weak signal at an amplification selected by the computer is discussed. The first technique for scaling down a signal is not unlike the selection of inputs discussed earlier: the scale factor is selected by a switch. The second technique uses a fast switch to sample the input at a given duty cycle. We will show examples of these techniques now. Then we show how the amplification of a signal can be controlled by a computer.

We now consider a mechanism for reducing an analog signal by a factor controlled by an output port of a microcomputer. This mechanism might be used on a microcomputer-controlled digital meter to select the range of the voltmeter. Suppose an input voltage in the range 0 to 500 volts is to be reduced to a voltage in the range 0 to 0.5 volts to be used in the next stage of the meter. See figure 5-11a.

The 4051 selects one of the resistors, connecting it to ground. That

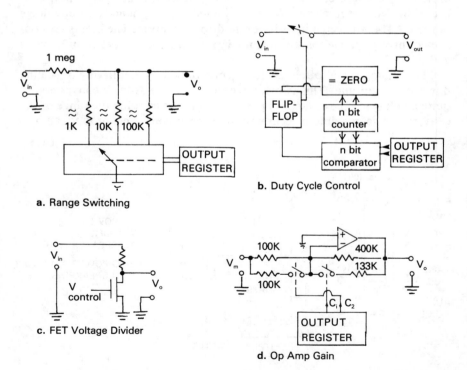

Figure 5-11. Computer Control of Amplification

resistor becomes part of the voltage divider that reduces the input voltage to be within the range needed by the next stage. The other resistors, not selected by the 4051, are effectively connected to very large resistors (turned off analog switches) so they disappear from the circuit. The voltages across all the switches are kept within 0.6 volts of ground because the computer will select the appropriate resistor to divide the input voltage so the next stage gets a voltage in its range. Thus, the analog switch is not corrupted by unwanted current flow, such as we worried about in the last section. This technique can be used to reduce the magnitude of incoming analog signals under the control of a microcomputer.

Another very useful technique is to open and close a switch at a very fast rate—about ten times the maximum frequency of the analog signal being processed. See figure 5-11b. If the analog switch is closed, the amplification is unity; if open, the amplification is zero, and if open fifty percent of the time, the amplification is one half. The microcomputer can control the *duty cycle* of the switch (the percent of time the switch is closed) to control the scaling of the analog signal. The output of this switch has a fair amount of high frequency noise, which can be eliminated by passing it through a low pass filter. Since an analog switch can operate well at ten megahertz, making the control signal frequency as high as possible eases the requirements on the low pass filter. A simple way to control the duty cycle is to use an n-bit binary counter, a comparator fed from an output port, and a set-clear flip-flop. The counter should be clocked fast enough so that it completes its $2^{**}n$ count cycle at about ten times the maximum frequency of the analog signal because that will determine the frequency of the switch control. When the counter passes zero, the flip-flop is set. When the value in the counter is equal to the value in the output register, as determined by the comparator, the flip-flop is cleared. Its output controls the switch, so the duty cycle of the switch is proportional to the number in the output register. A single counter can be used with a number of comparator/flip-flop/switches to control several analog signals. For instance, an octave filter used in sophisticated stereo systems has a band-pass amplifier for each octave so that the listener can compensate for irregularities in the reproduction of each octave. Ten comparator/flip-flop/switches can control the amplification of each octave from a microcomputer. This would enable a microcomputer automatically to "calibrate" a stereo system by adjusting the amplification of each octave as tones are generated and responses are measured under its control.

Two other techniques that are useful for scaling an analog signal deserve mention. A field effect transistor (FET) behaves like a fairly linear resistor provided that the voltage across it, from drain to source, is not too high. The resistance is proportional to the voltage from gate to drain. Alternatively, the resistance of a light sensitive FET is proportional to the light shone on it. Used in an opto-isolator, a light sensitive FET can be used as any of the resistors in a voltage divider or an operational amplifier circuit. See figure 5-11c. Finally, some operational amplifiers (like the CA3080) have a pin whose voltage controls the amplification. These devices can be controlled by a microcomputer by its sending out a voltage to adjust the light of the opto-isolator FET or the gain of a suitable operational amplifier. Finally, the level of a signal can be determined and used to adjust the amplification of these devices automatically in an *automatic gain control* (AGC) circuit. An AGC circuit is sometimes useful to adjust the input voltage to a filter to prevent saturating it.

Amplification (greater than one) must be done with an OP AMP but can be controlled by means of analog switches. By effectively connecting or disconnecting a resistor R_1 in parallel with another resistor R_2, the resistance can be changed from R_2 to $(R_1 \times R_2)/(R_1 + R_2)$. The two resistors in an inverting amplifier can be switched by this method to alter the gain. Consider figure 5-11d. If control signals C1 and C2 are HL, the amplification is one; if HH, the amplification is two; if LL, four; and if LH, eight. A second stage cascaded onto this one could be built to have amplification 1, 16, 256 or (a rather high) 4096, and so on, so the computer can select the amplification by setting these control signals to the analog switches. Amplification ratios lower than two provide closer control and can be obtained by appropriate resistors in the circuit.

5-3.3 Nonlinear Amplification

The final type of signal conditioning is the nonlinear modification of analog signals. A number of fascinating circuits have been advanced to multiply and divide one analog signal by another, or to output the square root or log or sine of an analog signal. Unless the signal is too fast, however, hardware-software tradeoffs usually favor doing this processing in the microcomputer. Three special cases often favor analog hardware signal conditioning—absolute value, logarithmic function, and sample-and-hold. These are shown below. See figure 5-12.

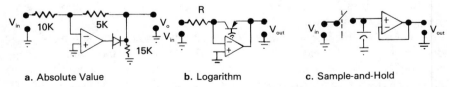

a. Absolute Value   b. Logarithm   c. Sample-and-Hold

Figure 5-12. Nonlinear Signal Conditioning

A diode is capable of extracting the absolute value of a waveform, and this is the basis of the AM radio detector. An accurate absolute value function is sometimes very useful, as for example, when an input voltage that ranges from plus one to minus one volt is to be measured by an analog to digital converter that is only able to measure positive signals, perhaps having only a single-ended five-volt supply. Figure 5-12a puts a diode into the feedback loop of an OP AMP to increase the linearity of the absolute value function. For positive inputs, the diode disconnects the OP AMP so the output is connected to the input via the feedback resistor R_2. For negative inputs, the OP AMP simply inverts the input to get the output. Using a CA3140, this circuit can derive the absolute value of sine waves at frequencies even beyond 100,000 hertz.

The logarithm of an input voltage is sometimes obtained using analog signal conditioners because audio levels, light levels, and so on, are logarithmically related to voltages measured by transducers. Conditioning the analog signal by a logarithmic function drastically compresses the range of signal that has to be converted by an analog-to-digital converter. A transistor has its emitter current I related to its emitter voltage V by the exponential law

$$I = (e**(V/a) - 1)$$

where a is a constant. A transistor can be put into a feedback circuit of an OP AMP to derive a logarithmic function signal conditioner. See figure 5-12b. The output V_o is related to the input V_{in} by

$$V_o = A \log (V_{in}/B)$$

where A and B are constants that depend on the resistor in the circuit, and on the transistor and its temperature.

The last of the nonlinear signal conditioners of particular use in microcomputer systems is the sample-and-hold circuit. Sometimes used by itself to sample an input signal at a precise time, it is also an important building block in digital-to-analog converters, covered in section 5-5, and in multiple output data acquisition systems. See figure 5-12c. The signal is input through an analog switch. When the switch is on, the voltage on the capacitor quickly approaches the input voltage. When the switch is off, the voltage across the capacitor remains steady. The voltage follower makes the output voltage equal to the voltage across the capacitor without taking current from the capacitor that would change its voltage, even though the output may have to supply considerable current to the device it feeds. Turning the switch on causes this circuit to *sample* the input. A microcomputer output register can control the switch in order to sample an incoming waveform

at a precise time so that the output voltage from the sample-and-hold circuit
can be converted to a digital value.

5-4 A Keyboard and LED Display Module

We now consider the design of a typical keyboard and light emitting diode
(LED) display module. This example shows some alternatives among
analog and digital hardware and software to solve the problem of contact
bounce. This design is also important as a module you might expect to see
on a lot of microcomputers.

This example could well have been introduced in chapter 3 as an application of parallel I/O, and indeed we did that in an early version of this
book. However, parallel I/O is just a small part of the design: analog circuits or functions which can be performed either by analog, digital, or software techniques are also part of the design. So we put this discussion here,
after analog circuits have been introduced. Besides, it offers an opportunity
to review parallel I/O, which we have been ignoring as we introduced other
concepts. It is a good opportunity to tie together the material of the
previous three chapters.

5-4.1 Key Debouncing

A keyboard is a collection of switches. Switches have some imperfections
including electrical noise and *contact bounce*. The former is the false signal
picked up by the wires due to motors, fluorescent lights, lamp dimmers, and
so on. It is more likely to be a problem in a keyboard module that has to be
mounted where the user wants to have it than in a microcomputer that can
be properly enclosed and isolated from noise. The latter is due to the
dynamics of a closing contact. Though a contact appears to close firmly and
quickly, at the speeds at which the computer runs, the motion appears
slowed and the contact bounces like a ball as it closes. This generates a rag-
ged signal, as we observe below.

A signal switch is normally connected as in figure 5-13a. The resistor
serves to pull the voltage V to high if the switch is open; the voltage drops to
low if the switch is closed. Since we normally think of a variable associated
with such a switch as true when the switch is closed, the signal V is in
negative logic. This choice is due to the nature of TTL logic, which requires a
low resistance connection to ground to input a low signal reliably.
Therefore the resistor is connected to positive five volts and a switch is connected to ground. Although this configuration is not necessary for MOS integrated circuits, they usually use it to be compatible with TTL, in case an

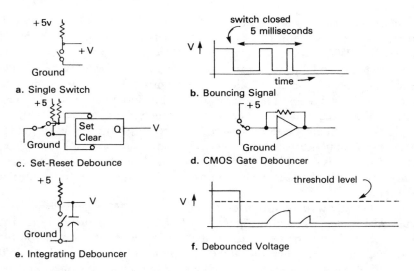

Figure 5-13. Contact Bounce and Its Prevention

existing design using TTL is converted to a microcomputer implementation. This signal can be attached to any input device, such as an M6821 configured as an input, or the 81LS95 discussed earlier. In the following example, we connect it to the most significant bit of the A device because it can be easily tested in the program, and the A device has an internal pull-up resistor so the resistor in figure 5-13a is not needed outside the M6821. If the B device were used, or if an 81LS95 were used as an input device to read the signal from this switch, a separate pull-up resistor would be used.

The noise and contact bounce problem can be solved in analog or digital hardware or in software. The signal V due to closing the switch shown in figure 5-13a is shown in figure 5-13b. The signal falls and rises a few times within a period of about five milliseconds as the contact bounces. Since a human cannot press a switch at a rate faster than twenty milliseconds, a *debouncer* will recognize that the switch is closed if the voltage is low for about ten milliseconds, and that the switch is open if the voltage is high for about ten milliseconds.

The bouncing problem can be reduced by using a good switch. A mercury switch is much faster, and an optical switch, where a beam of light from an LED to a photodetector is interrupted, or a Hall-effect switch, where the magnetic flux by a semiconductor is changed, are free of bounce. It is not difficult, however, to eliminate bounce. Hardware solutions include an analog circuit using a resistor and capacitor to integrate the voltage, and two digital solutions include using set-reset flip-flops or CMOS buffers and double throw switches. These are discussed below.

In the commonly used set-reset debouncer (figure 5-13c), the switch wiper sets or clears a flip-flop when it contacts the top or bottom plate, respectively. When the switch wiper was up (the flip-flop output was therefore high) and the wiper is moved down, the output remains high because the (negative logic) set and clear signals are false. The first instant the wiper hits the bottom plate, it clears the flip-flop by asserting the clear input. As it bounces (it does not bounce up enough to make contact with the top plate) it continually clears the already cleared flip-flop, so the output remains low. A similar effect occurs when the wiper is moved to the top plate, and the flip-flop is repetitively set on each bounce. In either case, the output changes just once when the wiper is moved to the other plate, so the output is debounced.

A better way to debounce uses a noninverting CMOS gate with a high input impedance as shown in figure 5-13d. The wiper normally holds the gate input, and thus the gate output, high or low when it is resting on the top or bottom plate. When the wiper is moving, the resistor tends to hold the input where it was. On the first bounce, the output changes, and remains at that level as the wiper leaves the plate, because of the resistor. Successive bounces do not change the output. Thus, the output is debounced.

Several analog debouncers are possible. We will look at the integrating debouncer because it leads to the software technique that we advocate. Figure 5-13e shows how easy an integrating debouncer can be implemented. The input circuit functions like an analog comparator: the input to the microcomputer is high if the voltage sensed by the comparator is above a threshold level. The waveform for the voltage across the capacitor and the threshold are shown in figure 5-13f. While a comparator can be used to sense the voltage level precisely, any gate, and the input to the M6821 in particular, can be used as a not-too-accurate comparator. Then an integrating comparator can be implemented by simply connecting the peripheral data input of the M6821 through a capacitor to ground.

Software solutions include the *wait-and-see* technique and the software simulation of the *integrating debouncer* discussed above. In the wait-and-see technique, when the input drops indicating the switch might be closed, the program waits ten milliseconds and looks at the input again. If it is still low, the program decides the key has indeed been pressed. If it is high, the program decides the input signal was noise, or the input is bouncing and a later examination will surely show the key is pressed. In either case, the program returns to wait for the input to drop.

The integrating debouncer can be simulated by keeping a binary number in accumulator B that represents the voltage across the capacitor in the hardware approach. If the input is low, indicating the switch is closed, the count is incremented, else the count is decremented. This count more or less simulates the voltage across the capacitor. A threshold is used to determine if the key is closed. Suppose accumulator B is initially set to one and the input is sampled every millisecond. Then when the count is above ten, the key surely is pressed. This technique is shown in the program below. The key signal is input to the most significant bit of the A device of an M6821 whose data register is at location $8000. (In order to use this routine in a few later examples, the two high order bits are made input bits.) This device is configured in the reset handler routine by the following ritual:

```
CLR   $8001
LDD   #$3F04
STD   $8000
```

The following program can test this input, remaining in a loop until the key is closed, then when it is closed, jumping to location L2.

```
     NAM    DEBNCE
     LDB      #1      INITIALIZE NUMBER OF
                      "CLOSURES" TO 1
L0   LDX     #125     SET UP A DELAY LOOP
LP   LEAX    -1,X     TO WAIT ABOUT 1 MILLISECOND
     BNE      LP      LOOP UNTIL TIME OUT
     CMPB     #10     SWITCH CLOSED FOR 10
                      MILLISECONDS?
     BEQ      L2      IF SO, GO TO NEXT ROUTINE
     LDA    $8000     GET INPUT FROM SWITCH IN MSB.
     BMI      L1      IF HIGH (NEGATIVE) THEN
                      SWITCH NOT CLOSED
     INC       B      OTHERWISE (CLOSED) WE INCRE-
                      MENT THE COUNTER
     BNE      L0      IF COUNT CHANGES FROM $FF
                      TO 0
     LDB     #$FF     THEN RESET TO $FF (SATURATE
                      COUNTER)
     BRA      L0      REPEAT CHECK OF KEY
L1   DEC       B      IF KEY WAS OPEN, DECREMENT
                      COUNT
     BNE      L0      IF IT CHANGED FROM 1 to 0
     LDB      #1      THEN RESET IT TO 1 (SATURATE
                      COUNT)
     BRA      L0      REPEAT CHECK OF KEY
L2   RMB       0
     END
```

The first line initializes the count to one. The next three lines provide a one-millisecond delay. The count is then tested for the threshold, ten. If the threshold is achieved, go to the next program. The next line inputs the switch signal in the leftmost bit, and this is tested in the next line. If high, the switch is not pressed, and the bottom four lines decrement the counter, else the four lines above it increment the counter. Note that, on incrementing and decrementing, we guard against the count cycling through the threshold value of ten, or we would have the effect of a repeat key you sometimes see on a keyboard. This is conveniently done by testing the result of incrementing or decrementing the count for zero: if it reaches zero it is reset to its former value.

The above program can be improved by providing hysteresis much as a schmitt trigger comparator in hardware improves the integrating debouncer. When the count reaches ten, and the key is sensed closed, the count is changed to $FF, so that if noise decrements it after it has been sensed it will not reflect such a change of the decision made about whether the key is closed. If the count is decremented and reaches $F4, which indicates the switch has been open for ten milliseconds, the count is reset to one. This simulated hysteresis makes the switch highly immune to noise and quite usable with cheap, bouncy, switches. Modifications to include this feature are simple, and are left as an exercise for the reader.

5-4.2 Keyboard Scanning Techniques

A single key is sometimes all that is needed. Both the hardware and software approaches given above are often used: the best one depends on cost analysis as in any hardware-software tradeoff. On the other hand we are often in need of tens of switches as in a typewriter keyboard. Again, there are both hardware and software approaches and they are mutually analogous. The principles are discussed below.

Keyboards are arranged in arrays for the sake of describing the connections, although physically they can be arranged for the convenience of the user. Using terminology from core memory arrays, a *linear select* keyboard uses one decoding and selecting device and is useful for on the order of ten keys. A *coincident select* or matrix keyboard uses two decoding and selecting devices to determine which key was pressed by coincidental recognition of the row and column the key is in. An eight-key linear select keyboard is shown in figure 5-14a, and a sixty-four-key keyboard is sketched in figure 5-14b. Though there are dozens of good keyboard designs, these two are used here because with them we can extend the example above to introduce the key ideas in a nice way. The selector is an analog switch such as a CMOS 4051. For a given address A output from the low order three bits of the M6821, the Ath input on the left is connected to the output on the right through a small (200-ohm) resistance. In the coincident select keyboard, a decoder such as the 74LS138 is used to select a column. For a given address B output from the next three low order bits of the M6821 to the decoder, the Bth column is made low while the others are made high.

The keyboards have to be *scanned* to determine which key is pressed. For the moment, we assume no keys are pressed or only one key is pressed. A scanning program can search for the pressed key, then the debounce routine described above can be used to verify the key is closed.

The scanning program will be described for the linear select keyboard, using the hardware in figure 5-14a. The initialization of the M6821 is the same as that used earlier in this section, and the following routine can precede the debounce program described above so the key found by the scanner will be debounced.

	NAM	SCAN
L	INC	$8000
	BMI	L
	DEC	$8000
	END	

The routine uses several capabilities of the M6821 to advantage. The low order six bits of the device have been configured by the initialization ritual

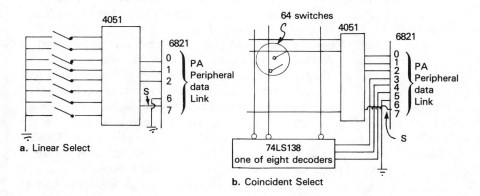

a. Linear Select

b. Coincident Select

Figure 5-14. Keyboard Structures

as a readable output register, so an instruction like INC $8000 will increment them, but the high order two bits are input, so they are not affected by this instruction. The most significant bit is the signal from the switch selected by the low order three bits output from the device. The next low order bit is always a false value. (This prevents the carry from the INC operation from propagating into the most significant bit.) Then the instruction INC $8000 will first read the device, including the scanning count in the low order three bits and the input from the switch in the high order bit, increment this number, set the condition code, and store the result back in the device. Note that the N condition code is true if the signal S was low: the switch selected by the low order bits that were in the device output register was closed. Even though the number counts from zero to sixty-three, only the low order three bits are used, so the count seen by the selector counts from zero to seven repetitively until a key is seen to be closed. The condition code sensed the key selected by the count before it was incremented, so the scan count should be decremented before it is used to select the key sensed by the debounce routine.

The program for the coincident select keyboard scan is actually identical to the one for the linear select keyboard. Suppose this program is executed using the hardware in figure 5-14b on the peripheral data lines of the M6821. If the three bits sent to the decoder are held constant while the scan program samples keys, any key in the column selected by those three bits will be scanned, and the debounce program will be entered whenever any one of them appears to have been pressed. If a key in any other column were pressed, the scan program would not see any different signals (as long as three bits to the decoder do not change). If the three bits to the decoder are allowed to change naturally by the INC instruction, all the columns will be sampled one after another, and as each column is sampled, all keys in it will be sampled by the scan routine. The same scan routine used by the linear select keyboard works with this keyboard too.

The scan and debounce routines shown above have some limitations. It is possible to eliminate the hardware selector and decoder modules by using both devices in an M6821, one to shift a low bit to scan the columns and another to input all eight row signals to be studied by software. The principle uses singuary rather than binary number scanning, and the patterns are rotated instead of incremented. This is often desirable because it reduces the number of hardware components; however, it uses more lines to an M6821. If these lines are needed for some other function, like controlling an LED display, two small chips can be used in place of another M6821.

The above technique assumes that only one key is pressed at a time. If we allow two keys to be pressed simultaneously, and this is often done by a proficient keyboard user as he presses a new key before releasing the key he was pressing, the program might keep picking up the first key and not see the new key if it sees that one first in its scan. Any technique that can correctly recognize a new key even though $n - 1$ keys are already pressed and are still down is said to exhibit n-*key roll-over*. Two-key roll-over is a common and useful feature, and can be achieved with most keyboards, but for larger numbers one must guard against sneak paths through the keys. Sneak paths appear when three keys at three corners of a rectangle are pushed, so that the fourth key seems to have been pushed because current can take a circuitous path through the pressed keys when the fourth key is being sensed. This can be prevented by putting diodes in series with each switch to block this sneak path current, but the solution is rather expensive and *n*-key rollover is not usually that useful. The *n-key lock-out* technique works like N-key roll-over except that if the user presses n-keys before releasing the keys, the computer recognizes only the first key and ignores the other n-1 keys without getting confused.

These improvements can be made using the software approach. The hardware approach for keyboard scanning and debouncing actually uses these principles. A special purpose integrated circuit connects to the keyboard and executes routines like the ones above: the microprocessor connects to an output from them, from which the code for the key appears. Though this takes all the effort out of keyboard interfacing, it adds another large chip to the hardware, and the microprocessor may be twiddling away in a delay loop anyhow while it awaits a command entered through the keyboard. Software scanning and debouncing is therefore rather commonly done.

5-4.3 Displays

We now extend the example to include a display for the keyboard. The hardware and software to support the keyboard and the display are quite similar and can be shared. These two modules are both used very often for user input/output. The LED, the LED display, and the scanned display will be studied in turn.

Recall that an LED is a diode that emits light if about ten milliamperes of positive current flows from anode to cathode. These diodes can be arranged in the form of a block 8, a diode per bar in the figure 5-8. To save pins, either the cathodes are tied together internally or the anodes are internally tied. The first is called a *common cathode* LED display, and the cathode is connected to ground. See figure 5-15a.

In order to display a digit, the LEDs are turned on or off in each segment. Using the lettering system shown in figure 5-15a, which is widely used in practice, a *seven-segment code* is the values of the variables g through

a. The seven-segment code for the number two is TFTTFTT. The representation of the number in the computer is hexadecimal (or binary coded decimal). This representation has to be recoded into its seven-segment form, and the seven segment variables have to be applied to the display to turn on the LEDs. This can be done in hardware or software. In the hardware approach, a *seven-segment decoder-driver* integrated circuit chip is used. The hexadecimal number from the computer output device is input to this chip, and its output is attached to the display LEDs. In the software approach, the hexadecimal number is converted by a routine, usually a table lookup routine, into the desired seven-segment code, which is then output to the LEDs. Since the output device may be able to supply only about 1 milliampere, a *segment driver* integrated circuit amplifies the signal. Figure 5-15a shows a popular segment driver, the 75491, which was designed for the high volume calculator market. In order to use it with a microcomputer, a pull-up resistor on its input is often needed. If the input to the 75491 is high, current flows through the transistor. This current, limited by the small (100-ohm) current limiting resistor, goes through the LED to light it.

A typical program to generate the seven-segment code for a display uses table lookup. Suppose a table TBL stores the seven-segment codes for the digits: the ith row is the code for the ith digit, and hexadecimal number to be displayed is in accumulator A. This routine will output the code through an output device at location $8002.

```
NAM     LOOK
LDX     #TBL     GET ADDRESS OF TABLE IN X
LDA     A,X      GET 7-SEGMENT CODE IN A
STA     $8002    OUTPUT IT
END
```

A single display may be needed in some applications, but we are often in need of several displays. Just as the concepts used for the single switch can be easily expanded to a keyboard, the technique above can be easily expanded to handle multiple displays. One way to handle multiple displays is to have one output device for each display. Alternatively, the displays can be *multiplexed* as we will show in the following example. Multiplexing is usually used because it saves the cost of several output devices, but sometimes it generates noise which might be intolerable, for instance, if a sensitive radio is near the display. In that case, separate displays have to be used.

In multiplexed displays, the cathode of a common cathode display is connected to ground through a transistor. If the transistor is turned off, no current can flow through any of the LEDs in the display, so it appears dark regardless of the signals applied to the anodes. Suppose n displays are con-

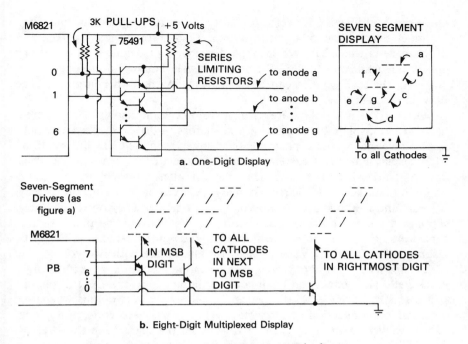

Figure 5-15. Seven-Segment Displays

nected, corresponding anodes connected to a segment driver as in the previous example, and the transistors connected to a second output device so that only one is turned on. If the first transistor is turned on, and the program above is executed, the number in accumulator A is displayed on the first display. If another number is put in accumulator A and the second display is turned on, that number is displayed in the second display, and so on. The number can be read from a table, for instance. The displays are turned on, one at a time, as the numbers to be displayed are picked up from the table, for instance. The displays are turned on, one at a time, as the numbers to be displayed are picked up from the table by a table interpreter and are entered by putting them in accumulator A and executing the above program. Each is turned on for the same amount of time. Note that each display is on for $1/n$th of the time. The current limiting resistor is made smaller so that n times as much current is sent through the LED so it will be as bright as if it were driven as a single display. See figure 5-15b.

Multiplexed displays are widely used in calculators. The *digit driver* 75492 integrated circuit has six transistors capable of being used in the cathode line of these displays, and the *peripheral drivers* like the 75451 have two NAND gates, each connected to a transistor, that can be used in this application. Multiplexing is useful for up to about ten displays: beyond that too much current has to be put through the LEDs for the small percentage of the cycle in which they are scanned. Even with six displays, if something goes wrong while one display is being driven so it remains on for longer than one sixth the scan time, it can be burned out by the rather large currents flowing through it.

Other types of displays are used. A liquid crystal display is configured like an LED display, but the bars are capacitors. A digit is displayed by putting voltages across the appropriate bars, much as in the LED display. If an LCD display has direct current across the capacitor, however, it weakens due to polarization of the chemical in it. An alternating voltage has to be imposed to darken it. If the rms voltage is below about one volt, the display is clear, and if above about two volts, it is opaque. The control circuitry supplies a voltage of zero, one, two, or three volts to the plates of the capacitors. The common connection analogous to the cathode in the LED display is sent a square wave of one volt alternating with two volts if the digit is not selected, and of zero volts alternating with three volts if the digit is selected. The connection analogous to the anode in the LED display is sent a square wave too. If the segment square wave is two volts whenever the common connection of a selected segment is at zero volts, and is one volt whenever common is at three volts, then the segment in the selected digit will have enough rms voltage to darken. If the segment square wave is one volt when the common connection of a selected terminal is zero volts, and two volts when common is three volts, the segment does not have quite enough voltage across it to darken. Note too that none of the segments of the nonselected digits have enough rms voltage to darken. When one digit is selected, all the segments to be darkened in it are given a sigmal that will darken them. One digit is scanned at a time. This technique provides the required alternating voltage free of DC to protect the LCDs. If the number of digits scanned this way increases, however, the rms voltage of the segments to be darkened decreases so the ratio of the clear to dark levels gets too small to work reliably. Thus LCDs can be multiplexed, but ony about three or four can be multiplexed together. A six-digit display would be implemented as two separate three-digit multiplexed displays. Finally, incandescent, gas discharge, and fluorescent seven-segment displays are also used, and self-scanning PANAPLEX displays can be used for user messages.

The reader might perceive the similarity between the keyboard scan and the display scan hardware and software. Indeed, the decoder that selects the column of the keyboard can also select the digit to be displayed, and as the rows are read from the keyboard the segments can be driven to display the digit through another output device. A number of variations of this technique can be implemented. The reader is invited to feast his imagination on them.

5-5 Converters

We often convert analog signals into digital signals and vice versa. Also, we convert analog amplitude signals into analog frequency signals and vice versa. These conversions are now discussed. The first subsection describes the digital-to-analog converters that are commonly available for microcomputer I/O systems. The next subsection describes the analog-to-digital converters. Though they seem to be more common than digital-to-analog converters, we discuss them later because some analog-to-digital converters use digital-to-analog converters inside them. Finally, the frequency-to-voltage and voltage-to-frequency converters are discussed.

Before we discuss the different converters, we introduce some important concepts that cover the various converters. In general, the analog input is either sampled, using a sample-and-hold circuit or its equivalent, or integrated using an integrator circuit or its equivalent. Analog output is either produced in samples, or is output from an integrator. Integration smooths out the signal, reducing noise, but limits the upper frequency signal components. Sampling provides a "snap-shot" of the data—and the noise too. In sampling converters, another problem is caused by high frequencies. The *sampling rate* is obviously the rate at which the data samples are taken. The *Nyquist rate* is one half the sampling rate. Components of the signal that have higher frequency than the Nyquist rate "beat" against the frequency of the Nyquist rate in the same manner as radio frequency signals are "beat" against the frequency of a local oscillator in a radio, generating *alias* frequency components. For example, if a component has a frequency equal to the sampling rate, it will appear as a direct current component. In order to eliminate the generation of these alias components, a low-pass filter is used to eliminate all frequencies above the Nyquist rate.

5-5.1 Digital-to-Analog Converters

Three basic digital-to-analog converters (D-to-As) are introduced now: the summing amplifier, the ladder, and the exponential superposition D-to-As. The summing amplifier converter most readily shows the basic principle behind all D-to-A converters, which is that each digital bit contributes a weighted portion of the output voltage if the bit is true, and the output is the sum of the portions. The ladder converters are easier to build because the resistors in a ladder network can be trimmed precisely without much effort. Ladder networks for these D-to-A converters are readily available, quite fast, and inexpensive. The exponential superposition converter is quite a bit slower and less accurate, but does not need precision components, so it would be very useful in microcomputer based toys or appliance controllers. These converters are examined now, in turn.

The summing amplifier can be used in an D-to-A converter, as in figure 5-16a. Keeping in mind that the output voltage is

$$V_o = -R_f \times (V_1/R_1 + V_2/R_2 + \ldots)$$

if $V_1 = V_2 = \ldots = 1$ volt, and R_i is either infinity (an open switch) or a power of two times R_f (if the corresponding switch is closed), then the output voltage is

$$V_o = C_1/2 + C_2/4 + C_3/8 + \ldots$$

Where C_i is one if the switch in series with the ith resistor is closed, zero otherwise. An output device can be used to control the switches, so the ith most significant bit controls the ith switch. Then the binary number in the output register, considered as a fraction, is converted into a voltage at the output of the summing amplifier. Moreover, if the reference input voltage is made V volts rather than one volt, the output is the fraction specified by the output register time V volts. V can be fixed at a convenient value, like ten volts, to *scale* the converter. Usually, a D-to-A converter is scaled to a level such that for largest output value the summing amplifier is nearly, but not quite, saturated, to minimize errors due to noise and offset voltages and currents. Alternatively, if V is itself an analog signal, it is multiplied by the digital value in the output register. This D-to-A converter is thus a *multiplying D-to-A converter*, and can be used as a digitally controlled voltage divider, an alternative to the range switch and duty cycle control techniques for amplification control.

Although conceptually neat, the above converter requires using from eight to twelve precision resistors of different values, which can be difficult to match in the two-to-one ratios needed. An alternative circuit, an R-2R *ladder network*, can be used in a D-to-A converter that uses precision resistors all of which have values R or $2 \times R$ ohms. This network can be used as a voltage divider or a current divider: the former is conceptually simpler but the latter is more commonly used. See figure 5-16b for a current ladder D-to-A converter. A pair of analog switches for each "$2R$" resistor either connect the resistor into the " $-$ " input to the OP AMP or to ground, depending on whether the control variable is high or low, respectively. The currents through these switches, from left to right, vary in proportion to $1/2$, $1/4$, $1/8$, and so on, as can be verified by simple circuit analysis. If the ith control variable is true, a current proportional to $2^{**}-1$ is introduced into the " $-$ " input of the OP AMP, which must be counterbalanced by a negative current through R_f to keep the " $-$ " input at virtual ground, so the output voltage proportional to $2^{**}-i$ is generated. The components for each input i are added, so the output is proportional to the value of the binary number whose bits control the switches. Like the previous A-to-D converter, this one can be scaled by appropriately selecting the voltage V_{in} and can be used as a digitally controlled amplification device. It, too, is a multiplying A-to-D converter.

A program for outputting a voltage by means of either a summing or an $R-2R$ D-to-A converter is very simple, of course. One merely stores the number to be converted onto an output register that is connected to the converter.

A ladder network for a converter can be obtained as an integrated circuit for six to twelve bits of accuracy. The chip contains the switches and the resistors for the circuit. The output settles to the desired voltage level in less than a microsecond in a typical converter, so the programmer usually does not have to worry about settling time.

The last converter uses a sample-and-hold circuit to sample a voltage that is the sum of exponential voltages corresponding to bits of the digital word being converted. The circuit, in figure 5-16c, is simplicity exemplified. Some preliminary observations on an exponential waveform and the superposition principle are offered. Consider an exponential wave form as shown in figure 5-16d. Note that for such a signal, there is a time T (not the time constant of the network though) at which the signal is one-half the initial value of the signal. And at times two times T, three times T, four times T, and so on, the signal level is one-fourth, one-eighth, one-sixteenth, of the initial value, and so on. Furthermore, in a linear circuit, the actual voltage can be computed from the sum of the voltages of each waveform. This is called superposition. Now if a sample-and-hold circuit samples at a given

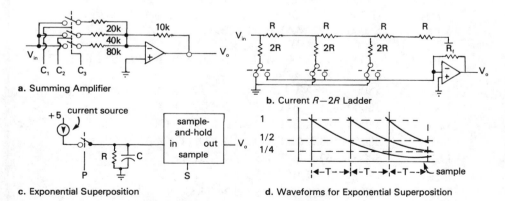

a. Summing Amplifier

b. Current $R-2R$ Ladder

c. Exponential Superposition

d. Waveforms for Exponential Superposition

Figure 5-16. D-to-A Converters

time a voltage that is a sum of exponential voltages, an exponential waveform that was started T time units before will contribute one-half its initial value; one that was started two times T time units before will contribute one-fourth its initial value; one started three times T units before will contribute one-eighth its initial value, and so on. Thus, by generating or not generating each of the exponential waveforms, from left to right in figure 5-12d, the voltage sampled will or will not have a component of one-eighth, one-fourth, one-half, and so on. These waveforms are generated by asserting control variable P if the shifted bit is true, as the least significant bits are shifted out each T time units. This closes the switch if the bit shifted out is true, so that the current source pumps a charge into the capacitor to generate the exponential that contributes its component of the sampled voltage. The control variable S is asserted to sample the waveform after all bits have been shifted out. The sampled voltage is the desired output of the D-to-A converter. The output can be scaled by selecting an appropriate current source, but this A-to-D converter does not make a good multiplying converter because dynamically changing the input current level a bit will destroy its accuracy.

A program to convert an eight-bit number in ACCA to a voltage is shown below. It assumes that an M6821 output register at location $8000 is a readable output device, and bit zero controls the switch via control variable P in figure 5-16c. It also assumes that an address decoder supplies an address trigger (as discussed in section 4-1.1) to assert the S control signal and thus sample the data whenever the address $8004 is generated in a read or write operation.

```
NAM    EXSP
CLR    $8001    MAKE $8000 THE DIRECTION REGISTER
LDX    #$FF04   PUT $FF IN DIRECTION, $04 IN CONTROL
STX    $8000    TO MAKE ALL BITS READABLE OUTPUT SO
                LSR WORKS
STA    $8000    PUT NUMBER IN OUTPUT REGISTER, OUT-
                PUT LSB TO A/D
LSR    $8000    NEXT LSB TO A/D CONTROL
LSR    $8000    3RD BIT TO A/D CONTROL
LSR    $8000    4TH BIT TO A/D CONTROL
LSR    $8000    5TH BIT TO A/D CONTROL
LSR    $8000    6TH BIT TO A/D CONTROL
LSR    $8000    7TH BIT TO A/D CONTROL
LSR    $8000    MSB TO A/D CONTROL
LDA    $8001    PULSE S TO SAMPLE THE COMPOSIT
                EXPONENTIAL SIGNAL
END
```

The first three lines initialize the M6821 to output the least significant bit of the data register and make the other bits act lke a read/write memory word (that is, make them "output" bits too). The next line stores the data to be converted into the data register. Note that this will cause the least significant bit to be sent to the A/D converter to generate an exponential signal if the bit is true. Then the number to be converted is shifted seven times to generate the other seven exponential waveforms. Finally the address $8004 is generated, so the address decoder will output a pulse to the S line to cause the sample and hold module to sample the waveform. As explained earlier, this waveform contains components from each output bit if that bit was true, and the component generated by the most significant bit is twice as big as the component for the next, and so on.

Accuracy of this simple converter is limited to just a few bits. The sample-and-hold circuit loads the capacitor, and the current source does not supply a fixed current if its output is stopped and started. Nevertheless, this converter requires a minimum of adjustment. The resistor is adjusted so the decay time T discussed above corresponds to the time to execute the LSR instruction in the above program. This simple converter would be most suitable, for instance, where a microcomputer controls a toy train by controlling a voltage supplied to the motor.

5-5.2 Analog-to-Digital Converters

In a manner like that of the previous section, six different analog to digital converters (A-to-Ds) are introduced. These have different costs, accuracies, and speeds. We discuss them in approximate order of decreasing speed and cost. The parallel and pipeline converters are fastest, followed by the delta and successive approximation converters and the ramp converters.

The *parallel* A-to-D converter uses comparators to determine the input voltage and can be made almost as fast as the comparators. Accuracy is limited, however, due to the cost of the comparators. Figure 5-17a shows a typical three-bit converter that has a range of zero to seven volts, for ease of discussion. The resistor divider network establishes reference voltages for each comparator, from top to bottom, of zero, one, two, . . . seven volts. If the input voltage V_{in} is between i - 1 and i volts, the i bottom comparators output a true value. A priority encoder module encodes this set of values to a binary number that is the most prior true input address, which is i.

A variation of the parallel converter, a *pipeline converter*, consists of n identical stages, as shown in figure 5-17b, to achieve n bits of accuracy. The signal V_{in} is sent to the input of the leftmost stage, and the output V_{out} of each stage is then sent to the input of the next stage to the right. Suppose the voltage range is V_{max}. The output of the comparator is either V_{max} if the V_+ input is higher than the V_- input of the comparator or else it is zero volts.

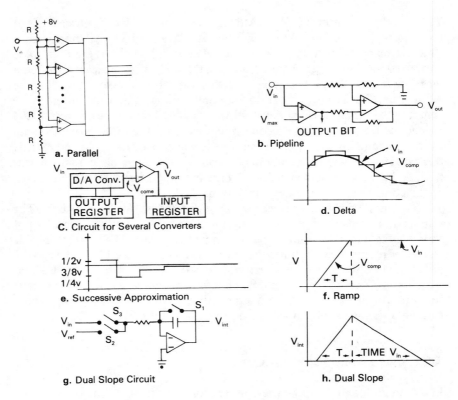

Figure 5-17. A-to-D Conversion Techniques

If the input is above half V_{max}, then half V_{max} is subtracted from the input and then doubled, otherwise the input is just doubled in the differential amplifier that feeds the output V_{out}. If a steady signal is fed into the input, V_{in}, then as the signal flows through the stages, bits from most significant bit are obtained from each stage, being true if half V_{max} was subtracted, otherwise being false. Moreover, the conversion is actually done as the leading edge of the analog signal flows through each stage. It is possible, then, to begin the next conversion just as the first stage has settled, even though later stages may yet be settling. Its rather like oil flowing through a pipeline. This kind of system is, then, called a pipeline. Recently, an experimental six-bit pipeline converter was reported, which had an incredible eight-gigahertz conversion rate. Digital oscilloscopes, anyone?

Successive approximation, delta, and ramp converters can be implemented with the hardware shown in figure 5-17c. The programs differ for each method. For *delta* or *servo* conversion, a D-to-A converter outputs a voltage V_{comp} which is compared to V_{in}. If V_{comp} is greater than V_{in}, then V_{comp} is diminished, otherwise V_{comp} is increased by a small amount. Assuming V_{in} changes slower than V_{comp} can change, V_{comp} should "track" V_{in} in the manner of a feedback control, or servo system. By another analogy to communications systems, the digital output changes by delta increments, as in delta modulation systems. Figure 5-17d shows a varying V_{in} and a tracking V_{comp} for a delta converter. A program for an eight-bit delta converter is shown below. It assumes that location $8000 is an output register, whose output is converted by the eight-bit D-to-A converter to V_{comp}, and location $8001 is an input register, whose sign bit is true if V_{in} is greater than V_{comp}.

```
L1  TST   $8001   INPUT BIT TO SIGN CONDITION CODE
    BMI     L2    IF 1 (NEGATIVE) THEN GO TO INCREMENT
    DEC   $8000   ELSE DECREASE OUTPUT VOLTAGE
    BRA     L1    REPEAT TEST AND ADJUSTMENT
L2  INC   $8000   INCREMENT OUTPUT, INCREASE OUTPUT
                  VOLTAGE
    BRA     L1    REPEAT TEST AND ADJUSTMENT
```

The reader can observe that the number in location $8000 can be read at any time, and it tracks the input voltage. A servo converter can also be built using digital hardware, so that a processor is not tied up in the loop shown above, but the technique is identical. Servo converters are as fast as the comparator, D-to-A converter, and up-down counter that track the input. However, like OP AMPs, they have a slew rate limitation that may be unacceptable.

A *successive approximation* converter uses the same circuit, but requires a program that embodies a different principle, the principle of divide-and-conquer. We observe the same technique in long-hand division. Suppose the input is in the range zero to V_{max}. The D-to-A converter is so loaded as to output $V_{max}/2$. If the comparator senses V_{in} greater than $V_{max}/2$, then the D-to-A converter is set to output $V_{max} \times 3/4$, else it is set to output $V_{max}/4$. Note that this is done by either adding or subtracting $V_{max}/4$ from the current output, depending on the result of comparing this output with V_{in}. In successive trials, $V_{max}/8$, then $V_{max}/16$, $V_{max}/32$, and so on, are added or subtracted from the value output to the D-to-A converter. The comparison voltage V_{ref} approaches V_{in} as shown in figure 5-14e. The subroutine is shown below. We write it as a subroutine because we will call this subroutine in a program in section 5-6.

Accumulator A is generally output in line five, and the word on the top of the stack is added to or subtracted from A. These are initialized to half the range so the D-to-A converter will initially try $V_{comp} = V_{max}/2$. In the loop, in line three, the adjustment value is divided by two, so that in the first loop

```
          NAM        SUCCES
S         LDA        #$80    START AT MID VALUE, AS FIRST
                             GUESS
          PSHS         A     COPY, TOP STACK WORD HOLDS
                             "ADJUSTMENT"
L1        LSR          ,S    DIVIDE ADJUSTMENT VALUE BY 2 TO
                             ADJUST NEXT BIT
          BEQ          L3    IF ZERO, ALL BITS HAVE BEEN
                             ADJUSTED
          STA        $8000   OUTPUT TOTALIZED VALUE TO COM-
                             PARE TO INPUT
          TST        $8001   LOOK AT COMPARATOR, SIGN BIT IS
                             COMPARATOR OUTPUT
          BPL          L2    IF LOW (POSITIVE) THEN SUBTRACT
                             ADJUSTMENT
          ADDA         ,S    ELSE ADD ADJUSTMENT TO
                             TOTALIZED VALUE
          BRA          L1    REPEAT TO ADJUST NEXT BIT
L2        SUBA         ,S    SUBTRACT ADJUSTMENT TO TRY
                             LOWER VOLTAGE
          BRA          L1    THEN REPEAT TO ADJUST NEXT LESS
                             SIGNIFICICANT BIT
L3        PULS       A,PC    RETURN TO CALLER
          END
```

$V_{max}/4$ will be added to or subtracted from the comparison voltage, in the second execution of the loop, $V_{max}/8$ will be added or subtracted, and so on. Next, the adjustment value is examined: if it has become zero the conversion must be complete. If so, a jump to L3 completes the program. Otherwise, that number in accumulator A is output to try the comparison voltage V_{comp}, in line four. The comparator output is tested in line five. If V_{in} is greater than V_{comp}, then accumulator B is added to A to get the next comparison voltage, else it is subtracted. (This program always leaves the least significant bit true, regardless of the input; this can be fixed by further processing.) Successive approximation converters are quite fast, because each execution of the loop determines one more digit of the result. Moreover, by implementing this technique in hardware (called a successive approximation register), the computer can concentrate on other things as the voltage is being converted.

A *ramp* analog-to-digital converter can use the same circuit as in figure 5-17c, or a simpler circuit as in figure 5-17g. Simply, in figure 5-17c, the comparator voltage V_{comp} is initialized to zero by clearing location $8000, then is gradually increased by incrementing $8000 until V_{comp} greater than V_{in} is sensed by the comparator. See figure 5-17f. The circuit shown in figure 5-17g uses a *dual slope* technique shown in figure 5-17h. The output voltage from the integrator, sensed by the comparator, is initially cleared by closing only switch S1. Then, by closing only S2 for a specific time T, the reference voltage $-V_{ref}$ is integrated, charging the capacitor in the integrator. Lastly, only S3 is closed, so that the voltage V_{in} is integrated to discharge the capacitor. The time to discharge the capacitor is proportional to V_{in}. Moreover, the time is proportional to the average value of V_{in} over the time it is integrated, which nicely reduces noise we do not want to measure, and the accuracy of the converter does not depend on the values of the components (except V_{ref}), so this converter is inexpensive. It is, however, the slowest converter. It finds great use, nevertheless, in digital voltmeters, multimeters, and panel meters, because it can achieve about twelve bits (three and a half digits) of accuracy at low cost, and it is faster than the eye that watches the display.

5-5.3 Frequency-to-Voltage and Voltage-to-Frequency Conversion

Related to the digital-to-analog converter, a *frequency-to-voltage converter* (FVC) outputs a voltage that is proportional to the frequency of the input sine wave. For high frequencies an FM detector serves this function. Several integrated circuits are available for detecting FM signals. For a broad range of frequencies, a phase locked loop can be used. The error voltage used to lock the oscillator in the loop to the frequency of the incoming signal is proportional to the difference between the frequency to which the oscillator is tuned to, and the frequency of the incoming signal. For audio frequencies, a common technique is to trigger a one-shot with the leading edge of the input signal. The output is a pulse train, where the pulses are of constant width and height and occur with the same frequency as the input signal. See figure 5-18a. This signal is passed through a low-pass filter to output a signal that is proportional to the area under the pulses, which is proportional to the frequency. The LM3905 is especially suited to this application, as it is a one-shot (monostable) with built-in voltage reference and an output transistor that is capable of producing output pulses of precise height. See figure 5-18b. Another way to convert frequency to voltage is to use an integrated circuit specially made for the vast automobile market to implement a tachometer, since a tachometer senses spark pulses whose frequency is proportional to engine speed, and it outputs an analog level to a meter to display the engine speed. This technique can be used with subaudio frequen-

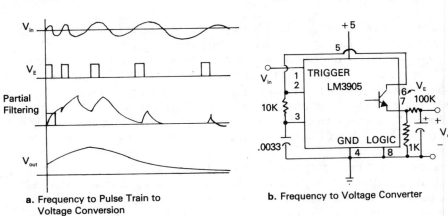

a. Frequency to Pulse Train to
Voltage Conversion

b. Frequency to Voltage Converter

Figure 5-18. Frequency-to-Voltage Conversion

cies, since it is designed to measure low-rate spark pulse trains. Frequency-to-voltage converters have the advantages that information is carried by the frequency of a signal on a single wire, which can be easily isolated using opto-isolators, and that this signal is remarkably immune to noise and degradation due to losses in long wires from microcomputer to output. The signal they carry has to pass through a low-pass filter, however, so its maximum frequency is much lower than the frequency of the carrier that is being converted to the voltage.

The final analog converter of interest is the voltage-to-frequency converter. This generates a square wave whose frequency or period is proportional to the input voltage V_{in}. See figure 5-19a. Internally, V_{in} is integrated until the integrated voltage reaches a reference voltage V_{ref}, whence the integrated voltage is cleared. An output pulse, occurring as the integrator is cleared, has a frequency that is proportional to the input V_{in}. If desired, this can be fed to a toggle flip-flop to square the signal as its period is doubled. With the reversal of the role of the reference and input voltage, so that the reference voltage is integrated and compared to the input voltage, the period of the output is proportional to the voltage V_{in}. This makes a voltage-to-period converter. Noise on V_{in} is not averaged out in this technique though. Other circuits are used for VFCs, but the principles are similar to those discussed above. VFCs can be quite accurate and reasonably fast: the teledyne 9400 (see figure 5-19b) accurately converts voltage to frequency to about thirteen bits of accuracy and is that accurate after two cycles have occurred on the output wave. This means the converter is faster for higher voltages, since they result in higher frequencies, than for lower voltages. Used in an integrating mode, moveover, the VFC can reduce noise like the dual ramp converter. The VFC is of particular

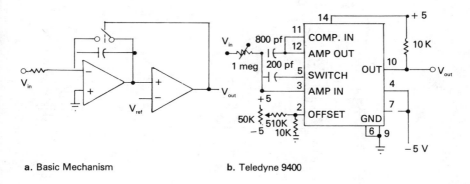

a. Basic Mechanism   **b.** Teledyne 9400

Figure 5-19. Voltage-to-Frequency Conversion

value where the microprocessor has a built-in counter to measure frequency, especially since the frequency carrying signal is easy to handle, being carried on only one wire.

5-6 Data-Acquisition Systems

A *data-acquisition system* (DAS) consists of switches, a D-to-A converter,
and signal conditioning circuits so that several inputs can be measured, and
several outputs can be supplied, under the control of a microcomputer.

A DAS can be purchased as a printed circuit board, or even as a
(hybrid) integrated circuit module. Such a DAS would be better to use than
the system we discuss below, but we introduce it to show how such a system
works, and to bring together the various concepts from previous sections.
Finally, in this section, we will show how a DAS can be used to implement a
digital filter or feedback control system.

The DAS described in this section is shown in figure 5-20. From left to
right, an analog switch selects an input among eight inputs for the comparator. This will be used to measure the input voltages. The D-to-A converter is used with the comparator to implement the A-to-D converter to
measure the inputs and to supply the output voltages. The analog switch
and voltage followers on the right implement sample-and-hold circuits that
act like analog flip-flops to store the output voltages after they have been set
by the microcomputer. In the following discussion, location $8000 will be
an output register to the D-to-A converter, location $8001 will be an input
whose sign bit is true if V_{in} (selected by the analog switch) is greater than
V_{comp}. Location $8002 will be a readable output port that addresses both the
analog switches. If, for instance, a three is put in this register, then input

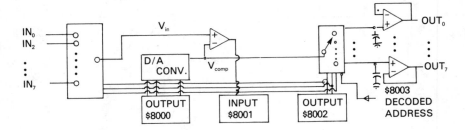

Figure 5-20. A Data-Acqusition System

three is sent to the comparator (as V_{in}), and the output of the D-to-A converter is made available to the sample-and-hold circuit that supplies output three. Finally, the enable of the analog switch is connected to the microcomputer address decoder to generate an address trigger. If the microcomputer addresses location $8003, as it does in two memory cycles in the execution of an instruction like INC $8003, then the address decoder will provide a one-microsecond pulse, which will enable the analog switch for that time. Recall that, when enabled, the addressed input is connected to the output of the switch, but when not enabled, all inputs and the output are not connected.

The data-acquisition system is controlled by a program, which will now be discussed. This program will be called as a subroutine whenever the inputs are to be measured and the outputs are to be adjusted. Eight output values are stored in a table TBL, so that TBL[0] is converted to a voltage on output zero; TBL[1] on output one, and so on; and TBL is loaded with the desired values just before this subroutine is called. After returning from the subroutine, the eight inputs are converted and stored, to keep things simple, in the same table. TBL[0] will store the binary number equal to the voltage on input zero; TBL[1] will be the voltage on input one, and so on. The program is now shown:

```
      NAM       DAS
      LDB       #7       PUT 7 TO THE SELECTOR ADDRESS
      STB       $8002    VIA OUTPUT PORT $8002
      LDX       #TBL+8   START AT BOTTOM OF TABLE
L1    LDA       ,-X      GET ENTRY FROM TABLE
      STA       $8000    OUTPUT IT VIA D/A CONVERTER
      INC       $8003    SEND TWO ADDRESS PULSES TO
                         SAMPLE AND HOLD
      LBSR      S        EXECUTE SUCCESSIVE APPROXIMA-
                         TION ROUTINE "SUCCESS"
```

STA	0,X	ROUTINE RETURNS DIGITAL VALUE IN ACCA
DEC	$8002	SELECT NEXT LOWER ANALOG INPUT/OUTPUT
BPL	L1	LOOP IF MORE TO INPUT AND OUTPUT
RTS		RETURN TO CALLER
END		

The first three lines initialize the output register that selects inputs and outputs to select the last one, and it initializes the index register to access the last row of the table TBL. Thereafter, in the loop, a number is read from the table to the D-to-A converter via output register $8000 and then the output analog switch is enabled for two consecutive memory cycles by executing the instruction INC $8003. The address trigger technique discussed in section 4-1.1 is used here. This instruction should read the word at $8003, increment it, and write the result there. But no output register or RAM word is at this location, so nothing is actually done by the microprocessor. However, location $8003 is accessed twice. This enables the analog switch twice. At this time, the output of the D-to-A converter is sampled by the sample-and-hold circuit that feeds output seven, since the analog switch addresses the bottom position. The voltage output from the D-to-A converter is now sampled, and will remain on this output until it is changed again, when this subroutine is called again. Thus, the sample-and-hold behaves rather like an analog storage register. Next, a successive approximation subroutine like that discussed in the previous section is called. The subroutine converts the bottom input, since output register $8002 is seven, to a digital value that is left in accumulator A. This value is then stored in the bottom row of the table TBL. The index register and the contents of output register $8002 are decremented to output row six of TBL to the sixth output, and put the value of the sixth input into row six of TBL, in the next iteration of the loop. When all rows are output and input, this subroutine is left. The above routine can be made more useful if two tables are used, one for outputs and a different one for inputs, but more code would be needed, and it would not show any important new ideas.

The above DAS and subroutine can be used in control systems. A brief sketch of their uses will now be offered to round out the discussion of this chapter. The three main applications are collection of analog data, generation of analog signals, and feedback control.

The microcomputer is admirably suited to collect analog data. The DAS and subroutine discussed above can collect a sample of up to eight analog inputs. The collected data could be stored in a table, transmitted across a data link, or operated on. The programs for these operations should be simple enough so that they are not spelled out here. Data collection using microcomputers has a unique advantage over simpler techniques that

should be stressed, however. Its software can execute functions on the incoming data. In particular, the function can correct errors in the measurement apparatus, as is discussed below.

Suppose the incoming data has value x, but the measurement apparatus
reports the value as $y = F(x)$. The function F can be empirically obtained by
inputting known values of x, then regarding the values of y. Suppose F is an
invertible function and the inverse function is G; then $x = G(y)$. The software can read y from the measurement apparatus then compute $G(y)$ to get
the accurate value of x.

A number of techniques can be used to evaluate some arbitrary function
$G(y)$ such as might be obtained for correcting errors. The well-known
Taylor-series expansion is sometimes useful, but to evaluate such a
polynomial may take a long time and accumulate a lot of rounding error. A
better technique is to evaluate $G(y)$ as a continued fraction $G(y) = A/\big(B +
G'(y)\big)$, where $G'(y)$ is y or else is a continued fraction. The most suitable
technique for microcomputers, however, is the *spline* technique. Just as a
complex curve is often drafted by drawing sections of it with a ''French
curve,'' the complex function $G(y)$ is approximated by sections of simpler
functions (called splines) like parabolas. See figure 5-21. Given a value y, we
determine which section of $G(y)$ it is in to choose which spline to evaluate.
This is done by comparing y against the values y_i that separate the splines. A
fast way is to test y against the middle y_i, *then if* y is less than y_i check y
against the y_i a quarter of the way across the scale, or else check against the
y_i three quarters of the way, and so on, in the same manner as the successive
approximation technique for A-to-D conversion. Once the section is determined, evaluate the function by evaluating the spline. If the spline is a
parabola, then $X = A \times y^{**}2 + B \times y + C$ for some constants A, B, and
C. The values y_i for the boundaries and the constants A, B, and C, can be
stored in a table. Software routines to search this table to select the correct
spline, and to evaluate the spline, are quite simple and fast on a microcomputer.

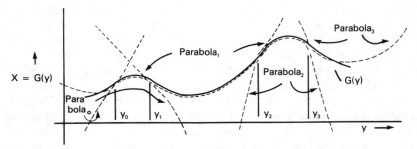

Figure 5-21. The Spline Technique

Analog signals can also be converted to digital values, then filtered using digital techniques, rather than filtered using OP AMPs as discussed earlier in this chapter. Digital filtering is discussed below as a feedback control technique.

In a manner similar to that above, if analog values are to be output from a microcomputer, errors in the output apparatus may be corrected in software. If the true output value is y, but if x is sent to the output, the output is actually $y = F(x)$; then if F is invertible and G is the inverse of $x(x = G(y)$, the microcomputer can evaluate $G(y)$ and send this value to the output system. The program that evaluates $G(y)$ precompensates for the error to be made in the output apparatus.

A test system might be designed using the above techniques to output some analog voltages to the thing being tested then measure the voltages it returns. While these systems are important, the feedback control system is even more important and interesting. Figure 5-22 shows the classic model of the feedback control system. The entire system has a stimulus x (or a set of stimulae considered as a vector) as input, and an output z (or a set of outputs, a vector z). The system that outputs z is called the *plant*. The plant usually has some deficiencies. To correct these, a *feedback system* is implemented as shown in figure 5-22, which may be built around a microcomputer and DAS. Note that the microcomputer and DAS are in the feedback loop, and the machinery being controlled is in the main "plant." The output of this system, an error signal, is added to the stimulus signal x, and the sum of these signals is applied to the plant. Feedback control systems like this have been very successfully used to correct for deficiencies in the plant, to provide stable control over the output z.

Three techniques have been widely used for feedback control systems. The proportional integral differential, the linear filter, and the multi-input multi-output controllers are discussed below.

The simplest and most popular controller is called the *proportional in-*

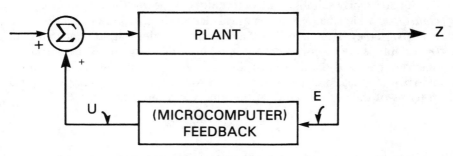

Figure 5-22. Feedback Control

tegral differential controller (PID). Its form is easy to implement on a microcomputer. The output of the feedback system U is a weighted sum of the current input to the feedback E, the integrated value of E, and the differential value of E:

$$U = A \times E + B \times \int_o^t E(t)\, dt + C \times d(E(t))/dt$$

Integration is nicely approximated in a microcomputer by adding each input value to a number in memory each time the inputs are sampled. If the feedback control system is working correctly, the inputs will be positive and negative, so this running sum will tend to zero. The differential is simply approximated by subtracting the current value from the last value of the input.

A more general kind of controller can be implemented as a digital version of a filter. (As a filter, it can be used to correct errors in analog measurement and output systems as we discussed above.) A *digital filter* is defined by a *Z-transform*. A *Z*-transform is an expression like:

$$D(z) = \frac{U(z)}{E(z)} = \frac{A_0 + A_1 \times Z^{**}-1 + A_2 \times Z^{**}-2 + \ldots A_n \times Z^{**}-n}{1 + B_1 \times Z^{**}-1 + B_2 \times Z^{**}-2 + \ldots + B_n \times Z^{**}-n}$$

This expression is evaluated in a microcomputer as follows. Call the input at time k, E_k, and the output at time k, U_k. Then the output U_k at any given time is just the weighted sum of the inputs and outputs of the n prior times:

$$U_k = A_o \times E_k + A_1 \times E_{k-1} + \ldots + A_n \times E_{k-n}$$
$$- B_1 \times U_{k-1} - \ldots - B_n \times U_{k-n}$$

The program should keep the vectors A, B, E, and U. Each time it updates the most recent output value U_k, it can shift all values of E and U back one place to get the output U_k at the next time k.

A particularly suitable control technique is the *multi-input multi-output controller*, which has a mathematical definition as follows. Let E be an (eight-variable) input and U be an (eight-variable) output, and S be an (n-variable) state vector, stored in a table in memory. A, B, C and D are matrixes having suitable dimensions. Then the controller is defined by matrix multiplication equations that give the next value of the state vector S in terms of the current value of the state vector and the input E:

$$S = A \times S + B \times E$$

and that give the output values in terms of the current value of the state vector and the input:

$$U = C \times S + D \times E$$

These equations can be implemented by subroutines to perform matrix multiplication and vector addition, together with the subroutine that exercises the DAS to get the input vector X and to output the values of Z.

These techniques show how a microcomputer with a DAS can implement simply multiple input analog measurement systems, multiple sources of analog output voltages with programs to correct for nonlinear errors or to filter the data digitally, or one of several feedback controllers. All we have to do is to determine the coefficients for the formulas above. That is a nontrivial problem, but it is treated in many excellent texts on control theory. Our only intent in this chapter was to show that, once a desired control system has been defined, it can be implemented easily in a microcomputer.

5-7 Conclusions

This chapter has covered a lot of ground. Several analog devices and circuits commonly used in microprocessor I/O systems have been examined. We studied transducers that convert physical properties like distance into and from analog voltages. We studied analog circuits that amplify and condition these signals. A keyboard and display system was examined, and we saw many analog digital and software alternatives for the functions that it needs. The A-to-D and D-to-A converters were surveyed, and the data-acquisition system was studied. Finally, software techniques for compensating for nonlinearities and for filtering the digitized signals were discussed.

In general, most I/O devices have some analog circuitry. On one extreme, some analog controllers use only OP AMPs without a microprocessor. This seems to be the best way to implement fixed function controllers, especially if the frequencies of the signal can be higher than the Nyquist rate of an economically acceptable microprocessor-based system. On the other hand, we may implement everything that we can in software, minimizing the analog hardware. This appears attractive where flexibility is valuable and the signal rates are not higher than the Nyquist rate of an economically acceptable system. In between, just about every design has some analog hardware to implement filtering or power amplification, some software to control the operation, and some digital hardware to free the microcomputer to do something else as the digital hardware controls the system. A good designer, therefore, must be aware of the analog devices and circuits, and must be aware of the advantages of the different ways to implement some functions that can be implemented in analog or digital hardware, or in software.

This chapter should provide sufficient background for the reader to be able to understand what the analog circuitry in an I/O device is supposed to be doing, and to be able to sort out many of the analog, digital, and software alternatives for implementing important I/O functions. If the reader wants further information, we recommend Garrett's *Analog Systems for Microprocessors and Minicomputers*, published by the Reston Publishing Company. Many of the concepts we have introduced in this chapter were extracted from or inspired by that fine book. Applications notes from linear integrated circuits manufacturers, and even catalogs from some of them, have a wealth of useful information about how to use the chips they make. National Semiconductor's two books *Linear Applications Handbooks I and II* are very good, as is the catalog for Analog Devices Incorporated. Finally, *Electronics* mazagine provides design information on the use of these analog circuits, and other trade and hobby magazines often show interesting and useful circuits.

The reader should now be ready to use analog circuits in microcomputers. We now turn our attention to frequency analog signals, and then to communications systems that are used in microcomputer I/O.

Problems

Note

Problems 1, 5, 12, 13, and 25 are paragraph-correction problems. See the problem section at the end of chapter 1 for guidelines for these problems. Guidelines for software problems can be found there, and guidelines for hardware problems can be found at the end of chapter 2.

1. *A transducer changes physical properties, such as distance, to or from voltages or frequencies. The most accurate position measurements can be made using a potentiometer. Acceleration can be measured by measuring distance at several specific times and integrating the results in software. A light emitting diode is clear when no voltage appears across it, and is opaque when a voltage appears across it. The photoresistor is the fastest light-to-voltage transducer, but it is nonlinear. Very high temperatures are best measured with a diode, whose output voltage is 2.2 volts per degree Kelvin. Pressure is generally measured by converting pressure to heat, and measuring the temperature.

2. A stepping motor has three windings and the power signals for them are called A, B, and C. These are singulary (only one is asserted at a time), and the stepping motor is made to go clockwise by making A, B, and C run in the sequence TFF FTF FFT TFF . . . and counterclockwise by making them run in the sequence FFT FTF TFF FFT. . . . Each time the next pattern is output in either sequence, the stepping motor rotates seven and one-half degrees in the direction indicated by the sequence. (a) Write an initialization routine and a subroutine with two entry points CW and CCW that will cause the stepping motor to rotate seven and one-half degrees clockwise, and seven and one-half degrees counterclockwise, respectively. Use a global variable SMTR on page zero to remember the pattern, which will be output on the three least significant bits through an output register at location $8000. (b) Write a routine to rotate the motor at one rotation per second. Use the subroutine in part (a) and use real-time synchronization. (c) Assume an input at location $8001 has most significant bit true when the motor has moved an object to a terminal position, which is the most counterclockwise position, otherwise the bit is false. Write a routine to position the object N positions clockwise from the terminal position where each position corresponds to a seven and one-half-degree rotation of the motor. Assume the object position is initially unknown, and the number N is in accumulator A, so the object has to be position in the terminal position first, then stepped out to the Nth position. Use real-time synchronization, and assume that the motor can be pulsed for ten milliseconds with each pattern

to cause it to rotate. (Part (c) is basically the mechanism used to position the head on a floppy disk.)

3. A gear has a tooth every ten degrees of rotation, the teeth are five degrees wide, and two wiper contacts are two degrees apart. These contacts output a low signal when they touch a tooth. (a) Write a (Mealy) sequential machine description of the state transitions, where the internal states are the signal pair on the contacts, LL, LH, HL, and HH, and the input states are CW for moving clockwise, CCW for moving counterclockwise, and NUL for no movement. The leftmost contact value of the pair corresponds to the more counterclockwise of the two wiper contacts as they appear close together. (b) Write an initialization routine and interrupt handler that will keep track of the position of the gear. The more counterclockwise of the two contacts is connected to the CA1 input of an M6821 A device (data/direction register at $8000, control at $8001, and cause a FIRQ interrupt each time the signal falls) and the other contact can be read as the most significant bit of the A device. The position of the gear, in thirty-sixths of a revolution, will be kept as a double-precision signed number POSN, positive numbers indicating clockwise rotation. (When the machine is turned on, we will just assume that the position of the gear is defined to be zero.)

4. A home temperature control will control a furnace and an air conditioner based on the temperature measured in the home. The temperature in degrees can be read from an input device at location $8000, the furnace and air conditioner are controlled by writing a word into an addressable latch at location $8000, such that writing zero there turns off the air conditioner, writing one there turns it on, writing two there turns off the furnace, and writing three there turns it on. (a) Show the logic diagram of this I/O system, using the 74LS259 addressable latch and 81LS95 bus driver. Use incompletely specified decoding, assuming that the program uses addresses zero to $3FF, $8000 for these devices, and $FC00 to $FFFF. (b) Suppose the desired temperature is stored at location SETTMP. Write a complete program to control the furnace and air conditioner to adjust the home temperature to this value. If the temperature is three degrees cooler than the desired temperature, turn on the furnace (fully), but turn it off when the temperature is one degree lower (because residual heat will cause the temperature to rise after the furnace is off); if the temperature is three degrees higher, turn on the air conditioner (fully), but if the air conditioner was on within the last two minutes, do not turn it on (because the back-pressure in the compressor has to dissipate or the motor will stall when it is turned on). Use real-time synchronization, assuming the E clock rate is one megaHertz.

5. *Bipolar transistors have very high input impedances and are commonly used to measure bipolar (AC) voltages. The VFET or Darlington transistor is a good output for a microcomputer for controlling direct cur-

rent. SCRs can be used to control AC. A single SCR alone can control both positive and negative cycles of an AC power signal. Proportional cycle control is most attractive for microcomputer systems because it provides the most precise control over the amount of power applied to the load. Proportional cycle control is commonly used to control the heat of an electric range. An operational amplifier has two inputs, and it outputs a voltage that is a large number times the difference between the voltages on the inputs, as long as the OP AMP is in the saturated mode. An integrator uses a capacitor on the input to an OP AMP in order to sample the incoming voltage. A comparator is an OP AMP used in the saturated mode. A modern OP AMP such as the CA3140 has very high input impedance, which is useful in microcomputer I/O systems because it allows the use of small capacitors and permits the sensing of minute currents from transducers such as *pH* measurement devices. The analog switch allows one to switch a digital signal as a result of a comparison of an analog signal. The timer is a useful device which is most commonly used to convert a voltage into a frequency.

6. Write a routine to control an incandescent lamp using proportional cycle control. Assume the most significant bit of an input at location $8000 is true when the sixty-hertz power signal is positive, and false otherwise, that the number in LGHT is the number of degrees of phase that the light should be on in every half cycle (8.333 milliseconds), and the most significant bit of the output at $8001 has to be pulsed high for exactly five microseconds to fire the Triac that controls the lamp. Use real-time synchronization and assume the E clock rate is one megaHertz.

7. For each of the circuits in figure 5-23, show the output voltage V_o as a function of $V_1, V_2, \ldots$, (and V_o for circuit d).

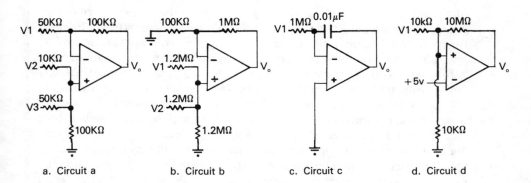

Figure 5-23. Some OP AMP Circuits

8. Section 5-2.3 discussed in detail the limits of input voltages, and other parameters, for positive five-volt single supply use of the CA3140. Discuss all the limits and parameters that are different, and give their values, for plus or minus fifteen-volt dual supply use of this same OP AMP.

9. Show the logic diagram for a 555 timer and eight resistors that can be put into the timing resistor position (R_2 in figure 5-8) using a 4051 analog multiplexer. The multiplexer will be controlled by an output register. Show all connections from the output register and the analog multiplexer to the timer.

10. Show a diagram of an amplifier whose gain is controlled by an output register. The (4-bit) unsigned binary number N in the register sets the gain to -N. Use a CA3140 OP AMP, 4066 analog switch, and resistors in the range of 100 kilohms to 10 Megohms, show pin numbers and values of all components, including bypass capacitors, so that the circuit is ready to be built.

11. Show a diagram for a circuit that uses two CA3140 OP AMPs to output the absolute value on V_{abs} and the (logical) sign on SGN of an input voltage V_{in}. Show all pin numbers and bypass capacitors and the values of all components, so that the circuit is ready to be built.

12. *Filters are used to remove noise from the signal being measured or output. A high-pass filter has capacitors connected to ground and to the output to short out the low-frequency components and integrate them out of the signal. A light pen develops a signal that corresponds to the average brightness of the CRT screen, so a high-pass filter is commonly used to eliminate the noise, which is a higher frequency "signal." A Butterworth filter is often used in digital systems because it delays all frequency components about the same, so that square waves do not develop humps or grooves. Analog switches are useful for selecting inputs and for nonlinear signal conditioning. One of the ways a microcomputer can control the loss of a signal is to chop it at a fixed frequency, but so that it is chopped off for a proportion of each cycle that corresponds to the loss. Three nonlinear functions that are often performed in analog hardware are absolute value, logarithm, and sample-and-hold. The logarithm function is often used before an A-to-D converter because microcomputers have difficulty multiplying, and multiplication can be performed by adding the logarithm.

13. *Key bounce is a problem where the user bangs on the key repeatedly when he wants something done. It can be eliminated by a sample-and-hold circuit that takes a "snap-shot" of the signal just once. Software debouncing is rather rarely done in microcomputers because it takes too much of the valuable time of the microcomputer to monitor the key. Keyboards are often used on microcomputers because the user may want to enter different commands, and a set of keys is most easily used. Linear selection is often used for a keyboard that has a lot of keys like that of a typewriter. N-key

roll-over is a property of keyboards wherein the microcomputer can correctly determine what keys were pressed, and in what order they were pressed, provided that no more than N keys are pressed at one time. Two-key rollover is commonly used in microcomputer systems but is rather inadequate for most adept users, who often hold several keys down at once. The LED seven-segment display is used on many inexpensive microcomputer systems because it uses very little power. LCDs have to be multiplexed carefully, because they require AC (square wave) signals, and the difference in rms voltage between a clear and an opaque segment is rather small. Therefore we do not multiplex more than two or three LCDs on the same drive circuitry. A typical keyboard system is often integrated with a multiplexed display system because the hardware to scan the keyboard can also be used to scan the display.

14. Write a program that uses three counts of hysteresis to debounce a switch (as in DEBNCE in section 5-4.1). The count of the number of closures is initially one and is incremented each time the switch is closed, as in that program, but is set to $F8 (-8) when the closure is recognized after the count reaches $10, and is set to eight when the count reaches $F0 (− $10) because we recognize that the switch is indeed open. This program should exit to a routine DOIT when the key has been recognized pressed, but that routine will jump to label RETN in your program when it is finished. At that time, your program should assume the key is still pressed, so it will not repeat the program DOIT until the key is released and pressed again.

15. Show the output of a logic analyzer, left column being the R/W signal, the next two columns the address and data bus values in hexadecimal, and each row for successive memory cycles, for two complete executions of the loop in the program SCAN (section 5-4.2). Assume that in the beginning of the first execution, the readable output register is two and the third key is the only one pressed.

16. Write the table for the program LOOK (section 5-4.3) so that the hexadecimal number in accumulator A will be converted and output to light the correct LEDs to display the number. Your answer should be in hexadecimal, not binary, in a FCB assembler directive or two, and you should display the numbers six and nine without their "tails," "one" should appear on the right of the display, and B, C, and D should be lower case letters.

17. Write a reentrant 6800 program equivalent to the program LOOK in section 5-4.3.

18. Section 5-4.3 showed a technique for multiplexing LCD displays. Assuming the voltages are zero, one, two, and three volts and each segment is displayed for one millisecond, draw an oscilloscope trace for the following waveforms, so that the top trace is the waveform on one plate of a LCD display segment and the bottom trace is the waveform on the other plate.

The single waveform will have four (one-millisecond) sections: (a) for a segment that is off, in a digit that is off (clear segment); (b) for a segment that is on, in a digit that is off (clear segment); (c) for a segment that is off, in a digit that is on (clear segment); (d) for a segment that is on, in a digit that is on (dark segment).

19. Suppose the current source in figure 5-16a is one microampere. What is the largest value of resistor that will apply at most four volts to the input to the sample-and-hold circuit when the program EXSP in section 5-5.1 is executed, and what should the capacitor value be for this resistor, assuming a one-megahertz clock and that $FF in the output register will produce 1.99 volts.

20. Show a diagram of a summing D-to-A converter (like figure 5-16a) that outputs the value of a four-bit two's complement number in volts (for example, 1100 puts out negative four volts). Use a CA3140 OP AMP and 4066 analog switches and use resistors in the range 100 kilohms to 10 megohms. Show all pins and component values, and show the bypass capacitors so the circuit is ready to be built from your diagram.

21. Write a program to follow SUCCES (section 5-5.2) to determine the least significant bit of the result.

22. Write a reentrant 6800 program equivalent to the program SUCCES in section 5-5.2.

23. Write a routine to evaluate a spline as specified by a table. The table has a row for each parabola, and a column for the larger limit y_i on the interval where that parabola is to be used, and three columns from left to right for the constants A, B, and C, the coefficients of the parabola ($G(y) = A \times y^{**}2 + B \times y + C$). The parabolas are in successive rows of the table in order of increasing values of y_i, so the ith parabola should be evaluated by your routine if the input y is between y_i in that row and y_i in the row above it, and the last row has $y_i = 0$ as a marker of that row. Assume input y in accumulator A, and all y_is are unsigned eight-bit numbers, and all A, B, and C values in the table are two's complement numbers.

24. Write a digital filter program equivalent to the Z transform $(3 - 2 \times Z^{**} - 1)/1 + 4 \times Z^{**} - 1)$. Evaluate the filter function repetitively on the input, read at $8000, so that the filtered output is fed out the output at location $8001.

25. *Converters are based on integrators or sample-and-hold circuits. The sampling converters have a Nyquist rate, which is the rate at which they sample the analog signal. A high-pass filter is commonly used to remove frequencies below this Nyquist rate to prevent alias signals from appearing. D-to-A converters include ladder networks, commonly available on integrated circuits, and exponential superposition converters, which are exceptionally accurate yet very cheap. D-to-A converters like the successive approximation converter are able to sample the input signal quite rapidly,

but parallel and pipeline converters are the fastest, using more hardware to achieve the greater speed. A frequenty-to-voltage converter is based on a very accurate one-shot that is triggered at the rate of the input frequency, and whose output is filtered through a low-pass filter to recover the voltage. A tachometer is a good voltage-to-frequency converter, but is limited to low frequencies. A data acquisition system uses sample-and-hold circuits to sample the input signals and uses a D-to-A converter to develop the output voltages and a reference voltage for an A-to-D converter. The A-to-D converter can use delta, ramp, or successive approximation programs to measure input voltages.

6

Counters and Timers

The counter-timer is one of the most flexible of the recently developed large scale I/O integrated circuits. It can generate a square wave. The square wave can be used to generate sine waves, or any periodic wave. Sine waves can be used in cassette tape recorders, telephone systems (touch-tone), and signals to the user (bleeps). The counter-timer can be used to generate single shot pulses. These can control motors, solenoids, or lights to give precisely timed pulses that are independent of the timing errors to which the real-time programmed microprocessor is susceptible, such as those of dynamic memory and DMA cycle steals, and interrupts. The counter-timer can provide interrupts itself to coordinate a program: to effect an instruction step or a real-time clock. To effect an instruction step, the timer is set up as the monitor is left, so that it allows one instruction to be executed in the user program before the interrupt returns control to the monitor. The monitor is used to examine or modify memory or registers, then the monitor is left, and the next instruction in the user program is executed, and so on. A real-time clock can be effected if the timer interrupts every millisecond. The module can be used to count the number of events (falling edges of a signal input to the module), and thus the number of events in a fixed interval of time (the frequency). It is also capable of measuring pulse width and period. Several things can be converted to the period of a signal: voltage can be converted using the voltage-to-frequency converter integrated circuits, and resistance or capacitance can be converted to the period of a waveform using a linear timer integrated circuit like the ubiquitous 555. We also observe that a single signal can be easily isolated using optical isolators so the voltage of the system being measured can be kept from the microcomputer and the user. (However, more bandwidth is needed for FM signals.)

The counter-timer is the principal component, then, in interfacing to frequency analog signals. These signals, like FM radio signals, are easier to handle than amplitude analog signals and comparatively free from noise. We observe that, at the time of writing, the use of amplitude analog signals is pervasive in interface circuits, but we feel that frequency (or phase) analog signals will become equally important.

The primary object of this chapter is to present the principles of using the counter-timer module. To make these principles concrete, the M6840 counter-timer is introduced; however, we start by hiding its general purpose flexible control, showing those rituals that are used to initialize it without

307

much explanation of why they are performed. Later, the details of control are explained, so the reader can implement his own variations of the ideas presented in the chapter. Although this is not the optimum way to describe the M6840 as a chip, we believe that this approach better teaches the theory and philosophy behind the use of counter-timer modules.

A further object of this chapter is to emphasize a fundamental principle of top-down design. Chips like the timer are so fascinating that the designer may decide to use them before he examines the alternative hardware and software techniques. This is an instance of bottom-up design: I have got this marvelous counter chip, now where can I use it? As we chided in an earlier chapter, this is rather like the popular TV character, Carnak the Magnificent, who answers a question that is sealed in an envelope, giving the answer before he knows the question. Bottom-up design is especially evident whenever a new and powerful integrated circuit like the counter-timer appears on the market. This design approach generally leads to bad designs, so we will constantly emphasize the need to examine alternatives, and we will discuss some of the alternatives to using this counter timer chip.

This chapter should acquaint the reader with the hardware and software of the counter-timer chip and with alternative techniques using a simple parallel I/O port and more hardware or a parallel I/O port and more software. He should be able to connect a counter-timer like the M6840 to a microcomputer and write software to generate square waves or pulses or to measure the frequency or period of a periodic wave or the pulse width of a pulse. With these techniques, he should be able to interface to I/O systems that generate or use periodic signals or pulses, or to interface through voltage-to-frequency or frequency-to-voltage converters to analog I/O systems.

6-1 The Simple M6840 Module

We introduce the bare essentials of the counter-timer chip in this section for further reference in this chapter. A data sheet on this chip is provided in *The Complete Motorola Microcomputer Data Library*, for further details. The module has three almost separate and identical devices. Each device has a sixteen-bit read-only *counter register*, a corresponding sixteen-bit write-only *latch* to reinitialize the counter each time it counts to zero, and an eight-bit write-only *control register*. The three counters have a common read-only *status register* to identify device interrupts. Each device has three connections to the outside world—negative logic *clock* C, negative logic *gate* G, and positive logic *output* O. The designers chose to make the counters with sixteen bits because this corresponds to about four and a half decimal digits of accuracy—enough accuracy for control systems. Eight bits would be too small and more than sixteen bits would be inconvenient to handle in a microcomputer. Three devices were put in this chip because relatively few pins are needed, and three could be put on a contemporary large scale integrated circuit. Although we often need but one, the flexibility of the counter-timer seems to allow new applications, so we do not mind the small extra cost for the spare devices. Figure 6-1 shows the block diagram of the module.

Suppose, for concreteness, the module is addressed at locations $8000 through $8007. The control registers and status register are at locations $8000 and $8001, and each latch-counter register is at a pair of locations below $8002. Using two locations for each latch-counter allows them to be accessed by the LDD and STD instructions for convenient handling. LDD $8002 will read the current contents of the counter register of the first device and STD $8002 will write into the corresponding latch. Similarly, LDD $8004 and LDD $8006 will read the counter register of the second and third devices, respectively, while STD $8004 and STD $8006 will write into the latches of the second and third devices. LDA $8001 will read the common status register, while STA $8001 will write into the control register for the second device. Using the same technique that we saw in the M6821, bit zero

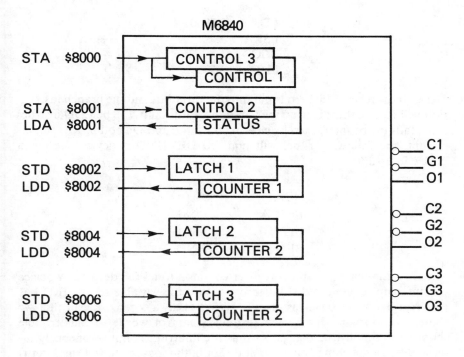

Figure 6-1. The M6840

of the control register of the second device is like a seventeenth address bit used to select the other control registers: if that bit is zero, STA $8000 will store into the third device control register, if one, into the first device control register. Note that the control registers are write-only and the status register is read-only. Do not try to increment a control register in an INC $8000 instruction, since arithmetic operations on memory require readable output registers.

For most of the following examples, we need only one device, which is the first device. To store a word in accumulator A into the control register, we execute the ritual:

```
LDB      #1
STB      $8001
STA      $8000
```

The first two lines merely put a T in bit zero of the control register for device two, so that the third line can store the desired word in the control register for device one. Using the gadfly approach, the following ritual will loop until the device interrupt for device one is set:

```
L    LDA      $8001
     LSRA
     BCC          L
     LDD      $8002
```

Here, status register bit zero is put into the carry bit, and the branch instruction will loop in these instructions until the status bit is T. The LDD instruction reads the counter, thereby clearing the interrupt. On polling after an interrupt, the following ritual will jump to DEVHND if device one has a device interrupt:

```
LDA          $8001
EOR A        #$81
BITA         #$C1
BEQ          DEVHND
```

The first line reads the status register common to all the devices. A device one interrupt is indicated if bit zero is T and the variable on the IRQ bus pin, read from bit seven, is also T. Bit six is always zero. Recall that we should test for one zero when reading a control word, so that trouble shooting is simplified, that is, so that the interrupt is not erroneously indicated when the chip is burned out or not in the socket. To test this, status bits seven and one are inverted and the BIT instruction checks the resulting bits zero, six, and seven for false. In the interrupt handler, the device interrupt is cleared by reading the counter, as in the LDD $8002 instruction.

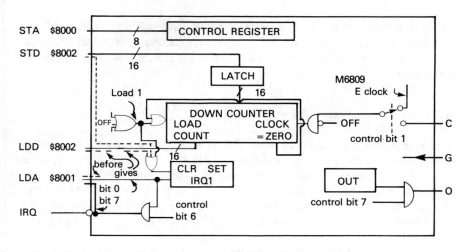

Figure 6-2. The Basic Counter Device

Here we discuss the several counter and interrupt request signals for device one. The counter register has control variables LOAD and CLOCK, a one-bit output =ZERO, and a sixteen-bit output COUNT. The IRQ1 flip-flop has SET and CLR inputs. A flip-flop OUT drives the output pin O. Control bit zero, called OFF, turns the timer off if asserted. When the device is off, words in the latch are also put into the counter. When on, the counter can be decremented each time its CLOCK signal falls. If control bit one is T, the M6809 E clock is used, if F, the signal on the clock pin for this device is used to decrement the counter. Each time the counter reaches zero, the output =ZERO is true, and the sixteen-bit number in the latch is loaded into the counter register on the next falling CLOCK edge. If the number were n, the counter counts modulo $n + 1$. The IRQ1 interrupt request flip-flop is set as a function of the mode, but is always cleared when LOAD is asserted to load the counter or when the counter is read just after the status register is read. IRQ1 can be read as status register bit zero. IRQ2 ANDed with control bit six can be read as status bit seven, and outputs on the IRQ pin can be read in negative logic to connect to a wire-OR bus line. Finally, OUT is ANDed with control bit seven to drive the output pin O.

6-2 Signal Generation

We can generate square waves and pulses for external hardware. We can also generate interrupts for the microcomputer that can be used to time operations: this includes the timing of output signals. This section will consider the generation of signals with the M6840 and with alternative hardware and software techniques. The generation of square waves, and subsequent generation of arbitrary repetitive waveforms, will be considered first. The next subsection shows the techniques for generation of pulses. The last section shows how interrupts used to implement real-time clocks can be generated.

6-2.1 The Gated Square-Wave Generator

The object of this section is to show how to generate square waves, and with them, how to generate other periodic signals. We first address the problem of generating square waves with the desired period, because it is fairly easy to generate any other periodic signal from a square wave. Most of the section will concentrate on the use of a counter-timer chip such as the M6840. But before that is fully discussed, we will consider alternatives, which use more software or some analog or digital hardware.

A very economical way to generate a square wave is by means of a software loop that outputs alternate ones and zeros to an output port. The only hardware needed is a single flip-flop with an address decoder suitable to load, say, the least significant bit of a word written at location $8000. The following program shows how simple is this operation.

```
        NAM     SQUARE
        CLR A
L1      STA A   $8000
        INC A
        LDA B   #N
L2      DEC B
        BNE     L2
        BRA     L1
        END
```

The outer loop increments accumulator A, which complements the least significant bit each time the loop is executed, and then outputs the least significant bit. A delay loop is executed N times (N is supplied by the programmer). The output will change every $12 + 5 \times N$ microseconds (if the M6809 has a 1-megahertz clock), so the output period will be $24 + 10 \times N$ microseconds.

This simple approach is often indicated because of its low cost. It has some basic limitations, however, as we now discuss. The minimum period (maximum frequency) is limited to the microcomputer clock period divided by twice the time to execute the outer loop. Without the inner delay loop, the minimum period is twenty microseconds. The period is controlled by supplying the appropriate value of N. Other values can be selected by putting instructions with the appropriate execution time inside the loop to stretch it out; however, a different routine is needed for each desired value of the period. A routine to handle arbitrary period values would be rather hard to implement. Moreover, if the microcomputer handles an interrupt while in this loop, the timing will be upset. Direct memory access will cause similar timing problems, and so will the use of cycles to refresh dynamic memories. Finally, the microcomputer is unable to do any other useful work while executing the routine to output a square wave. Nevertheless, this approach is recommended wherever a square wave with a fixed period, or a small number of periods, is needed and neither interrupts, nor direct memory access, nor dynamic memory refresh, nor running any other programs while the square wave is generated, are done.

Note that this approach can be generalized. If a full word is output, the ith bit from the right has $2**i$ times the period of the right bit in the above example. Also, noting the similarity to the traffic light controller discussed in chapter 3, almost any pattern sequence could be output in a manner similar to this.

Two analog hardware solutions use a voltage controlled oscillator or a timer like the 555. The microcomputer can output a voltage via an analog multiplexer that selects voltages from taps on a voltage divider chain, or via a D-to-A converter, which can control the frequency of a voltage-to-frequency converter. This approach permits several discrete voltages or an almost continuous range of voltages to select several fixed frequencies or an almost continuous range of frequencies from the oscillator. Alternatively, the resistor in a timer module like the 555 can be selected by an analog multiplexer. The microcomputer output register supplies the address to the analog multiplexer to select the resistor, and thus the period of the output signal. A circuit like this one will be discussed later in the chapter, wherein the microcomputer selects different joysticks to control a 555 so that the microcomputer can read the period of the signal and thus determine the position of the joysticks.

Analog hardware techniques provide almost continuous control without side-effects due to interrupts and can be operated at higher frequencies than the microcomputer clock. They are, however, subject to noise and inaccuracies due to dependence of voltages on temperature, aging, and so on.

Two digital hardware solutions are to build a programmable counter or a multistage binary counter with taps at each stage, using digital integrated circuits. A *programmable counter* is an integrated circuit able to count when clocked, and able to load a word into the counter when a load command is signaled. If this word is supplied by an output register and is loaded each time the counter increments to its largest number and cycles to zero then the period of the counter is determined by the word in the output register. A second technique uses a selector whose address is specified by an output port. The selector chooses an input from a stage i of the counter to output a signal with period $p/(2**i)$. It allows scaling of the frequency by factors of powers of two.

Digital hardware techniques provide frequencies as accurate as the frequency that is used to clock the counter, and these can easily run at a 35-megahertz input frequency. They also are immune to the effects of interrupts and so on; however, they require more integrated circuits, which can increase the size and cost of the final product.

The M6840 counter-timer can be used to output square waves. We will consider the configuration of the device, the ritual needed to configure it, and the software to use it as a square wave generator. Then we will discuss an application of two devices for generating touch-tone signals.

In order to configure a simple square-wave generator, we put $92 in the control register and a number n in the latch. The gate input G is grounded (this is easy to forget). Then if the M6809 clock frequency is one megahertz, a square wave with period $2 \times (n + 1)$ microseconds will appear on the output pin O. See figure 6-3.

To set up this simple generator, the following ritual is executed. Assume that the desired waveform has period $2 \times (n + 1)$ and n is in the D accumulator.

```
STD     $8002
LDB      #1
STB     $8001
LDB     #$92
STB     $8000
```

The STD instruction puts the number n into the latch. The next two instructions expose the control register for device one, and the next two set it to $92, which configures device one to be a square-wave generator.

This generator is gated. The gate input G must be low, or the counter will not count. The user may want this option for some applications. Note that the counter is loaded from the latch at the moment the G input falls,

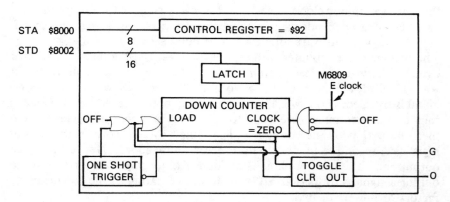

Figure 6-3. A Gated Square-Wave Generator

because the one-shot triggers at that moment to cause the LOAD control to be asserted. This means that, when gating is used, clean square waves will be generated that are low for $n + 1$ memory cycles after the gate signal falls, then alternately high and low for each $n + 1$ cycles after that. If the user only wants a square-wave generator, he must remember to ground the G input.

We now consider an application of this oscillator to the production of touch-tone signals. A *touch-tone* signal is a pair of sine waves having frequencies that represent the digits used in dialing a telephone. A touch-tone generator can generate these signals so that the microcomputer can dial up on the telephone, and it can generate such tones to be sent via radio remote control, to be stored on cassette tape, or whatever. In a top-down design, one must consider all the relevant alternatives. There are integrated circuits that output touch-tone signals in response to keyboard contact closings, but these would require the microcomputer to act like the keyboard to such a chip. Analog switches in place of the keys can be controlled by an output port. (A few other alternatives are also possible.) The number of chips, though, would be at least two, if not more. Next, we consider generating a square wave with $2N$ times the frequency of the sine waves that make up the touch-tone signal and using an N-stage Johnson counter to generate the sine wave. To consider these approaches, we have to study the touch-tone signals and the Johnson counter, as we now do.

A touch-tone signal consists of two sine waves transmitted simultaneously over the phone. Table 6-1 shows the tones required for each digit that can be sent. Table 6-1A shows the mapping of digits to frequencies shown in table 6-1B, and table 6-1B shows the frequencies in hertz and

Table 6-1
Touch-Tone Codes

Table 6-1A
Touch-Tone Digit to Frequency Mapping

Table 6-1B
Touch-Tone Frequencies

Digit	Frequencies	Frequency	Hertz	Counter
0	R4, C2	R1	697	$59
1	R1, C1	R2	770	$50
2	R1, C2	R3	852	$48
3	R1, C3	R4	941	$41
4	R2, C1	C1	1209	$33
5	R2, C2	C2	1336	$2E
6	R2, C3	C3	1477	$29
7	R3, C1	C4	1633	$25
8	R3, C2			
9	R3, C3			

the corresponding values of n to be put in the counter devices to generate the desired frequencies, as they will be used later in the example. Thus, if you want to send the digit 5, send two superimposed sine waves with frequencies 770 Hertz and 1336 Hertz.

In order to produce a sine wave, a Johnson counter is almost ideal. This counter is actually just a shift register whose output is inverted then shifted back into it. See figure 6-4. A four-bit Johnson counter would have the following sequence of values in the flip-flops:

$$
\begin{array}{cccc}
L & L & L & L \\
H & L & L & L \\
H & H & L & L \\
H & H & H & L \\
H & H & H & H \\
L & H & H & H \\
L & L & H & H \\
L & L & L & H \\
\end{array}
$$

As described in Don Lancaster's marvelous little book, *The CMOS Cookbook*, published by Howard Sams, these counters can be used to generate sine waves simply by connecting resistors whose values are 33,000 ohms to the first and third stages, and 22,000-ohm resistors to the second stage of the shift register. See figure 6-4. Although the wave will look like a stair-step approximation to a sine, it is free of the lower harmonics and can be filtered if necessary. Moreover, using more accurate values of resistors and a longer shift register, it is possible to eliminate as much of the low-order harmonics as desired before filtering. In this case, if we want a sine wave with frequency F, we clock the shift register with a square wave whose period should be $1/(8 \times F)$ seconds.

Now we consider ways to implement two square wave generators whose frequencies take on each one of four values. A software solution would need two microcomputers since a whole microcomputer would have to be dedicated to outputting just one square wave; or a rather complex program just might be possible; or a table could be read out to supply the right sequences, but a different table would be needed for each frequency and each table would be quite long. The digital and analog hardware solutions require more than two chips, so we consider the M6840. Note that it has three independent counter-timers, so two square waves can be implemented. This design, using an M6840 to control a pair of Johnson counters, needs only two chips, so we will select it. (Be warned, however, that using the M6840 is not always the most suitable way.)

Consider now the approach to generating a sine wave with frequency F

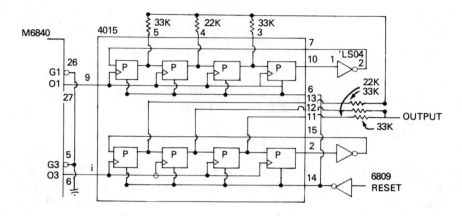

Figure 6-4. A Touch-Tone Generator

using the M6840 to drive a four-stage Johnson counter. Note that the number n in the latch should be $(1,000,000/(16 \times F)) - 1$. The values to be stored in the latches for the touch-tone codes are shown in the right half of table 6-1B. For instance, to send the digit 8, we put the numbers $48 and $29 in the latches of two counters, which will each generate a sine wave to comprise the signal.

Two devices are used to generate the two sine waves required by the touch-tone signal. The external connections are shown in figure 6-4. Note that the gate inputs to the two devices are grounded to enable the counters, and that the CLEAR control on the shift register is connected to the microcomputer RESET bus line to insure that the shift register does not have some unusual pattern in it after power is applied. The desired signal is simply the sum of the sine waves produced by two shift registers, and is obtained merely by connecting to the common points of the resistors. The subroutine TTONE to send a touch-tone code is shown below. Here, we assume that the desired periods for the signal have been obtained, for instance by table lookup in table 6-1B, and are now in index registers Y and U. Counter devices one and three are used. Counter one is set up exactly as in the previous example. Counter three is set up in exactly the same way, except that bit zero of control register must be F to set up control register three.

```
NAM     TTONE
STY     $8002
STU     $8006
CLR      B
```

```
STB      $8001
LDA      #$92
STA      $8000
INC      B
STB      $8001
STA      $8000
RTS
END
```

The first two lines put the period value n for the sine waves into the latches. It really does not matter which period is put in which counter, since the outputs are just added. The next two lines set up control register two so that the following two lines can put the control word $92 into control register three. The following two lines set up control register two so that the last line can put $92 into control register one. This program initializes the counters to output the desired signal. The microcomputer can turn to other things without need to attend to the counters. When desired, the waveform can be stopped by setting the OFF bit, by putting the control code one into control register one. This is easily done as follows:

```
LDA      #1
STA      $8001
STA      $8000
```

A slight variation of this technique can be used to generate any periodic waveform. The square wave can be used to increment a counter which supplies an address to a read-only memory. It can output words to a D-to-A converter, and can store the desired pattern to be developed. Thus, generating a square wave can generate other periodic waves. Finally, as discussed in the previous chapter, a square wave can be integrated to get a ramp signal, and this can be shaped by nonlinear analog techniques. Also, as in music generation, a periodic signal can be shaped by attenuating it under control of an output port to apply attack and decay characteristics in a music synthesizer.

The M6840 is seen to be a valuable tool in generating square waves, which can be used to generate other periodic waves using Johnson counters or read-only memories and D-to-A converters. Nevertheless, the designer must not assume that this chip, or any counter-timer chip, is so much better than any other generator. He must consider the software approach as well as the hardware approaches to pick the best one for his application.

6-2.2 The Pulse Generator

Like the square wave generator, a pulse generator has many uses. The device normally outputs a false value, but outputs a true value for a specified time after each time it is triggered. It can be triggered by software, or by an external signal, and, as for the square-wave generator, there are software and hardware techniques to implement it. The software technique to supply a pulse triggered by software merely outputs a true, waits the required time, and then outputs a false value. To react to an external signal, the external signal can be sensed in a gadfly loop or can generate an interrupt so that the pulse is generated when the signal arrives. Like the software square-wave generator, the software pulse generator is susceptible to timing errors due to interrupts, direct memory access, and dynamic memory refresh cycles. A 555 timer can act like a pulse generator triggered by a microcomputer or an external signal, and the length of the pulse, determined by the value of a resistor and capacitor, can be controlled by selection of the resistor by means of an analog switch controlled from an output port. One-shot integrated circuits can also be controlled in like manner. Finally, the counter-timer chip can be used to generate pulses either when the computer starts them or when they are started by an external signal, and the pulse length can be controlled by the computer, as we now discuss.

In this section, we show how a counter device in the M6840 can be used as a pulse generator. The configuration for a pulse generator is set up by putting the control code $A2 into the control register and the pulse width in the latch. Then the device appears as shown in figure 6-5. Suppose the number n is in accumulator D. Initialization can be done as follows:

```
STD     $8002
LDA     #1
STA     $8001
LDA     #$A2
STA     $8000
```

The one-shot can be triggered in hardware by means of a falling signal on the gate input or in software by execution of a STD $8002 instruction. When triggered, if n is the number in the latch, the output will go high for n clock cycles. Due to a delay in setting the OUT flip-flop, the output goes high the cycle after the STD instruction or the falling edge of the gate input triggers the one-shot, and goes low when the counter reaches zero. The output is high for n clock periods (not $n + 1$ as in the square wave

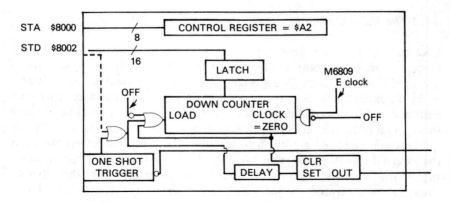

Figure 6-5. A Single-Shot Pulse Generator

generator). After a pulse is generated, the output remains low until the device is triggered again.

A pulse can be generated entirely under software control, using real-time programming and a bit of a parallel output register to output the pulse. The M6840 provides significant advantages, however. The pulse width is precisely timed to within a memory cycle time, which is usually one microsecond, and this time is not affected by processor interrupts, dynamic memory refresh requests, or other subtle problems that affect the timing of real-time programs. This is quite useful in automobile engine control, where the pulse width controls the amount of gasoline injected into the engine, the spark timing, and other key factors in running the engine. A counter-timer chip with three timers is sufficient to control an engine so that the microcomputer can measure input signals and compute the values of the pulse widths to be put in the timers. In fact this is why the M6840 was developed to be the way it is—to appeal to the vast automobile industry.

Pulses are used for a lot of things. We consider the problem of dialing the telephone that uses a *rotary dialer*. A relay connected in series with the dialer contacts will be pulsed to dial the number. The telephone standards require the relay to be closed for at least forty milliseconds and then opened for at least sixty milliseconds for each pulse: the number of pulses corresponds to the number being dialed. A six-hundred-millisecond pause is needed between each number being dialed. The alternatives to be considered are a software approach using a single-bit output device to control the relay, an approach using the M6840 as a pulse generator, and an approach using additional digital or analog hardware. Each designer has his own preferences. In fact, we really wanted to use the M6840. But unless the pulse generation and the timing are done by the M6840 so that the microcomputer can do something else that it has to do, it turns out that the program is actually less efficient using the extra chip than using a simpler approach using real-time synchronization. Therefore, we swallow our pride and implement the dialer using real-time programming.

The routine uses a simple subroutine DEL that outputs the value in the least significant bit of accumulator A to the relay, and then waits N times twenty milliseconds, where N is in accumulator B. The main routine dials a number by outputting a true value for $N = 2$ to the subroutine, then a false value for $N = 3$ to it, this being repeated for each pulse. The subroutine is called with a false value and $N = 30$ to provide the spacing between digits as required by the telephone company.

```
        NAM     DIAL
DIAL    PSHS      A     SAVE AS LOCAL VARIABLE
L1      LDD    #$102    OUTPUT HIGH FOR 2 × 20
                        MILLISECONDS
        BSR     DEL
        LDD     #$3     OUTPUT LOW 3 × 20 MILLISECONDS
        BSR     DEL
        DEC      ,S     COUNT DOWN NUMBER OF PULSES
        BNE      L1
        LDD     #30     OUTPUT LOW FOR 30 × 20
                        MILLISECONDS
        BSR     DEL
        PULS    A,PC    DELETE LOCAL VARIABLE, RETURN
                        FROM SUBROUTINE
*
DEL     STA    $8000    OUTPUT LEAST SIGNIFICANT BIT TO
                        RELAY
L2      LDY   #$1250    SET DELAY FOR 1250 × 8 = 2000
                        MEMORY CYCLES
L3      LEAY   -1,Y     COUNT DOWN
        BNE      L3     TO DELAY 20 MILLISECONDS
        DEC      B      COUNT OUT NUMBER OF 20 MILLI-
                        SECOND EXECUTIONS
        BNE      L2
RTS
END
```

This example gives me an opportunity to relate one of the truly great stories in electronics—the invention of the dial telephone. It seems that in the 1880s Almond B. Strowger, one of two undertakers in a very small town, could not get much business. His competitor's wife was the telephone operator for the town. When someone suffered a death in the family, they called up to get an undertaker. The wife naturally recommended her husband, and not our poor friend, Almond. Necessity is the mother of invention. He contrived a mechanism using a celluloid shirt collar and some pins that could be operated by the caller, to use a stepping relay mechanism that would connect the caller to the desired telephone, so that calls for his business would not go through his competitor's wife. It worked so well that it became the standard mechanism for making calls all over the world. Even today, about a quarter of the telephones use this "step-by-step" or Strowger system.

6-2.3 A Real-Time Clock

Using a configuration almost identical to that of a pulse generator, a device can be used as a real-time clock, or as a trace mode interrupt. These applications will be covered in this section. In particular, an example using a real-time clock and a sine-wave generator to generate the tones for the "Kansas City Standard" tape recording format will show how precise timing can be achieved.

One of the peculiarities of the M6840 chip is that it turns out that the best way to use interrupts to time a program is to configure the device as a pulse generator. The other configurations of the device also produce predictable and useful interrupt signals, but in this configuration the counter is essentially independent of the gate input (as long as it is steady). In order to get an interrupt in n memory cycles, the number $n - 1$ is put into the latch, and the control code $62 is put into the control register. The interrupt request flip-flop IRQ1 will be set every $n + 1$ memory cycles. If the user promptly honors the interrupt and resets the IRQ1 flip-flop right after it is set, an interrupt will be generated every $n + 1$ memory cycles. The device appears as in figure 6-6.

The device can be triggered either by turning the OFF control false or by executing the STD $8002 instruction to load the latch. To set up the device to interrupt $n + 1$ memory cycles after OFF goes false, or after STD $8002 is executed, n is put into accumulator D and the following ritual is executed:

```
STD     $8002
LDA      #1
STA     $8001
LDA     #$62
STA     $8000
```

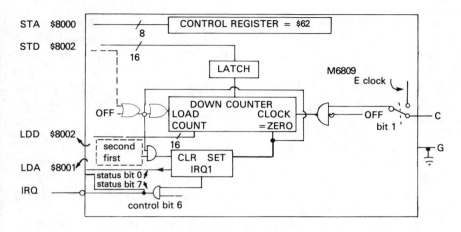

Figure 6-6. A Real-Time Clock

The processor will get an interrupt on the IRQ pin of the M8640 $n + 1$ memory cycles after STA $8000 causes the OFF bit to become false. The interrupt handler polling routine described in section 4-2.2 can test for the interrupt in device one and the interrupt can be cleared in the device handler as described in that section, and as is shown again below:

```
          LDA      $8001
          EORA     #$81
          BITA     #$C1
          BEQ        L
            •
            •
            •
     L    LDD      $8002
            •
            •
            •
          RTI
```

The interrupt is actually cleared in one of three ways. One way is to make the control variable OFF true. This turns off the device, and it is useful when the user does not want another interrupt from the device. Another is to read the control register first, then read the counter register right after that, before any other register or latch in the chip is read or written. This permits you to examine the counter without inadvertently clearing an interrupt when you examine it. One important feature of this method of clearing the interrupt flip-flop is that it does not reload the counter from the latch. Then the next interrupt will occur exactly $n + 1$ memory cycles after the last interrupt occurred. The last way is to store another number in the latch, by means of a STD $8002 instruction. This last technique not only clears the interrupt, but loads the latch with a new value n and causes an interrupt to occur in another $n + 1$ memory cycles.

Some useful alternatives to the above example are now considered. As shown in figure 6-6, the value in the counter can be read at any time by executing the LDD $8002 instruction. This value indicates how long the device will wait until it generates an interrupt. The program may want to know that value to decide whether to start a program that should not be interrupted by the real-time clock.

As shown in figure 6-6, control bits one and six determine whether the clock used by the counter is the M6809 E clock or the signal on the C pin for this device, and whether setting the IRQ1 flip-flop causes a processor interrupt, respectively. In the above example, both were true. If both are false, if $20 were put in the control register, the signal on the C pin would be used to clock the counter, and setting the IRQ1 flip-flop would not cause an interrupt. This configuration will be used in the next section to implement the measurement of frequency. We can use it in this section as a real-time clock using the gadfly technique.

Suppose we would like to build a logic analyzer that has a word recognizer. The output of this word recognizer is true whenever the word appears on the inputs with which the user intends to trigger the logic analyzer. The M6840 can count occurrences of this word, so that a program is executed after the nth occurrence. The program will be written so that it is in a gadfly loop testing device one's IRQ1 flip-flop until the counter reaches zero and sets IRQ1. The output from the word recognizer inputs to the C pin for device one. The number n is put into accumulator D and the following initialization ritual is executed.

```
STD     $8002
LDA     #1
STA     $8001
LDA     #$20
STA     $8000
```

The gadfly loop is executed as follows:

```
L    LDA     $8001
     LSRA
     BCC          L
```

The program will wait in this loop until the $n + 1$th word has been recognized by the word recognizer.

We now use the interrupt technique with the technique we used in the last section to produce the waveforms needed in the "Kansas City Standard" format for recording data on audio cassettes. We use this opportunity to introduce some of the details of this standard and the use of the SYNC instruction.

The personal computer market engendered the need to share software using inexpensive, readily available hardware for storage and transportation of data. The audio cassette tape recorder provided the best means for doing this. In order to exchange information, a standard format was defined by a convention that was sponsored by *Byte* magazine and held at Kansas City (the *Kansas City Standard*). The standard was set up so that even the slowest microcomputers, like the Intel 8008 could keep up with the data rate, and even the cheapest cassette recorders could be used. (However, one has to use good cassette tapes to record data reliably.) Its essential features are listed below:

1. *Bit Transmission*: A true T (mark) is eight cycles of a 2400-hertz sine wave. A false F (space) is four cycles of a 1200-hertz sine wave.
2. *Character Format*: A character is sent (left to right) FDDDDDDDDTT where D is a data bit (T or F), sent least significant bit first.
3. *Record Format*: A record is five seconds of T, followed by any number of characters. Characters can be separated by any number of Ts.

The heart of the problem is in generating precisely eight cycles of a 2400-Hertz sine wave, or precisely four cycles of a 1200-Hertz sine wave. The exact frequency is not critical; the tape recorder will introduce up to ten percent frequency variation. The generator must not produce a fraction of a sine wave, as these fractions introduce low frequency components to the signal that are emphasized by the cassette recorder and can saturate the record amplifier, distorting the signal. From the last section, we saw how easily the M6840 can generate a sine wave with one device. In this section, we find that another device can be used to interrupt the computer at precise times (about every 300th of a second). We will use the interrupt to change the frequency of the sine wave to send the next bit.

The gadfly approach should not be used to switch frequencies. If the gadfly loop takes n clock cycles, from zero to n cycles will elapse from when the counter reaches zero, requesting the next frequency be sent, until the frequency is changed. Although it is better, the common interrupt should not be used either. Since the longest instruction takes twenty cycles, from zero to twenty cycles could elapse. In either case, a fraction of a sine wave could be generated. In order to get around this problem, SYNC is used. It can respond to the interrupt within one memory cycle. Since the counter and the microcomputer are synchronized by the E clock, the use of the SYNC instruction can eliminate all uncertainty about when the frequencies are switched, so that no fraction of a sine wave is produced.

In order to simplify the example to convey the essential concepts, we will show a program that will send alternate true and false bits. The actual program will have to read the data to be sent, one word at a time, strip off bits least significant bit first, and use these bits to select the frequency of the sine wave. The hardware used by this example can actually be the same as that used by the touch-tone signal generator. One counter device (device three) is used to produce the sine wave, as in the touch-tone signal generator, and the other (device one) is used to generate interrupts. The output O of device one is held low by making control bit seven of its control register false, so it will not contribute an unwanted sine wave component to the waveform. The interesting part of the program uses the SYNC instruction. We will assume that only device one of the M6840 can interrupt the processor while it is executing that instruction. To generate a 1200-hertz sine wave using a four-stage Johnson counter, the number $(1,000,000/(16 \times 1200)) - 1 = 51.0833 - 51$ is put in the counter; to generate a 2400-hertz wave, 25 is put in it. To time out either four cycles of the 1200-hertz wave or eight cycles of the 2400-hertz wave, the number $(52 \times 16 \times 4) - 1 = 3327$ is put into the latch for device one, which causes an interrupt every 3328 microseconds. The setup routine and the main program are now shown:

	NAM	KCITY	
	ORCC	#$10	SET IRQ INTERRUPT MASK TO USE SYNC
	LDD	#3327	SET UP COUNTER 1 TO INTERRUPT
	STD	$8002	ABOUT 300 TIMES PER SECOND
	CLR B		
	STB	$8001	SELECT COUNTER 1
	LDA	#$62	CONTROL WORD FOR INTERRUPT
	STA	$8000	
	INC B		SELECT COUNTER 3
	STB	$8001	
	LDA	#$92	PUT IN CONTROL WORD
	STA	$8000	OUTPUT SQUARE WAVE
L1	LDD	#51	TO OUTPUT 1200 HERTZ
	STD	$8006	FROM COUNTER 3

```
SYNC                    WAIT HERE UNTIL 1/300 THS SECONDS
                        ARE UP
LDA        $8001        CLEAR IRQA1 BY READING
LDD        $8002        STATUS, THEN COUNTER
BRN                     COMPENSATE FOR TIME FOR BRA
LDD        #25          TO GENERATE 2400 HERTZ
STD        $8006        FROM TIMER 3
SYNC                    WAIT FOR 1/300 THS SECOND
LDA        $8001        CLEAR IRQ1 BY READING
LDD        $8002        STATUS AND THEN COUNTER
BRA        L1           THEN GO BACK TO OUTPUT 1200
                        HERTZ
END
```

The first line sets the I interrupt mask so that SYNC can be used like a gadfly loop. The next two lines set up the latch on the first device to allow it to interrupt the M6809 every 3328 microseconds. The next eight lines put $92 into control register three, so that it will generate the square waves to drive the sine-wave generator, and $62 in control register one so it will generate interrupts. The main part of the program is the loop from label L1 to the bottom of the program. The first two lines of this segment set up the latch in device three to generate 1200-hertz. Then the program executes an instruction, SYNC. This waits for a true (low) value on the interrupt line IRQ from the M6840. Meanwhile, counter one is decrementing. When it reaches zero, it sets its IRQ1 flip-flop, which causes the IRQ bus line to go low, which causes the microcomputer to finish the SYNC instruction. It is then necessary to clear the device interrupt (IRQ1) by reading the status and the counter registers. (A BRN instruction is put in the program to match the delay due to the BRA instruction to eliminate jitter. This point is cleared up later.) These next two instructions reload the latch in device three to send 2400-hertz sine waves. Again, the SYNC instruction is executed, and again, when the device one counter reaches zero, the SYNC instruction is completed. Although there is a delay D from when the device one counter is zero until when the device three latch is reloaded to send the new frequency, the same delay D occurs when we change from T to F, as from F to T, so the frequencies are switched every 3328 microseconds, and no partial sine waves are generated. Note that the BRN instruction is inserted to compensate for the BRA instruction in order to make the two delays D the same. This program will loop, that is, will go on forever, until the user turns off the machine; however, it shows the principles by which a program can generate the "Kansas City Standard" signals used to store and transport data for microcomputers.

Another useful application of the real-time clock is that of tracing instructions in a monitor. Although the reader is not likely to write a monitor since so many excellent monitors are available, such as JBUG, this application further illustrates the power of a real-time clock.

The trace operation is used to step through a program, one instruction at a time, so the monitor can examine registers and memory after the execution of each instruction. A trace operation works thus: as the monitor program is left, a timer is started. The timer allows all the remaining instructions in the monitor to execute, and interrupts the microprocessor just after it returns to the program being monitored, so that exactly one instruction is executed. The interrupt handler returns control to the monitor so it can examine the result of the instruction. The following program will start the counter in device one of an M6840 and return to the program being monitored:

```
LDD    #N
STD   $8002
LDA    #1
STA   $8001
LDA   #$62
STA   $8000
RTI
```

The number in the latch, N, is just large enough so that after the fifteen cycles it takes to execute the RTI and one cycle of the monitored program, the counter will count to zero and the interrupt will be recognized just as that first instruction is being executed. (It takes some additional time for the interrupt request bit IRQ1 to be set after the counter reaches zero, so the number N is not exactly sixteen, but that is beside the issue.) Of course, an instruction cannot stop in the middle of execution, so the interrupt will be honored at the end of the instruction, no matter how long it takes. The interrupt handler should test the M6840 thus:

```
LDA  $8001
EORA #$81
BITA #$C1
BEQ    L
```

The device handler should rest the timer so that it will not keep interrupting while the monitor program is examining the registers and so on:

```
L    LDA      #1
     STA     $8001
```

STA $8000

(To monitor)

The counter-timer chip is seen to be a valuable component for generation of pulses. But do not forget to consider the alternatives to this chip. Another could be better.

6-3 Frequency Analog Measurement

Converse to generating square wave or pulses, one may need to measure the frequency or period of a square wave or repetitive signal or the pulse width of a pulse. Many important outputs carry information by their frequency—tachometers, photodetectors, piezo-electric pressure transducers. The voltage-to-frequency converter integrated circuit can change voltages to frequencies economically with great accuracy. The frequency of output from a timer chip like the 555 timer is inversely proportional to the resistance and capacitance used in its timing circuit; therefore, measuring frequency can measure resistance or capacitance. Better yet, the period of the signal is linearly proportional to resistance and capacitance. Period can be measured directly. Moreover, for high frequencies, frequency is easier and faster to measure, while for low frequencies, period is easier and faster. The microcomputer is quite capable of inverting the value if necessary. For nonrepetitive waveforms, pulse width measurement is very useful. This can be done too. Also, the time between two events can be measured by using the events to set, then clear, a flip-flop. The pulse width of the output of this flip-flop can be measured. Sometimes the microcomputer has to keep track of the total number of events of some kind. The event is translated into the falling edge of a signal, and the number of falling edges is then recorded. Note that the number of events per second is the frequency. Thus, events are counted in the same way as frequency is measured, but the time is not restricted to any specific value.

In this section, the measurement of frequency is first studied. The counting of events is similar to this, and even though it will not be discussed explicitly, it can be done in the same way as the measurement of frequency. Period measurement is described next. A short example that shows how period measurement can be used to read the positions of several potentiometers is then presented. Finally, pulse width measurement is described.

6-3.1 Frequency Measurement

As with the square-wave generator and pulse generator, frequency and period measurement can be done by software in the M6809 using a simple input port, by digital hardware read by a parallel input port, by an analog technique, and by using a counter-timer chip like the M6840. The designer should consider all techniques—those based on software digital or analog hardware, and counter-timer—for frequency and period measurement. The main body of this section explains how the counter-timer module is used to measure frequency or period. Before this discussion begins, we will consider the other approaches.

The software technique for measuring frequency uses a parallel port at location $8000 whose most significant digit inputs the signal. If this signal comes from a mechanical switch, it must be debounced before being input to this port. Also, this input must be either low or high for at least one cycle (thirty-two microseconds) of the loop in the program below, and a one-shot may be necessary to expand a pulse on this input to satisfy this requirement. Finally, we assume that the frequency is less thn 65,000 hertz, so it can be counted in an index register. Then the following routine will measure the frequency.

	NAM	FREQM	
	LDY	#$8000	SET UP INDEX REGISTER FOR LDA ,Y
	LDD	#31250	SET TO LOOP FOR 1 SECOND
	LDU	#0	INITIALIZE COUNTER TO ZERO
L1	TST	$8000	TEST INPUT IN SIGN POSITION
	BPL	L2	IF IT IS NOW LOW, CHECK IF WAS HIGH
	LDA	$8000	GET HIGH VALUE TO ACCA FOR NEXT TEST
	NOP		COMPENSATE TIMING
	NOP		COMPENSATE TIMING
	NOP		COMPENSATE TIMING
	BRA	L4	LOOP AGAIN TO CHECK NEXT SAMPLE
L2	TST	A	CHECK LAST VALUE
	BMI	L3	IF LOW, DO NOTHING
	LDA	,Y	GET LOW VALUE TO ACCA FOR NEXT TEST
	NOP		COMPENSATE TIMING
	BRA	L4	
L3	LDA	,Y	GET LOW VALUE INTO ACCA FOR NEXT TEST
	LEAU	1,U	IF HIGH, THEN HIGH TO LOW TRANSITION OCCURRED

```
      NOP                  COMPENSATE TIMING
L4    LEAX        , – X    WAIT FOR 1 SECOND
      BNE         L1       SO COUNT AS AN EVENT
      END
```

The inner loop can take three paths, through the three consecutive NOP instructions if the input is high, through L2 and L3 if the input changed from high to low (an event), or through L2 and the next three instructions below it if the input is low and was low before. In all three paths, the timing has been adjusted using NOP instructions so each takes exactly thirty-two memory cycles, or thirty-two microseconds. We had to use a faster LDA ,Y instruction in two of the paths while the other used a slower LDA $8000 instruction to trim the timing. The loop is to be executed 1,000,000/32 or 31,250 times. The index register is initialized in the first line of the program so that it counts loop executions in the last two lines of the program. If the input changes from high to low, index register U is incremented to count the number of cycles of the input signal in one second. Thus, the loop takes one second, and the number of low to high transitions of the input in that time are counted in register U.

A digital hardware approach would use one or more counter ICs that can be cascaded to make up a counter of sufficient width. A parallel I/O register can be used to clear the counter and then read the counter output word, say, one second later. The counter can count input transitions from low to high between these two times. A note of caution is necessary if the width is greater than eight bits. If so, two or more eight-bit bytes will be read at different times, and the counter could be incremented between successive reads. The counter should be examined with this in mind. For instance, a sixteen-bit counter should be read, most significant byte first, then least significant byte, and then most significant byte again. If the readings of the most significant byte differ, the reading should be considered erroneous and should be tried again.

An analog approach would be to convert the frequency to a voltage, then measure the voltage. An FM demodulator, a frequency-to-voltage converter, or a tachometer module can convert high frequencies, audio frequencies, or subaudio frequencies into a voltage and the voltages can be measured by an analog-to-digital converter.

Finally, we focus on the use of a counter-timer chip like the M6840 for frequency measurement or event counting. One counter can count the number of high to low transitions of an input signal. The fixed interval of time can be measured out by another counter in the chip or by real-time programming. The latter technique is easier to explain, and will be considered below. The counting is done by device one in the M6809, though, which by putting $20 in the control register is configured as shown in figure 6-7.

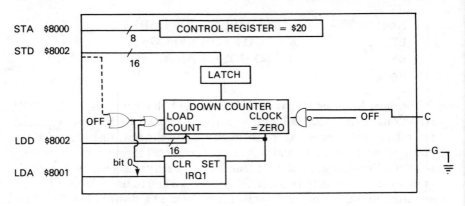

Figure 6-7. An Event Counter, or a Frequency Counter

A real time program to measure the frequency of the C input is shown below.

	NAM	FREQ40	
	LDD	#$FFFF	INITIALIZE LATCH,
	STD	$8002	AND THUS, COUNTER, TO LARGEST NUMBER
	LDX	#50000	SET UP LOOP TO TIME OUT 1 SECOND
	LDA	#1	TO ACCESS COUNTER 1 CONTROL
	STA	$8001	REGISTER, MAKE LSB OF $8001 TRUE
	LDA	#$20	COMMAND WORD TO COUNT INPUT EVENTS
	STA	$8000	TO COUNTER 1 CONTROL REGISTER
L1	NOP		EXPAND LOOP SO IT EXECUTES
	NOP		IN EXACTLY ONE SECOND
	NOP		
	NOP		
	NOP		
	NOP		
	LEAX	, – X	COUNT DOWN X REGISTER
	BNE	L1	TO WAIT 1 SECOND
	LDD	$8002	GET COUNT
	COM A		GET $FFFF-COUNT
	COM B		BY COMPLEMENTING EACH BIT

The usual initialization ritual puts $FFFF into the latch and $20 into the control register. Then the delay loop waits for one second. Since the loop is padded with NOP instructions so it executes in twenty microseconds, the loop counter, index register X, is loaded with 50,000. The device counter register is read. If i events occurred on the C input during the second that the program was in the wait loop, the counter would contain the value $FFFF $- i$. Then to derive the value of i, merely subtract the value read from the counter from $FFFF. An easy way to subtract $FFFF $- i$ is to complement all bits in the word i. The frequency in Hertz is left in accumulators A and B as a sixteen-bit binary number.

It is possible that the counter can overflow in one second, because it is only sixteen bits long and can be incremented every microsecond. When the counter is read, an erroneous number is returned indicating a low frequency. To alert the user, the IRQ1 flip-flop is set if the counter passes zero. If set, it indicates an overflow, and the number in the counter register is invalid. This bit can be read as bit zero of the status register, by a LDA $8001 instruction.

Each of the techniques described above has some advantages and disadvantages. The software approach is least expensive, requiring just a one-bit parallel I/O port. Interrupts, direct memory access operations, or dynamic memory refresh cycles can interfere with the timing, the processor cannot do anything else, and the maximum frequency is limited by the long time taken in the loop to sample the inputs. Nevertheless, it is often quite adequate. The counter-timer chip can use a gadfly loop to time out one second, while using the counter-timer to count events. This allows measuring frequencies up to half the microprocessor clock frequency, but interrupts and so on can interfere with the delay loop timing. If one counter is used to count events, and another is used to measure out a one-second time delay to cause an interrupt, then the two counters in the chip do all the work so the microcomputer is free to do other things and the measurement can be independent of interrupts, DMA, and dynamic memory refresh operations. The digital hardware technique using an external counter can directly measure much higher frequencies. The analog hardware method can be used with A-to-D converters, and is attractive if a data-acquisition system is already needed and has some free inputs to be used with this approach, but this method is prone to noise and errors in the analog signal. Choice of the best technique for any specific application requires some consideration of each of the above methods.

6-3.2 Period Measurement

We now turn to the direct measurement of the period of a waveform. Period can be measured in about the same way as frequency, but the roles of the reference signal that establishes the sampling time and of the signal being measured are interchanged. Then by analogy, period can be measured by software, digital or analog hardware, or a counter-timer chip like the M6840. Again, most of this section will concentrate on the counter-timer approach, using the M6840 as a concrete example, but the other approaches will be discussed first.

The software approach to period measurement is simpler than the software approach to frequency measurement. A counter is cleared, then the input signal is sensed in a gadfly loop until a falling edge occurs. Then the main loop is entered. Each time the loop is executed, the counter is incremented and the input value is saved. The loop is left when the input value from the last execution of the loop was true and the input value in this execution of the loop is false, that is, on the next falling edge. The counter then contains a number N, and the period is N times the time taken to execute the loop. The analog hardware approach uses a voltage-to-frequency converter where the input voltage and the reference voltage are interchanged (see section 5-5.3 for details). The digital hardware approach uses a reference clock to increment a counter. The counter is cleared on the falling edge of the input signal and stops counting (or else is examined) on the next falling edge of the input signal. Some reflection on these techniques shows that in each case the frequency measurement technique is used, but the roles of the reference frequency and the input frequency are interchanged.

The M6840 can be used to measure period, as we might expect. This is now discussed. In order to measure period, the control word $0A is put in the control register. Then the device is configured as follows:

The following program can be used to measure the period of a waveform. The first six lines initialize the control register and latch, as in the last

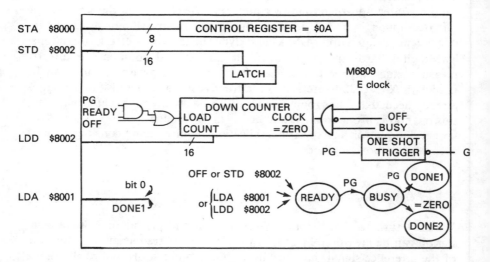

Figure 6-8. A Period or Pulse-Width Timer

case. The gadfly loop checks for entry into the first (DONE1) done state while timing its waiting period. Under worst case conditions, the device may be put in the ready state just after the falling edge of the G signal, which can have a period of 65,000 microseconds, so it can be in the ready state and in the busy state that long. If the loop takes eighteen microseconds, and the counter is decremented once each microsecond, then the device should enter the first done (DONE1) state before 3611 executions of the loop. If it does not, then the period is too long to measure, and the error should be reported.

```
         NAM      PERIOD
         LDD      #$FFFF    INITIALIZE COUNTER 1 TO A LARGE
                           NUMBER
         STD      $8002     TO A LARGE (UNSIGNED) NUMBER
         LDA      #1        PUT A T IN BIT 0 OF CONTROL
                           REGISTER 2
         STA      $8001     TO ACCESS CONTROL REGISTER 1
         LDA      #$0A      CONTROL WORD FOR PERIOD
                           MEASUREMENT
         STA      $8000     PUT IN CONTROL REGISTER 1
         LDX      #3611     DO GADFLY LOOP FOR 65
                           MILLISECONDS
L1       LDA      $8001     CHECK STATUS REGISTER
         BITA     #1        TO SEE IF COUNTER 1 IS DONE
         BNE      L2        IF SO, THEN LEAVE LOOP
         LEAX     ,-X       ELSE LOOP (UP TO 14000 TIMES)
         BNE      L1        IF NOT DONE BY THEN, IT IS IN
                           DONE2 STATE (GO TO ERROR
                           ROUTINE—PERIOD IS TOO LONG)
                 •
                 •
                 •
L2       LDD      $8002     GET COUNT
         COMB               SUBTRACT FROM $FFFF BY
                           COMPLEMENTING
         COMA               EACH BIT. THE RESULT IS IN
                           ACCUMULATOR D
```

Recall that the poplar 555 timer integrated circuit can generate a digital signal with period $P = A + B \times (R_a + 2 \times R_b) \times C$ where A and B are constants and R_a and R_b are the resistors and C is the capacitor shown in figure 5-8. The resistor R_b can be a "volume control" or "joystick," the wiper of which the computer may want to sense the position, or it may be a photoresistor or thermistor. In fact, under control of a parallel output port and an analog multiplexer, the computer can insert any of a number of resistors in place of R_b, so that the value of the selected resistor can determine the period of the signal, and the period can be measured by a counter-timer. This is a good way to "read" the potentiometers on a stereo console or a game or toy into the microcomputer.

6-3.3 Pulse Width Measurement

We define the *pulse width* of a signal to be the time from a falling edge to the next rising edge, that is, as the width of a negative pulse. The pulse width is defined this way because that is how the M6840 measures pulse width, even though we normally think of a pulse as a positive pulse. If a positive pulse is to be measured, it is inverted and measured as a negative pulse as discussed below. The reader may question why we may want to measure pulse width when we can already measure period, or vice versa. Usually, the signal being measured is an analog signal which is converted to a digital signal by a comparator. Normally, the period is independent of the threshold of the comparator, so it will be measured correctly. The pulse width can depend on the threshold of the comparator because the comparator will output a high signal when the input is above the threshold, so the pulse width depends on the shape of the input and the threshold. The pulse width is naturally better to measure if the waveform is not repetitive. In this case, period cannot be measured.

As usual, there are software, analog and digital hardware, and counter-timer based techniques for pulse-width measurement. They are all similar to the techniques for period measurement, except the analog hardware approach. In general, the main loop in the software approach is entered when the input signal falls and is left when that signal rises. The hardware counter is cleared when the input falls and counts until the input rises. The analog technique, however, uses an integrator rather than a voltage-to-frequency converter. The input signal is conditioned so that it is normally zero, and is a precise voltage when the input is low. This conditioned signal is merely integrated. After the pulse is over, the output voltage of the integrator is proportional to the pulse width.

Pulse width is measured by a counter-timer in a manner similar to that of period measurement. The period measurement function is controlled by a simple sequential machine having states ready, busy, done1, and done2. The program puts the device in the ready state in one of three ways: by asserting the OFF control bit, by writing into the latch, or by the sequence, read status, read counter. In the ready state, the device waits for a falling edge on the G input. When this occurs, the counter is initialized by loading it from the latch and the busy state is entered. In the busy state, the E clock decrements the down counter. If the next falling edge of the G signal occurs while the device is yet in the busy state, it enters the done1 state, but if the counter passes zero, it enters the done2 state. (If PG occurs as the counter passes zero, it stays in the busy state.) If in the done2 state, the counter has overflowed, and its value is not the period of the waveform. It remains in done1 or done2 until reinitialized to the ready state. When in the done1 state, it outputs a true value in bit zero if a LDA $8001 instruction is executed, so the user can test this bit using a gadfly loop to wait for the counting to be completed. When the bit is true, the counter can be read, as in the frequency measurement, and the period can be obtained by subtracting from $FFFF. However, if the period is too long, the device enters the done2 state. No indication is available that the device is in this state, but none is needed. If a sufficiently long timing loop is executed in the program as it waits for the device to enter done 1, and the loop runs to completion, then the the device must be in the done2 state, and the value in the counter is invalid because the counter has overflowed.

An example of pulse-width measurement is offered. In chapter 7, we will study the UART, which is used to communicate over a serial link. The UART requires a clock signal rate that is sixteen times the rate at which bits arrive on the serial link. The M6840 configured as a square-wave generator is well suited to this task (although special chips are also available for it). The M6840 is also suited to automatic determination of the bit rate and setting of the clock rate using pulse-width measurement. The sender should send the capital U character, ASCII code $55, repetitively. Each time this is sent, it generates five pulses (or six pulses if the parity is set even). The pulse rate can be measured using the M6840 then multiplied by sixteen to establish the UART clock, which can be loaded into the latch of one of the devices that is configured to generate a square wave.

The configuration of the device is the same as in figure 6-8, except that the control register should contain $1A rather than $0A, and the state transition from busy to done1 occurs when G is asserted rather than when PG is asserted. The program for getting the pulse width is identical to PERIOD except that LDA $0A is changed to LDA $1A to initialize the control register. The number obtained from that program should be the bit rate. It should be multiplied by sixteen to get the clock rate, but to generate that rate, one half the number minus one is put in the latch. Thus the number obtained from the period measurement is shifted left three times to multiply it by eight then decremented and put in the latch to set the clock rate.

6-4 A Comprehensive List of M6840
Device Configurations

We have looked at several specific examples of the use of the counter-timer device; however, we deliberately obscured the general configurability of the device and the setting of control bits to configure it in order to discuss the principles of its use. In this section, we turn our attention to those details that the user needs in order to tailor the device to an application that we have not discussed. We discuss the different configurations that produce signals and interrupts and then those that measure period and pulse width. We introduce a few new modes that do not warrant a section of discussion for themselves. Finally, we note a few points about the differences among the three devices in an M6840 chip and some details about connecting it to an M6809 microcomputer.

Table 6-2 illustrates the different configurations available for the generation of square waves and interrupts and measurement of frequency.

We discuss these options one at a time. When bit zero (in device one) is false, all devices decrement their counters. When it is T, all counters load

Table 6-2
Signal-Generation Modes

Control Bit	Value	Meaning
0	F	All counters count, load from latch when zero
	T	All devices OFF, no counting, latch loads counter
1	F	Counter clocked on falling edge of C pin signal
	T	Counter clocked on falling edge of M6809 clock
2	F	Counters behave as a combined sixteen-bit counter
	T	Counters behave as two separate eight-bit counters
3	F	Must be false for this set of modes
4	F	Loading latch also loads counter, clears interrupt
	T	Loading latch only loads the latch
5	F	Output OUT is square wave, G must be low to count
	T	Output OUT is a pulse, counting independent of G
6	F	IRQ pin no affected by IRQ1 flip-flop
	T	IRQI asserted causes IRQ pin to be low
7	F	Output O is low
	T	Output O is OUT flip-flop

their values from their latches continuously. Note that this bit, in device one, controls all devices. This feature permits easy synchronization of the devices in an M6840 chip; however, it also makes difficult the use of the other devices independently of device one. Bit one selects either the M6809 E clock or the signal on the C pin to decrement the counter. The signal on the C pin is actually sampled by the E clock, as it passes through some buffer flip-flops. To be recognized as a falling edge on the C pin, a signal must be high on one and low on the next falling edge of the E clock. The maximum frequency of the C signal is then half the frequency of the E clock, about 500 kilohertz. This is the Nyquist rate of the sampling circuit. Also, the signal on this pin, and on the G pin, affects the counter three memory cycles later, due to delays in the buffering flip-flops, but this does not affect most uses of the counter.

Bit two has been carefully disregarded up to now. If true, it converts the sixteen-bit counter into a tandem pair of eight-bit counters. Suppose that the accumulator D has high byte H and low byte L, and is stored in the latch of device one by the LDD $8002 instruction. Then the first eight-bit counter counts modulo $L + 1$. That is, when this counter becomes zero, the low byte L is loaded from the latch. Each time the first counter counts $L + 1$ falling edges of the clock, the second counter is decremented. If the second counter reaches zero, the high byte H is loaded into it from the latch. Thus, it counts modulo $H + 1$. The device as a whole completes a count cycle in $(L + 1) \times (H + 1)$ clock cycles. Note that if the latch has the value $0102 and if bit two is false, the counter counts modulo $0103, but if bit two were true, the first counter counts modulo 3 and the second counts modulo 2, so the device as a whole counts modulo 6. In generating square waves (bit five low), the OUT signal is low throughout the cycle except for the last L clock cycles. In generating one-shot pulses, the OUT signal is low from the time the device is triggered, for $((L + 1) \times H) + 1$ cycles, then high for L cycles, and then low until triggered again. This feature allows generation of a short pulse after the trigger was applied and a fairly long delay has elapsed. The tandem eight-bit counter mode is useful in generating the spark timing in an engine. It does not appear to be that useful, however, as some of the more recent timer chips from Motorola (timer-ROM, timer-CPU, and the like) have discarded this option.

Control bit three identifies the class of operation, and is false for the operations discussed now. It is true for the period and pulse measurement modes to be discussed shortly. If bit four is false, writing a value into the latch simultaneously writes it into the counter too, and clears the interrupt flip-flop as well. If it is true, the latch can be changed without causing these other effects. It is usually false in the one-shot mode to let the software trigger the device by executing the STD $8002 instruction. It can be made true if one wishes to change the latch without affecting the current state of the counter. Note that the counter is always loaded from the latch when it is zero and is clocked when OFF (bit zero) is true, or when the G pin signal falls, and note that IRQ1 is always cleared when OFF is true when the G pin signal falls, or when the counter is read after the status register is read.

If bit five is true, the device is configured as a square-wave generator (or asymmetrical "square wave" generator if bit two is true). If bit five is false, the device becomes a one-shot. When configured as a one-shot, the counter can be clocked regardless of the level of the G pin signal, so we use this configuration for the real-time clock and for measuring frequency. Note, however, that falling edges of the G signal retrigger the device, so this input should not be allowed to float.

Bits six and seven control the IRQ and O outputs. If bit six is true and IRQ1 is true, the IRQ pin signal will be low; otherwise its signal depends on the other drivers on this wire-OR bus line. Also, if bit seven is true and the OUT flip-flop has a true, the O pin signal will be high, otherwise it is low.

The reader is invited to review the previous examples in this chapter and determine for himself the setting of the control codes for each configuration. We will look at another example here to show how easily the control code can be established. Suppose one wants a time of day clock. In this example, hours are to be counted in military 24-hour time, and days are to be counted in calendar 365-day time from January 1. The clock timing is to be derived from the sixty-hertz power line signal, as in the last chapter. A chain of counters K1 through K5 should operate as follows: K1 should divide the sixty-hertz signal to deliver a one-hertz signal. K2 should count in seconds. K3 should count in minutes, K4 in hours, K5 in days. K1, K2, K3, and K4 count modulo 60, 60, 60, and 24, respectively. They can be handled by an eight-bit counter. K5, however, must be handled by a sixteen-bit counter. One M6840 can be configured for this application: the sixty-hertz signal is input to C1, the clock for device one, which is configured as a pair of tandem eight-bit counters to divide by sixty and to count in seconds. Output O1 is connected to clock C2 of device two. Device two is also a pair of tandem eight-bit counters to count in minutes and hours. Output O2 is connected to clock C3. Device three is a sixteen-bit counter to count days since January 1. The gate inputs should all be grounded. The control code for devices one and two are identical. To derive them, circle the T or F options in table 6-2 (or a copy of it), then tilt the table and read the code word. From top to bottom, we want the devices on (F), we want them externally clocked (F), we want separate eight-bit counters (T), and bit three must be (F). It does not matter what we assign to bit four because we do not expect to rewrite the latches after initialization, so we make it (F). Bit five determines the output, which we do not use, so it too is a don't care. The pulse mode, however, is slightly better, since the count input is independent of the level of the G signal. Thus, we select pulse mode (T). We do not want a processor interrupt, and we do not want an output, so bits six and seven are (FF). The control code is therefore FFTFFTFF or $24. The control word for device three differs only in bit two, since we want a sixteen-bit counter. It is therefore FFTFFFFF or $20. Incidentally, to complete this example, latch one is loaded with $3B3B, latch two with $3B17, and latch three with 364. To read the time, read all three counters twice to detect carry propagation while you read them, and if both readings agree subtract each of the first three bytes from $3B, the fourth byte from $17, and the last two bytes from 364, and then convert to decimal if desired. (If the two readings disagree, reread the counters.) The main point of this discussion is to show how easy it is to get the control code word that you need for any configuration you want.

We now consider the period and pulse measurement modes. Table 6-3 shows the settings of the control bits in a device to select various options.

Control bits zero, one, and two operate as in the signal generation modes. When set, bit zero forces all counters into the ready state (see figure 6-9). When cleared, the device stays ready until the G pin signal falls (PG is

Table 6-3
Pulse- and Period Measurement Modes

Control Bit	Value	Meaning
0	F	All counters count, load from latch when zero
	T	All devices OFF, no counting, latch loads counter
1	F	Counter clocked on falling edge of C pin signal
	T	Counter clocked on falling edge of M6809 clock
2	F	Counters behave as a combined sixteen-bit counter
	T	Counters behave as two separate eight-bit counters
3	T	Must be true for this set of modes
4	F	Enter done1 on falling edge of G (period)
	T	Enter done1 when G is high (pulse width)
5	F	IRQ1 is true if in done1 state (measure overflow)
	T	IRQ1 is true if in done2 state (alarm)
6	F	IRQ pin not affected by IRQ1 flip-flop
	T	IRQ asserted causes IRQ pin to be low
7	F	Output O is low
	T	Output O is garbage

true), which puts the device in the busy state to count out the period or pulse width. Bit one selects the M6809 clock if true, or the signal on the C pin if false. The internal M6809 clock is especially useful if it is generated by an accurate crystal-controlled oscillator. The C pin signal is useful if a slower rate of counting is desired. Note that one device acting as a square-wave generator can clock another device measuring period or pulse width. Note, however, that the signal on the C pin is buffered by flip-flops and cannot be faster than half the M6809 clock frequency. Bit two is normally set false, as period and pulse width are usually measured in binary. It is possible, but awkward, to measure them in decimal by putting $99 into the latches if bit two is true, but it is easier to measure in binary and convert to decimal in software.

Bit three is true for this set of modes. Bit four determines when the state can change from busy to done1. If false, the change occurs when the G pin signal falls. Note that the busy state was entered when that signal fell the last time. So the device is busy for one complete cycle of the sine wave. If bit four is true, the change from busy to done1 occurs when the G signal rises. Since the busy state was entered when that signal last fell, the device is busy for the time the G input is low. Thus the counter measures the width of the (negative logic) pulse.

Bits four and five change the sequential machine that sets the IRQ1 flip-flop. See figure 6-9.

The first two modes can be used to measure period or pulse width, as described in the last section. For frequency measurement (bits 5,4 = FF) IRQ1 is true if the device is in the done1 state. This indicates the counter has a valid measure of the frequency. A minor peculiarity of this mode is that if the counter passes zero exactly when the G pin signal drops (PG is asserted) the device stays in the busy state. For pulse width measurement (bits 5,4 = FT) the state changes to done1 when G is high (which is the time when G rises). In both the above cases, IRQ1 is true if the device is in the done1 state. The last two modes can be used to monitor a signal for too long a period or too long a pulse width. Both these modes merge the done1 state into the busy state, and IRQ1 is true if the device is in the done2 state. The frequency alarm (bits 5,4 = TF) reloads the counter each time the G pin signal drops, and stays in the busy state. If the counter passes zero, the done2 state is entered and IRQ1 is set. This can be used to monitor a frequency: if an interrupt is to occur if ever the period is longer than $n + 1$ clock cycles, the number n is put in the latch in this mode. The period alarm (bits 5,4 = TT) returns to the ready state whenever G is true. When G falls again, the counter is loaded from the latch and begins to be decremented. If it passes zero, the state changes to done2 and IRQ is set. This can be used to monitor pulse widths: if an interrupt is to occur if ever the G signal is low for longer than n clock cycles, $n + 1$ is put in the latch of a device in this mode.

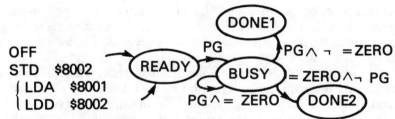

a. Bits 5,4 = FF (frequency measure)

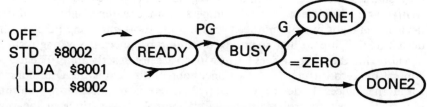

b. Bits 5,4 = FT (pulse width measurement)

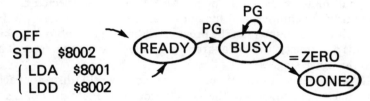

c. Bits, 5,4 = TF (frequency alarm)

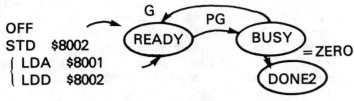

d. Bits 5,4 = TT (pulse width alarm)

Figure 6-9. State Diagrams for Period and Pulse Width

If control bit six is true, and IRQ1 is true, the IRQ bus line is made low, otherwise this device has no effect. Bit six can be true for the alarm configurations so that a processor interrupt occurs whenever the period or pulse width of the signal being monitored is too long. Bit six should be false when the gadfly technique is used while waiting for a device interrupt due to too long a pulse or period, or when the IRQ1 value indicates an error in measuring period or pulse width, as it is usually explicitly tested in these cases. Finally, control bit seven is normally false in these modes, as the output signal OUT is not defined.

Finally, we discuss differences among the three devices, and the connection of pins on this chip. Each device has its own clock, gate, and output pins, and its own device interrupt flip-flop. For instance, these pins and the flip-flop in device one are C1, G1, O1, and IRQ1, but those of device 2 are C2, G2, O2, and IRQ2. Also each device has its own counter and latch, but they share some hidden temporary registers. These should be read and written as a complete sixteen-bit numbers without reading eight bits of one device then eight bits of another because some short-cuts were taken in the design of the chip so that such mixed reading produces the wrong results. We note that the three devices in the M6840 are not exactly alike. The use of control bit zero differs. In device one, control bit zero is the OFF control for all the devices. In device two, control bit zero is an extra address bit that is used to select control register one or control register three at location $8000. The last device has an extra three-bit counter. If control bit zero is true, the signal input on the C pin or the M6809 clock (as selected by bit one) clocks this extra counter, and the output of the counter is used within the device to clock the counter. In the previous discussion, we always set bit zero to F. This disconnects the extra three-bit counter in device three, so it is identical to the other stages.

The M6840 has nine pins to connect to the outside world (three for each device) and nineteen to connect to the M6809 processor. Eight data pins are connected to the corresponding lines of the data bus. The five-volt power supply, ground, and reset bus line, and the R/W line are connected to the appropriate pins. The E clock must be connected to the Enable pin, and this signal may not be gated or otherwise modified. Register select pins RS0, RS1, and RS2 are normally connected to address bus lines zero, one, and two, respectively, in order to get the relative placement of registers shown in this chapter, and chip select pins CS0 (negative logic) and CS1 (positive logic) are connected to the address decoder that decodes some or all of the address lines fifteen to three and VMA, if used, to select the device. VMA must be connected to the decoder to prevent invalid addresses from disabling device interrupts caused by reading counter registers. It is often convenient to connect VMA to CS1 and the decoder output to CS0 because of the polarities of these inputs. Finally, the IRQ pin is connected to the IRQ bus line or to the NMI bus line if a device interrupt in this chip is to be handled by the IRQ handler or the NMI handler routines.

6-5 Conclusions

Frequency or phase analog signals are often generated naturally, by an AC tachometer, for instance, and may be used directly, in firing a triac, for instance. Even when the signal is first an amplitude analog signal, conversion to a frequency analog or a phase analog signal simplifies the noise isolation and voltage level isolation between transducer and microcomputer. Moreover, several hardware and software techniques, including those that use a counter-timer chip like the M6840, can be used to measure or generate frequency analog signals.

The counter-timer is a very useful and attractive I/O device for measuring or generating frequency or phase analog signals. It is useful in generating square waves, pulses, and timing interrupts, can measure events, frequency, period, and pulse width, and can monitor period or pulse width to interrupt the computer if too long a value is noticed. It is very attractive because a single wire sends the signal to or from the counter-timer. To the chip designer, it means that an I/O device can be put on a chip without using a lot of pins. While counters take up a nontrivial amount of area on the chip, that area is comparatively cheap, while pins are in much shorter supply. We see counter-timers appearing in read-only memory chips and CPU chips because of this principle. To the system designer, moreover, a single wire is easy to isolate with an optical isolator to prevent the voltages of the system under test from getting to the microcomputer and the user, as well as to isolate noise generated in that system from the microcomputer.

One of the temptations we face when a powerful and flexible chip like the counter-timer appears is to use it without thinking about it. Clearly, software control using a simple input or output device can be superior to control using the counter-timer, and other hardware approaches are more useful in other applications. We must not fall into the temptation of bottom-up design, looking too hard for uses for such a neat chip. We must thoroughly analyze the requirements of the problem. Nevertheless, this chip is so flexible that it is useful in a lot of the designs we use.

The M6840 is introduced to make concrete the discussion of the counter-timer module. It also offers an opportunity to show how a single chip is made more flexible by means of configuring the devices in it by setting the control word. This chapter prepares us for similar configuration techniques in communication modules, which we will cover in the next chapter.

You should now be familiar with the counter-timer chip in general and with the M6840 in particular. Connecting it to an M6809 and writing software to initialize it and use it should be well within your grasp. Moreover, you should be cognizant of alternatives to this chip, which you should be able to recognize whenever they are superior to the counter-timer.

Problems

Note

Problem 1 is a paragraph-correction problem. See the guidelines for this type of problem in the section at the end of chapter 1. The guidelines for programming problems are also there, and the guidelines for hardware design problems are at the end of chapter 2.

1.* Communication using frequency or phase is attractive because it can be accomplished using lower bandwidth channels than amplitude analog communication, and such signals can be generated or measured by counter-timer integrated circuits or chips that combine counter-timer functions with other functions. These combination chips are beginning to appear because the counter-timer does not require much surface area on a chip, and the transistors needed to build counter-timers need not be as good as those needed for A-to-D converters, so the inclusion of such a function on another chip does not raise the cost. Moreover, many functions require counting and timing. Pulses from a pulse generator can generate tones, and a Johnson counter can generate a stair-case approximation to a sine wave that is useful for touch-tone dialing and for cassette recording using the Kansas City Standard format. Pulses can be used to control automobiles, and interrupts from the timer can be used to implement real-time clocks. Frequency measurements can be used with a voltage-to-frequency converter to measure amplitude analog signals, and they can be used to measure the interval of time between two events. Period measurements are an alternative to frequency measurements, and one can always be obtained from the other by division; frequency measurement is preferable if the frequency is low because this will give more accuracy than period measurement. The M6840 should be used for these different generation and measurement functions if the software approach is susceptible to errors due to interrupt handling or DMA or dynamic memory refresh, but digital hardware or analog hardware approaches may be needed if the microcomputer software or M6840 approach is too slow.

2. Write a real-time square-wave generator that uses the least significant bit of an M6821 A device, at locations $8000 and $8001, to output a square wave with period $P = 10 \times (3 + N)$ microseconds. Assume the M6809 clock rate is one megahertz, and the unsigned binary number N is in accumulator A when the routine starts. (There are a few equally good solutions to this problem.)

3. A 555 timer and a binary counter are to be used to generate a square wave as determined by an output register FRQ. The low order three bits L of FRQ generate a square wave from the 555 with period $P = 2^{**}(L/8)$ and the next more significant 3 bits N select a tap from the binary counter

so the output period is $2^{**}N \times P$. Show a diagram using some 74LS161, 4051, and 555 chips, showing pin numbers and values of resistors and capacitors.

Note

The following guidelines should be used for all programs using the M6840.

Problems involving the M6840 will all assume it is addressed as in figure 6-1, using a one-megahertz E clock, and requesting interrupts on the IRQ line. Unless otherwise indicated, use the M6809 E clock to clock the counters in each device. All subroutines should assume that the control registers are unknown (as if the subroutine is called inside an arbitrary program) and must initialize them before using them. Results should be returned as unsigned binary numbers in accumulator D unless otherwise indicated. Each handler should be accompanied by a separate initialization routine that initializes the M6840 and all global variables as needed for the proper execution of the handler, and if the M6840 (output or interrupts) should be turned off, the ritual to turn off the M6840 should be included at the appropriate place in the handler.

4. Design a thirty-two-bit square-wave generator. Show the connections between the M6809 and M6840, and especially to the D, G, and C pins for devices one and two. Write a subroutine that generates a square wave from output O1 with period specified by the thirty-two-bit number in accumulator D (high order sixteen bits) and index register U (low order sixteen bits).

5. A *music synthesizer* has sixteen voices and is to be built with a device in the M6840, a parallel output register addressed at location $8008, a (256,4) PROM, a 74LS161, and a four-bit D-to-A converter. The M6840 output O1 clocks the 74LS161, which provides the low order four bits of the address of the PROM so that each voice is generated by sixteen samples of the repetitive waveform. The high order four bits of the output register provide the high order address of the PROM to select the voice. The output from the PROM is a four-bit two's complement number, which is converted to a voltage between negative eight and positive seven volts by the D-to-A converter. (a) Show a block diagram of the system. (b) Write a routine to generate a tone that is specified by the value in accumulators A and B. The four most significant bits of A are the octave and the four least significant bits are the note in the octave, such that A is represented by $0, B flat is $1, B is $2, . . ., A flat is $B; and the lowest octave is represented by zero. Low A has a frequency of 22.5 hertz and is represented by 0,0. The frequency of each note is the twelfth root of two times the frequency of the next lower note. The most significant four bits of accumulator B are the voice, which

will be used by the PROM, and the least significant bits are the length of the note, in sixteenths, where a sixteenth note is played for a quarter of a second. Use device three in the M6840 with a prescaler to time the processor using a gadfly loop so that when a note is over, exit from the loop will cause the next note to be generated. (Do not show the program that selects the next note. Hint: use table lookup to generate the basic frequency in the lowest octave, then shift it right to derive the required counter values.) (c) Show the table using FDB assembler directives and values in hexadecimal for the program in part (b).

6. Write a routine to generate a touch-tone dial sequence. The number to be called is in a vector, such as:

$$\text{NUM} \quad \text{FCB} \quad 5,5,5,1,2,1,2$$

The number is to be dialed by the generation of touch-tones, as in table 6-1, from devices one and three, and output as in figure 6-4. Each tone is on for fifty milliseconds and there is a mute period of forty-five milliseconds between tones. (These are the minimum times specified by the telephone industry.) (a) Write a subroutine TOTONE that will output the tone corresponding to a number that is in accumulator A and time that tone and mute period using real-time synchronization. Use a single table to convert the number into the values loaded into counters one and three, and show this table using FDB assembler directives and hexadecimal values. (b) Write a routine to dial the number that is stored in the vector NUM. It should call the subroutine TOTONE in part (a).

7. A widely available home remote control uses a high frequency signal that is superimposed on the sixty-hertz power line to transmit commands from a single command module to up to sixteen remote stations. Remote stations can turn appliances on or off or turn lamp dimmers up or down. The command module has a provision for a remote keyboard that communicates to it using ultrasonic signals. To avoid connecting to the power line, we would like to control the remote stations by sending the ultrasonic signals to the command module that would have been sent by the remote keyboard. Write a subroutine to generate ultrasonic signals to send commands via the O1 output of an M6840 to an ultrasonic transmitter to the receiver in the control module. A bit is sent for 8 milliseconds, a true is 4 milliseconds of 40-kilohertz square wave followed by 4 milliseconds mute output, and a false is 1.2 millisecond of a 40-kilohertz square wave followed by 2.8 milliseconds mute output. A command to send data bit D to remote station N is sent as follows: a true bit is sent, then a four-bit remote station number N is sent, most significant bit first, data bit D is sent, then the complement of the module number and data bits N and D are sent in the same order, and then sixteen milliseconds of a 40-kilohertz square wave is sent.

The data bit D is in least significant bit of accumulator A and the remote station number is in accumulator B. Use real-time synchronization to time out the sending of bits of the command.

8. The G1, G2, and G3 inputs of an M6840 are connected to a signal that pulses low at the moment that the sixty-hertz power line signal passes through zero. The three outputs O1, O2, and O3, are connected to pulse transformers that fire three triacs to implement proportional phase control of three lamps. Show a subroutine that sets up device N of the M6840 so that it outputs a waveform whose falling edge fires triac N at time D degrees in each half cycle. When this subroutine is called, N is in accumulator A, N is equal to one, two, or three, and G is an unsigned binary number in accumulator B.

9. The program DIAL in section 5-2.2 will dial a number on a conventional "step-and-repeat" telephone, but will tie up the computer while it is dialing the number. Write an interrupt handler for device one of the M6840 that will cause an interrupt every twenty milliseconds. On each interrupt, the most significant bit of the output at location $8008 should be given a value to control the relay in series with the dial contacts for the next twenty milliseconds. The output is implemented with a simple flip-flop and address decoder. Use global variables to keep track of what part of the sequence of numbers, what part of the number, and what part of a pulse has been output. (a) Write the handler to output just one number, which is in global variable N. (b) Write the handler to output the seven numbers in the vector NUM as in problem 6.

10. The Radio Shack TRS-80, a very popular microcomputer, uses a format (*TRS-80 format*) for storing data on cassettes that is quite different than the Kansas City standard. An output mechanism to write data on a cassette uses an address trigger, at location $8000, that will put a short positive followed by a short negative pulse on the tape. The TRS-80 format has the following characteristics, for "level II BASIC."

1. A word is eight bits, sent most significant bit first. A False bit is a short pulse followed by two milliseconds mute (with no pulses). A True bit is a short pulse, a millisecond mute, a short pulse, and a millisecond mute.
2. A record is a leader, a name, one or more data blocks, and an entry point address, where: The leader is 255 bytes of zero words and the sync code $A5; the name is the word $55 and the six-letter ASCII name of the record padded on the right with blanks (ASCII code $20); the data block is described below; the entry point is the word $78 and the least significant and then the most significant bytes of the starting address.
3. The data block is the block size, the data, and the checksum, where: the block size is the word $3C, the number of bytes in the block (00 represents 256), and the low byte and then the high byte of the address

of the first data word in the block; the data is up to 256 words to be stored in ascending addresses; the checksum is the eight-bit sum of the bytes in the address and data words.

(a) Write a subroutine WOUT to output a word in accumulator A by means of the address trigger onto a cassette using real-time synchronization. (b) Write a handler CASWD that is entered every millisecond which will output the word stored in global variable WD using the address trigger. Use a global variable TICK that tells how many milliseconds are left in the time to output the word. Use device one of an M6840 to request an interrupt each millisecond. (c) Write a program to output the contents of a buffer at location BUFFR of length LEN onto the cassette. The buffer is already completely formatted as described above, and contains all the words from the 255 zeros through to the high byte of the starting address. (d) Write an interrupt handler which outputs the contents of the buffer BUFFR of part (c). Use global variables to keep track of how many words are yet to be output (LEN), how many bits are to be output in that word, and where we are in the current word (TICK).

11. An *"alarm clock"* can interrupt the computer at a given time, within an hour, if two devices in the M6840 are used, one generating the clock signal for the other. The M6840 is connected so that device one will request an interrupt on the IRQ line, and device two will clock device one (02 is connected to C1). Write a routine ALARM that interprets a table of times that the "alarm" is supposed to "go off," so that when this happens, a program corresponding to the "alarm" will be executed. Suppose that a table of "alarms" is such that a row is stored thus:

FDB   TH,TL,GO

where TH is the two high order bytes and TL is the two low order bytes of a time interval T, and GO is the address of a routine that is to be started when that interval is over. The time T in row $i + 1$ is the time in microseconds to the time for "alarm" for row $i + 1$ since the "alarm" went off for row i. Each routine such as that beginning at location GO ends with an instruction BRA ALARM, and your routine, beginning at address ALARM, begins with a SYNC instruction to wait for the interrupt request signal on the IRQ line from the M6840.

12. Parts of a logic analyzer have been designed in the problems at the end of chapters 3 and 4. The apparatus also has counters to permit the data stored in and displayed by the analyzer to be the data on the bus before or after the pattern was recognized by the comparator. Assuming that the M6840 is synchronized to the data, which is changing each microsecond, the counters can allow N occurrences of the pattern C recognized by the comparator to occur, and then can allow M clock cycles before the time T_f

occurs. The (256) patterns that appeared on the buses before time T_f are displayed. The user can select N to be zero and M to be zero if T_f is to be the time the pattern occurred first, but the user can use another number N if the first N occurrences are to be ignored, as when the pattern appears inside a DO-LOOP. Another number M can be chosen if the M words after the comparator detects a match and $(256 - M)$ words before it are to be stored in memory and displayed by the logic analyzer. Show a block diagram of such a logic analyzer. It should be complete with M6821 output registers holding the comparator pattern C, a sixteen-bit address and one-bit R/W comparator, an M6840 counter-timer, memory for the patterns stored, and counters needed to address a (32,256) memory. The M6821 is addressed at locations $8008 to $800B in the normal way. Show clearly all the connections to C1, C2, O1, O2, G1, G2, and the logic needed to write the patterns into the memory. Finally, show a subroutine so that the comparator address C in accumulator D, the number N in index register X, and the number M in index register Y set up the logic analyzer.

13. A Kansas City standard signal can be generated using interrupts so the microcomputer can tend to other tasks. An M6840 is connected so that device one will generate interrupts for timing, and device three will output the square wave to clock the Johnson counters in figure 6-4, and a handler KCHND that will record data in the Kansas City standard that is stored in a buffer BUFFR. Do not generate the five seconds of T (mark) signals, and ignore the problem of generation of precise sine waves (this can be solved using the third device and a SYNC instruction so that device one generates an interrupt a little before the precise switching time determined by the other device using a SYNC instruction). Use global variable LEN to keep track of how many words are left in the buffer initialized to the length of the buffer and use global variable TICK, which indicates how many bits of the current word are yet to be output, to control your handler.

14. Rewrite the routine KCITY in section 6-2.3 for the M6800. Use the WAI instruction and write an interrupt handler to replace the SYNC instruction in the program KCITY.

15. Design a *voltmeter* using an isolated voltage-to-frequency converter. (a) Show a diagram of the complete system in enough detail to build it. Use the Teledyne 9400 (figure 5-19b), an optoisolator to isolate the voltage sensor from the microcomputer, and an M6840 to measure the frequency. (b) Write the subroutine VOLT to measure the frequency so that the voltage at the input of the hardware in part (a), in millivolts, is returned in accumulator D when the subroutine is executed.

16. Write the program FREQM (section 6-3.1) for the M6800. The frequency should be returned in accumulator B, an eight-bit unsigned binary number.

17. An AM tuner has a local oscillator which is tuned to a frequency that is 455 kilohertz higher than the frequency of a station that is tuned in, so that the "beat frequency" is the intermediate frequency that is amplified by the radio. Write a program to measure the frequency so that if device one has the local oscillator frequency divided by four on C1, the program will output the frequency of the station being received divided by four in accumulator D.

18. Design a *capacitance meter*. A capacitor of unknown value *C* is put in the timing circuit of a 555 timer, *C* being lower than 0.01 microfarads. (a) Show the hardware, pin numbers, and component values to build such a meter using an M6840 so that device A functions as a period measurement device. (b) Write a subroutine CAPAC that evaluates the capacitance, using real-time synchronization to detect counter overflow, to return the capacitance in picofarads in accumulator D.

19. Write a program to determine the period of a square wave in software, where the signal is input on the most significant bit of an input device at location $8000. The period, in microseconds divided by twenty, should be returned in accumulator D.

20. Write a program to read a cassette that was recorded using the Kansas City standard. An M6840 is used to determine the period of the incoming waveform on input G1 for every other sine wave recorded on the tape. The pattern of $1000 words on the tape after the five seconds of T are to be stored in a $1000-word buffer BUFFR, and real-time synchronization is to be used to monitor the counter for overflow.

21. Write a program to read a cassette that was recorded using the TRS-80 format. An M6840 device one is to measure the (negative) pulse width, which is the time between pulses. Assume the record is larger than $1000 words. The first $1000 words of data, except the header and the sync character, will be stored in a $1000-word buffer BUFFR exactly as it is recorded, but no attempt will be made to determine if the record is fully read into the buffer, nor that the checksum is correct, when the buffer is full.

22. Design a *frequency and phase meter* for audio frequencies, using an M6840. (a) Show a diagram for the system so that device one will measure the period of input V1, and device two will measure the time from rising edge of V1 to the next rising edge of a second input V2. (b) Write a subroutine to initialize an M6840 so that the hardware in (a) can be used to output the frequency in index register U and the phase in accumulator D. Use a subroutine DIV that divides the sixteen-bit unsigned binary integer in register U into the thirty-two-bit unsigned binary number in index registers X and Y, integer part in X and fractional part in Y, leaving the quotient in Y and remainder in X, but do not write this subroutine.

23. Design a TV sync signal generator using devices one and three of an M6840. Output O1 of device one is to supply the vertical sync pulse, which is four microseconds high, sixty microseconds low, repetitively. Output O2 of device two is to supply the horizontal sync pulse, which is clocked by the vertical sync pulse. The horizontal sync is high for twenty-six vertical pulses, and low for 234 vertical pulses. Show a routine to configure the M6840 to generate these signals.

7

Communication Systems

The microcomputer has many uses in communications systems, and a communications system is often a significant part of a microcomputer. This chapter examines techniques for digital communication of computer data.

Attention is focussed on the communications subsystem of a microcomputer, the part that interfaces slower I/O devices like typewriters and printers to the mcirocomputer. This is often a universal asynchronous receiver transmitter (UART). Because of their popularity in this application, UARTs have been used for a variety of communications functions, including remote control and multiple computer intercommunications. Their use, however, is limited to communicating short (one-byte) messages at slow rates (less than 1000 bytes per second). A technique that is suitable for sending longer messages (about a thousand bytes) at faster rates (about 1,000,000 bits per second) is the synchronous data link control (SDLC). This is especially useful for sending data between computers, or between computers and fast I/O devices. A third major technique, which sends a byte at a time rather than a bit at a time, is the IEEE-488 bus. This was developed for microcomputer control of instruments like digital voltmeters and frequency generators.

In this chapter, the UART, the SDLC, and the IEEE-488 communication techniques will be discussed. The overall principles of communications systems, including the ideas of levels and protocols, are introduced in the first section. The signal transmission medium is discussed next, to give some understanding of the problems and techniques of the communications engineer associated with moving the data. The UART and related devices that use the same communications mechanisms are fundamental to I/O interface design. We spend quite a bit of time on these devices to get a working knowledge of the hardware and software for them. They will probably find use in most of your designs for communicating with teletypes or teletype-like terminals, keyboards, and CRTs, as well as for simple remote control. Finally, we will look at the more complex communications interfaces that are used between large mainframe computers and that are used to control test and measurement equipment in the laboratory.

Communications terminology is rather involved. Parts come from the (comparatively ancient) telephone industry, parts from the computer industry, and parts of the terminology seem to be unique to digital communications. Communications design is an almost completely different discipline from microcomputer design. Moreover, the terminology for one kind of system, such as one using UARTs, is quite different from similar terminology for another kind of system, such as one using SDLC links. While it is important to be able to talk to communications-system designers, and to learn their terminology, we are limited in what we can do in this short chapter. We will use the terminology that is used in the so called X-25 protocol as much as possible, even for discussing UARTs, because we want to economize on the number of terms that we have to introduce, and the X-25 protocol appears to be a most promising protocol that is likely to be used with minicomputers and microprocessors. Nevertheless, you should be prepared to have to do some translating when you converse with a communications engineer.

On completing this chapter, you should have a working knowledge of UART communications links. You should be able to connect a UART or an M6850 to a microcomputer, and to connect a UART or an M14469 to a remote control station so it can be controlled through an M6850 or a UART. You should understand the basic strategies of communication systems in general, and the UART, SDLC, and IEEE-488 bus protocols in particular, so that you will know when and where they should be used.

7-1 Communications Principles

Before we begin to study the details of how microcomputers send information to each other and to remote devices via communication linkages, we will look at the overall picture. We will consider the ideas of peer-to-peer interfaces first. Then we will progress from the lowest level peer-to-peer interface to the higher level interfaces, examining the kinds of problems faced at each level.

Data movement is *coordinated* in different senses at different *levels* of abstraction, and by different kinds of mechanisms. At each level, the communication appears to take place between *peers*, which are identifiable entities at that level: even though the communication is defined between these peers as if they did indeed communicate to each other, they actually communicate indirectly through peers at the next lower level. See figure 7-1.

Consider this analogy. The president of company X wants to talk to the president of company Y. This is called *end-to-end* communication. Rather than do it himself, he has his secretary call up the secretary of the other president. This is referred to as *network control*. The secretary does not try to shout to the other secretary, but rather she dials the other secretary on the telephone. The telephone is analogous to the *link control* level—but even this communication is carried out at a lower level, the electronics and the electrical circuits that make the connection at the telephone exchange. This

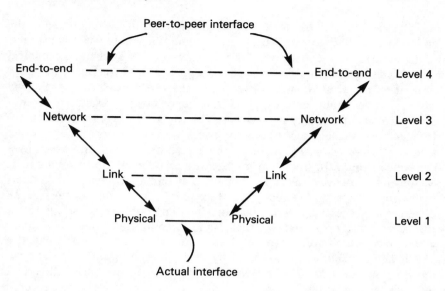

Figure 7-1. Peer-to-Peer Communication in Different Levels

is the *physical control* level. End-to-end communication is done between user (high level) programs. They want to send information to each other like the presidents in the example above. Network control is done at the operating system level. Like the secretaries, this software has to know where the other president is and how to reach him. Link control is done by I/O interface software and is responsible for setting up the link and disconnecting it so that the message can be sent. Physical control actually moves the data. In the design of I/O systems, we are primarily concerned with link control and secondarily with physical control.

The peer-to-peer interfaces are defined without specifying the interface to the next lower level. This is done for the same reasons that computer architecture is separated from computer organization and realization, as we saw in chapter 1. It permits the next lower level to be replaced by another version at that level without affecting the higher level. This is like one of the presidents getting a new secretary: he still gets to and talks to the other president in the same way, even though communication at the next lower level may be substantially changed.

We now discuss some of the issues at each of the levels. At the lowest level, the main issue is the medium and a secondary issue is the multiplexing of several channels on one link. The technique used to synchronize the transmission of bits may be partly in the physical interface level and partly in the link control level. This aspect of communications is covered too.

The *medium* that carries a bit of information is of great concern to the communications engineer. Most systems would probably use voltage level to distinguish between true and false signals. In other systems, mechanical motion carries information, or radio or light beams in free space or in optical fibers carry information. Even when the carrier is electric, the signal can be carried by current rather than voltage, or by the presence or absence of a particular frequency component. The signal can be conveyed on two frequencies—a true is sent as one frequency while a false is sent as another frequency (*frequency shift keying*). More than one signal can be sent over the same medium. In *frequency multiplexing*, n different messages are sent, each by the presence or absence of one of n different frequency components (or keying between n different pairs of frequencies). In *time multiplexing*, n different messages can be sent, each one in a time slot every nth time slot. A frequency band or a time slot that carries a complete signal that enables communication between two entities at the link control level is called a *channel*. Each channel, considered by itself, may be *simplex* if data can move in one direction only, *half-duplex* if data can move in either direction, but only one direction at a time, or *full duplex* if data can move in both directions simultaneously.

Usually, a bit of information is sent on a channel over a time period, the *bit time period*, and this is the same time for each bit. The *baud rate* is the inverse of this bit time period (or the shortest period if different periods are used). The *bit rate*, in contrast, is the rate of transfer of information, as defined in information theory. For simplicity in this discussion, the bit rate is the number of user information bits sent per time unit, while the baud rate is the total number of bits, both user information and synchronization and error checking bits, per time unit.

In general, a clock is a regular occurrence of a pulse, or even a code word, used to control the movement of bits. If such a (regular) clock appears in the channel in some direct way, the system is *synchronous*, otherwise it is *asynchronous*. In a synchronous system, the clock can be sent on a separate line, as the clock is sent inside a computer to synchronize the transmission of data. The clock can also be sent on the same wire as the data, every other bit being a clock pulse and the other bits being data, in the so called *Manchester code*. Circuitry such as a phase locked loop detects the clock and further circuitry uses this reconstructed clock to extract the data. Finally, in an asynchronous link, the clock can be generated by the receiver, in hopes that it matches the clock used by the sender.

Link control is concerned with how data is moved as bits, as groups of bits, and as complete messages that are sent by the next higher level peer-to-peer interface. At the *bit level*, individual bits are transmitted; at the *frame level*, a group of bits called a frame or packet is transmitted; and at the *message level*, sequences of frames, called messages, are exchanged. Generally, at the frame level, means are provided for detection and correction of errors in the data being sent, since the communication channel is often noisy. Also, since the frame is sent as a single entity, it can have means for synchronization. A frame, then, is some data that is packaged or framed, and sent as a unit under control of a communications hardware-software system. The end-to-end user often wishes to send data as a sequence of frames, as a single unit of data. The *message* corresponds to the user's unit of data.

At each level, a coordination mechanism is used. This is called a *protocol*. A protocol is a set of conventions that coordinate the transmission and reception of bits, frames, and messages. Its primary functions in the link control level are the synchronization of messages and the detection or correction of errors. This term, protocol, suggests an agreement between countries about how something is done, so the term fits a communication mechanism where sender and receiver operate under some mutually acceptable assumptions, but do not need to be managed by some greater authority like a central program. Extra bits are needed to maintain the protocol. Since these bits have to be sent, for a given data rate in bits per second the baud rate has to be greater as more extra bits are sent. The protocol should keep efficiency high by using as few as possible of these extra bits. Note that a clock is a particularly simple protocol, a regularly occurring pulse or code word. An important special case, the *handshake protocol*, is an agreement whereby the sender sends information to the receiver, who sends back an acknowledgment that the data is received in good condition or has some error. Note, however, that a clock or a protocol applies to a level, so a given system can have a bit clock and two different protocols, a frame protocol and a message protocol.

The third level of peer-to-peer interface is the network level. Here, we are concerned primarily about relationships between a large community of computers and the requirements necessary so that they can communicate with each other without getting into trouble.

The *structure* of a communications system includes the physical interconnections among stations as well as the flow of information. Usually modeled as a graph whose nodes are stations and whose links are communications paths, the structure may be a loop, a tree graph, or a rectangular grid (or a sophisticated graph like a banyan network or its homomorphic reduction).

A path taken by some data through several nodes is called *store and foreward* if each node stores the data for a brief time them transmits it to the next node as new data may be coming into that node, otherwise if it passes through intermediate nodes instantaneously (being delayed only by gate and line propagation) the path is called a *circuit* from telephone terminology. If such a path is half duplex, it is sometimes called a bus because it looks like a bus in a computer system.

Finally, the communication system is *governed* by different techniques.

This aspect relates to the operating system of the system of computers, which indirectly controls the generation and transmission of data like a government establishes policies that regulate trade between countries. A simple aspect of governance is whether the decision to transmit data is centralized or distributed. A system is *centralized* if a special station makes all decisions concerning which stations may transmit data, or it is decentralized or *distributed* if each station determines whether to send data based on information local to it. A centralized system is often called a *master-slave* system: the special station is the master and the other stations are called slaves. Other aspects of governance concern the degree to which one station knows what another station is doing, or whether and how one station can share the computational load of another. These aspects of a system are very important and are still the subject of considerable research and debate.

7-2 Signal Transmission

The signal is transmitted through wires or light pipes at the physical level. This section discusses the characteristics of three of the most important linkages. Voltage or current amplitude logical signals are used to interconnect terminals and computers that are close to each other. These are discussed first. The digital signal can be sent by sending different frequencies for a true and for a false signal (frequency shift keying). This is discussed in the next subsection. Finally, the optical link offers the unprecedented capability of sending data at very high rates. It will likely radically change our approach to communication systems. At the time of writing, however, it is still new and expensive. Some observations are offered on the optical link in the last subsection.

7-2.1 Voltage and Current Linkages

This section discusses the line driver and line receiver pair, the twenty-millampere current loop and the RS232 standard.

Standard high current TTL or LSTTL drivers can be used over relatively short distances, as the IEEE-488 standard uses them for a bus to instruments located in a laboratory. However, slight changes in the ground voltage reference or a volt or so of noise on the link can cause a lot of noise in these kinds of links. A *differential line* is a pair of wires in which the variable is on one wire in positive logic and on the other in negative logic. If one is high, the other is low. The receiver uses an analog comparator to determine which of the two wires has the higher voltage, and outputs a standard TTL signal appropriately. If a noise voltage is induced, both wires should pick up the same noise so the differential is not affected and the receiver will get the correct signal. Similarly, imperfect grounding and signal ringing affect the signal on both wires and their effect is canceled by the voltage comparator. A number of driver and receiver integrated circuits are designed for differential lines, but some require voltages other than positive five that may not be used elsewhere in the system. An integrated circuit suitable for driving and receiving signals on a half duplex line, using a single five-volt supply, is the SN75119, shown in figure 7-2a. If driver enable DE (pin 7) is high, then the signal on IN (pin 1) is put on line LA (pin 3) and its complement is put on line LB (pin 2), otherwise the pins LA and LB appear to be (essentially) open circuits. If receiver enable RE (pin 5) is high, then the output OUT (pin 6) is low if the voltage on LA is less than that on LB, or high if the voltage on LA is greater than that on LB; if RE is low, OUT is (essentially) an open circuit.

The twenty-milliampere current loop is often used to interface teletypes or teletype-like terminals to communications systems and computers. A pair of wires connect driver and receiver so as to implement an electrical loop through both. A true corresponds to about twenty milliamperes flowing through the loop, and a false corresponds to no current or to negative twenty milliamperes in the loop (for "neutral working" or "polar working" loops, respectively). A current is used rather than a voltage because it can be interrupted by a switch in a keyboard, and can be sensed anywhere in the loop. A current is also used in older equipment because the twenty-milliampere current loop was used to drive a solenoid, and a solenoid is better controled by a current than a voltage to get faster rise times. The current is set at twenty milliamperes because the arc caused by this current will keep the switch contacts clean.

A twenty-milliampere current loop has some problems. A loop consists of a current source in series with a switch to break the circuit, in series with a sensor to sense the current. Whereas the switch and sensor are obviously in two different stations in the circuit, the current source can be in either station. A station with a current source is called *active*, while one without is *passive*. If two passive stations, one with a switch and the other with a sensor, are connected, nothing will be communicated. If two active stations are connected, the current sources might cancel each other or destroy each other. Therefore, of the two stations, one must be active while the other is passive, and one must be a switch and the other must be a sensor. While this is all very straightforward, it is an invitation to trouble. Also, note that the voltage levels are undefined. Most twenty-milliampere current loops work with voltages like plus five or minus twelve or both, which are available in most communications systems, but some designed for long distance communication utilize "telegraph hardware" with voltages upwards of eighty volts. Therefore, one does not connect two twenty-milliampere current loop stations together without checking the voltage levels and capabilities. Finally, these circuits generate a fair amount of electrical noise, which gets into other signals, especially lower level signals, and the switch in such a circuit generates noise that is often filtered by the sensor. This noise is at frequencies used by 1200-baud lines, so this filter cannot be used in other places in a communications subsystem. The circuitry for a twenty-milliampere current loop can be built with an optoisolator, as shown in figure 7-2b. If the current through the LED is about twenty milliamperes, the phototransistor appears to be a short circuit; if the current is about zero milliamperes, it is an open circuit and the output is high. The diode across the LED is there to prevent an incorrect current from destroying the LED.

An interface standard developed by the Electronic Industries Association (EIA) and other interested parties has evolved into the RS232-C. A similar standard is available in Europe, developed by the Comite Consultatif Internationale de Telegraphie et Telephonie (CCITT), and is called the CCITT V.24 standard. These standards are supposed to be simple and effective, so that any driver conforming to one of them can be connected to any receiver conforming to it; and this has to cover the voltage levels used for the signals as well as the pin assignments and dimensions of the plugs. Basically, a false variable is represented by any voltage from plus fifteen to plus five volts, and a true by any voltage from minus five to minus fifteen volts (negative logic is used.) A number of specifications concerning driver and receiver currents and impedances can be met simply by using integrated circuit drivers and receivers that are designed for this interface—RS232 drivers and RS232 receivers. The MC1488 is a popular quad RS232 line driver, and the MC1489 is a popular receiver. See figures 7-2c and 7-2d. The driver requires plus twelve volts on pin fourteen and minus twelve volts on pin

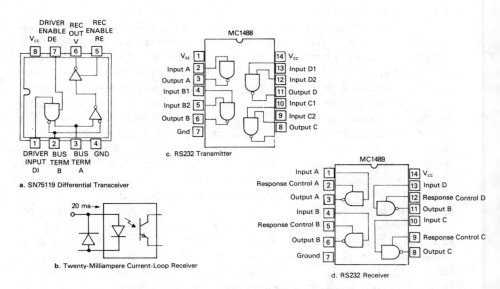

Figure 7-2. Drivers and Receivers

one. Otherwise, it looks like a standard quad TTL NAND gate, whose outputs are RS232 levels. The four receiver gates have a pin called response control (pins 2, 5, 9, and 12). Consider one of the gates, where pin one is the input and pin three is the output. Pin two can be left unconnected. It can be connected through a (33-kilohm) resistor to the negative supply voltage (pin 1) to raise the threshold voltage a bit. Or it can be connected through a capacitor to ground to filter the incoming signal. This controls the behavior of that gate. The other gates can be similarly controled.

The RS232 interface standard also specifies the sockets and pin assignments. The DB25P, a twenty-five-pin subminiature plug and the DB25S, the corresponding socket conform to the standard. The pin assignments are shown in table 7-1. For simple applications, only pins two (transmit data), three (receive data), and seven (signal ground) need be connected, but a remote station may need to make pins five (clear to send), six (data set ready), and eight (data carrier detect) twelve volts to tell the microcomputer that the link is in working order, if these signals are tested by the microcomputer. It does not hurt to wire these to twelve volts in a terminal when they are not carrying status signals back to the microcomputer.

Table 7-1
RS232 Pin Connections for D25P and D25S Connectors

Pin	Name	Function
1	Protective ground	Connects machine or equipment frames together, and is "earth"
2	Transmitted Data	Data sent from microcomputer to terminal
3	Receive Data	Data sent from terminal to microcomputer
4	Request to Send	(Full Duplex) enables transmission circuits (Half Duplex) puts link in transmit mode and disables receive circuitry
5	Clear to Send	Responds to Request to Send. When high, it indicates the transmission circuitry is working.
6	Data Set Ready	(telephone lines) The circuitry is not in test, talk, or dial modes of operation so it can be used to transmit and receive.
7	Signal ground	Common reference potential for all lines, should be connected to "earth" at just one point, to be disconnected for testing
8	Data Carrier Detect	Indicates a good signal is being received
9	+P	+12 volts (for testing only)
10	−P	−12 volts (for testing only)
11 · · · 25		Used for more elaborate options

7-2.2 Frequency Shift Keyed Links Using Modems

To send data over the telephone, a *modem* converts the signals to frequencies that can be transmitted in the audio frequency range. The most common modem, the Bell 103, permits full duplex transmission at 300 baud. Transmission is originated by one of the modems, referred to as the *originate modem*, and the other modem is referred to as the *answer modem*. The originate modem sends a true (mark) signal as a 1270-hertz sine wave and a false (space) as a 1070-hertz sine wave. Of course, the answer modem receives a true as a 1270-hertz sine wave and a false as a 1070-hertz sine wave. The answer modem sends a true (mark) as a 2225-hertz sine wave and a false (space) as a 2025-hertz sine wave. Note that the true signal is higher in frequency than the false signal, and the answer modem sends the higher pair of frequencies.

Some modems are originate only. They can only originate a call and can only send 1070- or 1270-hertz signals, and receive only 2025- or 2225-hertz signals. Most inexpensive modems intended for use in terminals are originate only. The computer may have an answer-only modem having the opposite characteristics. If you want to be able to send data between two computers one of them has to be an originate modem. So an answer/originate modem might be used on a computer if it is expected to receive calls but may also send calls. Whether the modem is originate only, answer only, or answer/originate, it is fully capable of sending and receiving data simultaneously, in full duplex mode. The originate and answer modes determine only which pair of frequencies are able to be sent and received, and therefore whether the modem is capable of actually initiating the call.

Modems have filters to reject the signal that they are sending, and pass the signals that they are receiving. Usually, Bessel filters are used because the phase shift must be kept uniform for all components or the wave will become distorted. Sixth order and higher filters are common to pass the receive signal and reject the transmitted signal and the noise, because the transmitted signal is usually quite a bit stronger than the receive signal, and because reliabiity of the channel is greatly enhanced by filtering most of the noise out. The need for two filters substantially increases the cost of answer/originate modems.

The module that connects the telephone line to the computer is called a *data coupler*. There is one that connects to the originator of a call and another that connects to the answerer. The data coupler isolates the modem from the telephone line to prevent lightning from going to the modem and to control the signal level using an automatic gain control, but the data coupler does not convert the signal nor filter it. The data coupler has three control/status signals. *Answer phone* (ANS) is a control command that has the same effect on the telephone line as when a person picks up the handset to start a call or answer the phone. *Switch hook* (SH) is a status signal that indicates that the telephone handset is on a hook, if you will, so it will receive and transmit signals to the modem. Switch hook may also be controlled by the microcomputer. Finally, *Ring indicator* (RI) is a status signal that indicates the phone is ringing.

Aside from the fact that data is sent using frequency analog signals over a telephone, there is not much to say about the channel; however, the way an originate modem establishes a channel to an answer modem and the way the call is terminated is interesting. The following discussion shows how the Motorola M6860 modem originates a call and answers a call.

Calling a modem from another, maintaining the connection, and terminating the connection involves handshaking signals *data terminal ready* (DTR) and *clear to send* (CTS) in both originate and answer modems. See figure 7-3a for a diagram showing these handshaking signals. If a modem is connected to an RS232C line, as it often is, data terminal ready can be connected to request to send (pin 4) and clear to send can be connected to the clear to send (pin 5) or the data set ready (pin 6), whichever is used by the computer. Figure 7-3b shows the sequence of operations in the modems and on the telephone line that show how a call is originated and answered by the Motorola M6860 modem chip. The top line of figure 7-3b shows the handshaking signals seen by the originator; the next line shows the originator modem; the center line, the telephone line signals; the next line, the answer modem; and the bottom line, the handshaking signals seen by the answerer. As indicated, the originator asserts the switch hook signal. This might be asserted by putting the telephone handset on the modem hook or by an output device that asserts this signal. This causes the command ANS (answer phone) to become asserted, which normally enables the data coupler electronics to transmit signals. The telephone is now used to dial up the answerer. (Seventeen seconds is allowed to dial up the answerer.) The answering modem receives a command RI (ring indicator) from the telephone, indicating the phone is ringing. It then asserts the ANS signal to answer the phone, enabling the data coupler to amplify the signal. The answerer puts a true signal, 2225-hertz, on the line. The originator watches for that signal. When it is present for 450 milliseconds, the originator will send its true signal, a 1270-hertz sine wave. The answerer is watching for this signal. When it is present for 450 milliseconds, the answerer asserts the CTS command and is able to begin sending data. The originator, meanwhile, asserts CTS after the 2225-hertz signal has been present for 750 milliseconds. When both modems have asserted CTS, full duplex communication over the communiation link can be carried out.

Some answer modems will automatically terminate the call. To terminate the call, send more than 300 milliseconds of false (space) at 1070-hertz. This is called a *break* and is done by your terminal when you

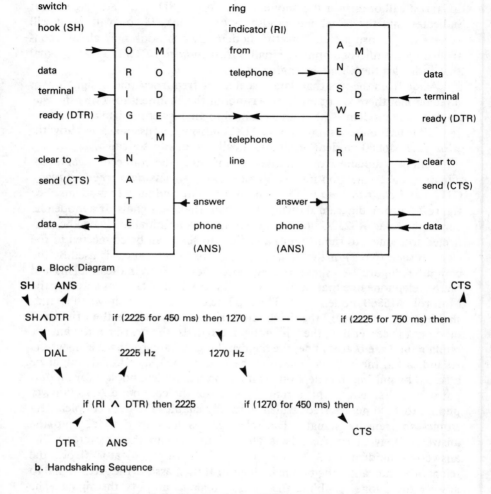

a. Block Diagram

b. Handshaking Sequence

Figure 7-3. Originating a Call on a Modem

press the "break" key. The answer modem will then hang up the phone (negate ANS) and wait for another call. Other modems do not have this automatic space disconnect: they terminate the call whenever neither a high nor a low frequency is received in seventeen seconds. This occurs when the telephone line goes dead or the other modem stops sending any signal. In such systems, the "break" key and low frequency sent when it is pressed can be used as an "attention" signal rather than as a disconnect signal.

7-2.3 Optical Data Transmission

Transmission of data using light is no longer science fiction. A light transmitter, such as a LED or LASER, modulates the signal on the light. This is usually sent on a *light fiber* to a receiver, commonly a photodiode. Data can be sent at 20 megabaud or even higher—a gigabaud is feasible. The product of the data rate and the distance traveled is a constant for any given light fiber, however, so that data sent over long distances has to be received and retransmitted every couple of miles.

Optical transmission will replace telephone lines in cities because one fiber can replace a few hundred pairs of copper wires. Bell telephone can recover enough copper from under New York City, we conjecture, to make that the largest copper mine in the world. Profits from the recovery copper may make installation of optical links quite attractive.

You may have noticed some of the problems with I/O LSI chips due to the fact that we are always short of pins. These problems will get worse as more and more logic can be put on the chip but the number of pins can not be increased proportionally. Optical links between integrated circuits may someday replace most of the pins on an integrated circuit, and most of the traces on a printed circuit board, so that the very dense logic on very large scale integrated circuits can get data in and out. Without the high capacity of optical links, we cannot get data into and out of those VLSI chips at a satisfactory rate. We are currently studying this problem.

Optical links in communications systems are a bit of an embarrassment because of their unprecedented capacity. What can you do with a gigabaud line? (This is bottom-up design.) They clearly have use for communication between large computers and might be useful in microcomputer systems that are used to handle large amounts of data traffic in communications systems. The extraordinary capacity can be used to distribute the components of a computer further. Your primary memory may be in another room. The organization of computing systems may be revolutionized.

While the technology is in its infancy, it is so important that we would like to mention a few of the exciting possibilities. One of these is called *ether-net*. The high capacity optical line is treated like the radio ether—different transmitters send to different receivers at frequencies or time-slices rather as ham radio oprators do. We are studying the *general propagating communication* (GPC) link. See figure 7-4. Each computer, or module, or integrated circuit, has a generate (G) input for data, a propagate (P) for control, and an output named C. The P control is normally asserted to cause the data to propagate through the module, but can be negated to inhibit the data. By inhibiting the data at different modules, we cut the communication link into segments that act independently of each other. In each segment, the OR of the G inputs is sent leftward, or clockwise. The rightmost module can broadcast data to all modules to its left on the same segment if all the other modules do not assert their G inputs. The leftmost module can collect the data from each of the G inputs in the same manner as a wire-OR bus collects data. Moreover, and this is very important, the segment can be made into a priority circuit, so that modules to the right in a segment have higher priority. If a module wants to compete for priority, it asserts the G signal. If the C signal is asserted, it means that some other module of higher priority is requesting a grant, so the module that receives such a signal should not be granted its request. The module that asserts G and receives a negated C is granted the request. Finally—perhaps you have recognized it—this is the carry circuit of a ripple adder. The optical linker can be used to link parts of an adder together. (We refer to the connections as G, P, and C, and to this link as GPC, because these are the names of the signals on a carry-lookahead generator, which is a faster implementation of the ripply carry logic of figure 7-4.)

The GPC is intuitively a good communication linkage because the P signal ANDed into the link can be used to cut the link at any desired point, while the G signal can be used to insert data just as is done on a wire-OR bus. Moreover, the ability to implement priority logic right on the communication linkage has profound effects. It is possible to establish the right to use a resource, including some time on the communication link, using a simple and efficient protocol, because the priority link does most of the work in hardware. By comparison, protocols to use the ether-net require more effort. The ability to break up the GPC into separate segments to get more data moved, and especially the ability to establish priorities, makes the GPC link attractive for optical communication systems.

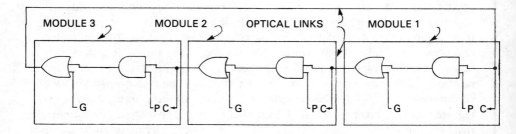

Figure 7-4. A GPC Linkage for Optical Communication

7-3 UART Link Protocol

By far the most common technique for transmitting data is that used by the *Universal Asynchronous Receiver Transmitter* (UART). This simple protocol is discussed here. Software generation of UART signals is quite simple and helps to show how they are sent. That will be discussed first. The UART chip is then discussed. The UART-like chip designed for the M6809 family, the M6850, will be discussed in the next subsection. A special remote control chip that uses the UART protocol is discussed in the final subsection.

7-3.1. UART Transmission and Reception by Software

As noted earlier, the Universal Asynchronous Receiver Transmitter (UART) is a module (integrated circuit) that supports a frame protocol to send up to eight-bit frames (characters). We call this the *UART protocol*. The UART protocol can be supported entirely under software control, without the use of a UART chip, or its equivalent. A study of this software is not only a good exercise in hardware-software tradeoffs, but is also an easy way to teach the protocol and is a practical way to implement communication in a minimum cost microcomputer. Therefore, we study it now. Nevertheless, we do warn the reader that most communication is done with UART chips or their equivalent and many of the minimum-cost microprocessors that have appeared recently (1979) have a built-in UART on the microprocessor chip itself.

In this section, we describe the format of a frame sent by a UART, which embodies the UART protocol. Then an M6809 program that can send such a frame is described. Finally, a program that can receive such a message is described.

The UART frame format is shown in figure 7-5. When a frame is not being sent the signal is high. When a signal is to be sent, a *start bit*, a low, is sent for one bit time. The frame, from five to eight bits long, is then sent one bit per bit time, least significant bit first. A parity bit may then be sent. The parity bit may be generated so that the parity of the whole frame is always even (or always odd). To generate even parity, if the frame itself had an even number of ones already, a low parity bit is sent, otherwise a high bit is sent. Finally, one or more *stop bits* are sent. A stop bit is high, and is indistinguishable from the high signal that is sent when no frame is being transmitted. In other words, if the frame has n stop bits ($n = 1$, 1 1/2, or 2) this means the next frame must wait that long before after the last

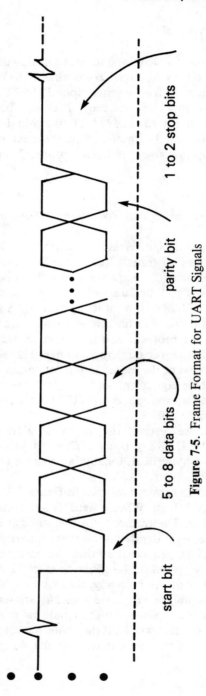

Figure 7-5. Frame Format for UART Signals

frame bit or parity bit of the previous message has been sent before it can begin sending its start bit. It can, however, wait longer than that.

In addition to the format above, the protocol has some rules for sampling data and for error correction. A clock is used in the receiver that is sixteen times the bit rate, and a counter that is incremented by each clock pulse is used to sample the incoming data. (The same clock is used in the transmitter to generate the outgoing data.) The counter is started when the input signal falls, at the beginning of a frame. After eight clock periods, presumably in the middle of the start bit, the input is sampled. It should be low. If it is high, the falling edge that started the counter must have been due to some noise pulse, so the receiver returns to examine the input for the leading edge of a start bit. If this test passes, the input is sampled after every sixteen clock periods, presumably in the middle of each bit time. The data bits sampled are reassembled in parallel. The parity bit, if one is used, is then sampled and checked. Then the stop bit(s) is (are) checked.

The following error conditions are defined. If the parity bit is supposed to be even, but a frame with odd parity is received, a *parity error* is indicated. This indicates that one of the frame bits or the parity bit were changed due to noise. Note that two errors will make the parity appear correct, but two wrongs do not make a right. Parity detection cannot detect all errors. Even so, most errors are single bit errors, so most are detected. If a stop bit is expected, but a low signal is received, the frame has a *framing error*. This usually indicates that the receiver is using the wrong clock rate, either because the user selected the wrong rate, or because the receiver oscillator is out of calibration. However, this condition can arise if the transmitter is faulty, sending frames before the stop bits have been timed out, or if more than one transmitter is on a link, and one sends before the other's stop bits are completely sent. Finally, most UART devices use a buffer to store the incoming word, so the computer can pick up this word at leisure rather than at the precise time that it has been shifted in. This technique is called *double buffering*. If the buffer is not read before another frame arrives and needs to fill the same buffer, the first frame is destroyed. This error condition is called an *overrun error*. It usually indicates that the computer is not paying attention to the UART receiver, since if it were, it would empty the buffer before the next message arrives.

The UART communication technique is based on the following principle. If the frame is short enough, a receiver clock can be quite a bit out of synchronization with the transmitter clock, and still sample the data somewhere within the bit time when the data is correct. For example, if a frame has ten bits, and the counter is reset at the leading edge of the start bit of the frame, the receiver clock could be five percent faster or five percent slower than the transmitter clock and still pick up all the bits up to the last bit of the frame without error. It will sample the first bit five percent early or five percent late, the second ten percent, the third fifteen percent, and the last fifty percent. This means the clock does not have to be sent with the data. The receiver can generate a clock to within five percent of the transmitter clock without much difficulty; however, this technique would not work for long frames because the accumulated error due to incorrectly matching the clocks of the transmitter and receiver would eventually cause a bit to be missampled. To prevent this, the clocks would have to be matched more precisely than is possible. Other techniques become more economical for longer frames.

A subroutine SUART to generate a signal compatible with the UART protocol is quite simple, as we discuss below. Assume an eight-bit word in accumulator B is to be sent in a frame with even parity and two stop bits. An output register at location $8000 outputs the least significant bit into the communication link. The following program uses a subroutine DELAY whose execution time is set to the time to send one bit. If the rate were 10 baud, this subroutine would delay 100,000 microseconds. The program below assumes that the output was high for some time, since the protocol requires a high signal when no frame is being sent. A low signal, the start pulse, is sent for one bit time. Then the data in accumulator B is output then shifted eight times so each bit is sent out the output port in its least significant bit position. Meanwhile, the parity is determined by exclusive ORing B into A, which makes the least significant bit of A the parity of the bits shifted out. The parity bit is then output. Finally, two stop bits are sent out. The whole purpose of "sending" these stop bits is to make sure that this routine is not called up too soon to send another frame. If this were done, the receiver would detect a framing error.

```
        NAM    SUART
SUART   CLR    $8000    SEND START BIT
        BSR    DELAY
        LDA    #8       SET COUNTER FOR 8 BITS OF DATA
        PSHS   A        SAVE ON STACK AS LOCAL
                        VARIABLE
        CLR    A        CLEAR PARITY BIT
L       STB    $8000    OUTPUT BIT
        BSR    DELAY
        PSHS   B        PUT B ON STACK
        EORA   ,S+      IN ORDER TO EXCLUSIVE-OR IT
                        WITH A
        LSR    B        NEXT BIT
        DEC    ,S       COUNT DOWN NUMBER OF BITS
                        SENT
```

```
BNE         L      LOOP UNTIL ALL SENT
STA      $8000     OUTPUT PARITY
BSR      DELAY
LDA        #1      STOP BIT IS HIGH
STA      $8000
BSR      DELAY     SEND STOP BIT
BSR      DELAY     SEND SECOND STOP BIT
PULS      A,PC     RETURN FROM SUBROUTINE,
                   DISCARD LOCAL VARIABLE
END
```

A subroutine RUART to receive a UART frame is also quite simple. Assume the protocol of the frame is as above, and the data is to be received from the most significant bit of an input register at location $8001, the low order seven bits of that register being zero. This data is assembled in the following subroutine into accumulator B. In addition to the DELAY subroutine, a subroutine HDELAY delays for one half of a bit time, in order to begin sampling the inputs in the middle of the bit times. The first part of the program waits for the falling edge of the input signal, which is the beginning of the start bit. HDELAY waits for the middle of the bit. If the input is not low, control returns to check for the beginning of the start bit again. Otherwise, after each full bit time, another bit is put into accumulator B (by ORing it in) and parity is updated in accumulator A. When the parity bit arrives, it is checked against the parity bit assembled in accumulator A. If they disagree, control goes to an error exit PARERR. Then, two stop bits are sought. If either bit is low, a framing error is reported, by branching to FRMERR.

Both the programs are simple enough to follow. They can be done in software without much penalty because the microprocessor is usually doing nothing while frames are being input or output. Essentially the same algorithms are executed inside the UART chip or an equivalent chip like the M6850 in an equivalent hardware alternative. The hardware alternative is especially valuable where the microcomputer can do something else as the hardware tends to transmitting and receiving the frames, or when it might be sending a frame at the same time that it is receiving another frame (in a full duplex link or in a ring of simplex links). In other cases, the availability of cheap, simple UART chips favors the hardware approach, while the simplicity of the program favors the software approach. The best design must be picked with care and depends very much on the characteristics of the application.

```
           NAM        RUART
RUART      TST        $8001
           BMI        RUART    WAIT FOR FALLING EDGE
           BSR        HDELAY
           TST        $8001    SEE IF INPUT STILL LOW
           BMI        RUART    IF NOT LOW, GO BACK AND
                               WAIT
           CLR        A        READY TO COMPUTE PARITY
                               BIT
           LDB        #8       INPUT 8 BITS OF DATA
           PSHS       B        SAVE AS LOCAL VARIABLE
L2         BSR        DELAY
           LSR        B        MOVE FOR NEXT BIT
           ORAB       $8001    INPUT NEXT BIT
           EORA       $8001    UPDATE PARITY
           DEC        ,S       ALL BITS INPUT?
           BNE        L2       IF NOT GO BACK
           BSR        DELAY
           CMPA       $8001    CHECK PARITY
           BNE        PARERR
           BSR        DELAY
           TST        $8001    CHECK FOR FIRST STOP BIT
           BPL        FRMERR
           BSR        DELAY
           TST        $8001    CHECK FOR SECOND STOP BIT
           BPL        FRMERR
           PULS       A,PC     RETURN FROM SUBROUTINE,
                               ELIMINATE LOCAL VARIABLE
           END
```

7-3.2 The UART

The UART chip is designed to transmit and receive signals that comply with the UART protocol (by definition). This protocol allows several variations (baud rates, parity bit, and stop bit selection). The particular variation is selected by strapping different pins on the chip to high or to low. The UART can be used inside a microcomputer to communicate with a teletype or a typewriter, which was its original use, or in an electronic equivalent of a typewriter such as a CRT display. It can also be used in other remote stations in security systems, stereo systems controlled from a microcomputer, and so on. Several integrated circuit companies make UARTs, and they are all very similar. We will study one that has a single supply voltage and a self-contained oscillator to generate the clock for the UART, the Intersil IM6403. A complete description is provided in appendix B.

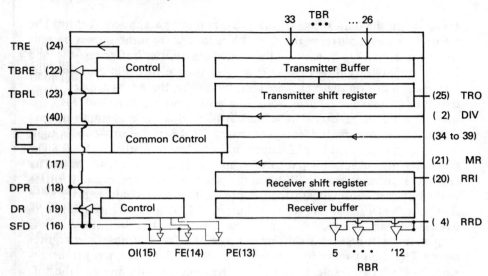

Figure 7-6. Block Diagram of a UART (IM6403)

The UART contains a transmitter and a receiver that run independently for the most part but share a common control that selects the baud rate and other variations for both transmitter and receiver. The common control is discussed first, then the transmitter, and then the receiver. The baud rate is selected by the crystal connected to pins seventeen and forty, and the divide control DIV on pin two. If DIV is high, the oscillator frequency is divided by sixteen, if low, by $2^{**}11$. This is the UART clock which is divided again by sixteen. If the crystal is a cheap TV crystal (3.5795-MHz) and DIV is low, the baud rate is close to 110, which is commonly used for teletypes. Master reset MR, on pin twenty-one, resets the chip when it is high. It is normally grounded. The other control bits are input on pins thirty-nine to thirty-five, and are stored in a latch inside the chip. The latch stores the inputs when pin thirty-four is high. This pin can be held high to defeat the storage mechanism so that the pin levels control the chip directly. Pin thirty-six selects the number of stop bits: low selects one stop bit, high selects two (except for an anomaly of little interest). If pin thirty-five is high, no parity bit is generated or checked, otherwise pin thirty-nine selects even parity if high, odd if low. Pins thirty-seven and thirty-eight select the number of data bits per frame: the number is five plus the binary number on these pins. The user generally determines the values needed on these pins from the protocol he is using, and connects them to high or low; however, these inputs can be tied to the data bus of a computer, and pin thirty-four can be asserted to load the control latch to effect an output register. The computer can then set the control values under software control when it executes the reset handler.

The operations of the transmitter and receiver are compactly and simply explained in the data sheets of the 6403, and are paraphrased below. The transmitter has a buffer register, which is loaded from the signals on pins thirty-three (msb) to twenty-six (lsb) when transmitter buffer register load TBRL (pin twenty-three) rises. If n (less than eight) bits are sent, the rightmost n bits on these pins are sent. Normally, these pins are tied to the data bus to make the buffer look like an output register, and TBRL is asserted when the register is to be loaded. When this buffer is empty and can be loaded, transmitter buffer register empty TBRE (pin twenty-two) is high; when full it is low. (SFD, pin sixteen, must be low to read out TBRE.) The computer may check this pin to determine if it is safe to load the buffer register. It behaves as a BUSY bit in the classical I/O mechanism. The data in the buffer is automatically loaded into the transmitter shift register to be sent out as transmitter register output TRO (pin twenty-five) with associated start, parity, and stop bits as selected by the control inputs. As long as the shift register is shifting out part of a frame, transmitter register empty TRE (pin twenty-four) is low. Figure 7-7 shows a typical transmission, in which two frames are sent out. The second word is put into the buffer even as the first frame is being shifted out in this double buffered system. It is automatically loaded into the shift register as soon as the first frame has been sent.

The receiver shifts data into a receiver shift register. When a frame has been shifted in, the data is put in the receiver buffer. If fewer than eight bits are transmitted in a frame, the data is right justified. This data can be read from pins five to twelve, when receive register disabled RRD (pin four) is asserted low. Normally these pins are attached to a data bus, and RRD is used to enable the tristate drivers when the read buffer register is to be read as an input register. If RRD is strapped low, then the data in the read buffer is continuously available on pins five to twelve. When the read buffer con-

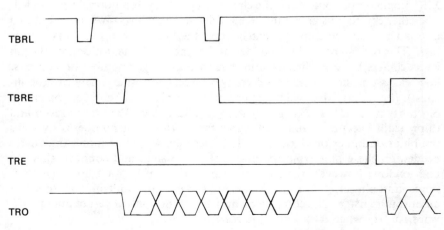

Figure 7-7. Transmitter Signals

tains valid data, the data ready DR signal (pin nineteen) is high, and the error indicators are set. (DR can only be read when SFD on pin sixteen is high.) The DR signal is an indication that the receiver is in the done state, in the classical I/O mechanism, and it requests the program to read the data from the receive buffer, and read the error indicators if appropriate. The error indicators are reloaded after each frame is received, so they always indicate the status of the last frame that was received. The error indicators and TBRE and DR can be read from pins fifteen to thirteen and twenty-two and nineteen when SFD (pin sixteen) is asserted low, and indicate an overrun error, a framing error, and a parity error, and that the transmit buffer is empty and that the receive buffer is full respectively, if high. The error indicators and buffer status indicators can be read as another input register by connecting pins twenty-two, nineteen, and fifteen to thirteen to the data bus, and asserting SFD when this register is selected, or if SFD is strapped low, the error and buffer status indicators can be read directly from those pins. When the data is read, the user is expected to reset the DR indicator by asserting data read to reset DRR (pin eighteen) high. If this is not done, when the next frame arrives and is loaded into the buffer register, an overrun error is indicated.

The UART can be used in a microcomputer system as follows. The control bits (pins thirty-five to thirty-nine) and the transmit buffer inputs (pins twenty-six to thirty-three) can be inputs, and the buffer status and error indicators (pins twenty-two, nineteen, fifteen to thirteen) and receive data buffer outputs (pins five to twelve) can be outputs. All the inputs and outputs can be attached to the data bus. TBRL, SBS, SFD, and RFD (pins twenty-three, thirty-six, sixteen, and four) are connected to an address decoder so that the program can write in the control register or transmit buffer register, or read from the error indicators or the read buffer register. The TBRE signal (pin twenty-two) is used as a BUSY bit for the transmitter, and the DR signal (pin nineteen) is used as a DONE bit for the receiver. We consider using the UART in a gadfly technique below, but the technique can be extended to interrupt or even DMA techniques. The program initializes the UART by writing the appropriate control bits into the control register. To send data using the gadfly approach, the program checks to see if TBRE is high, and waits for it to go high if it is not. When it is high, the program can load data into the transmitter buffer. Loading data into the buffer will automatically cause it to be sent out. If the program is expecting data from the receiver in the gadfly technique, it waits for DR to become high. When it is, the program reads data from the receive buffer register and asserts DRR to tell the UART that the buffer is now empty. This makes DR low until the next frame arrives.

The UART can be used without a computer in a remote station that is implemented with hardware. Control bits can be strapped high or low, and CRL (pin thirty-four) can be strapped high to load these values into the control register constantly. Data to be collected can be put on pins thirty-three to twenty-seven. Whenever the hardware wants to send the data, it asserts TBRL (pin twenty-three) low for a short time, and the data gets sent. It can examine TBRE (pin twenty-two) to be sure that the transmitter buffer is empty before it loads it, but if the timing works out so that the buffer will always be empty there is no need to check this value. It is pretty easy to send data in that case. Data, input serially, is made available, and is stable, on pins five to twelve. Each time a new frame is completely shifted in, the data in it is transferred in parallel into the buffer. RRD (pin four) would be strapped low to output this data in a hardware system constantly. When DR becomes high, new data has arrived, which might signal the hardware to do something with it. The hardware should then assert DRR high to clear DR. (DR can feed a delay into DRR to reset itself.) The buffer status and error indicators can be constantly output, if SFD (pin sixteen) is strapped low, and the outputs can feed LEDs to indicate an error, for instance. In a simple system when the hardware does not have to do anything special with the data other than output it, it can ignore DR and ignore resetting it via asserting DRR. In this case the receiver is very simple to use in a remote station.

7-3.3 The M6850

The M6850 is a "UART" that has been specially tailored to be used in an M6809 microcomputer. It is called an *asynchronous communications interface adapter* (ACIA) by Motorola. As noted before, we do not use the terms like PIA and ACIA because they are less specific than part numbers like M6821 or M6850, but we do not object to your using these terms. This section will discuss the highlights of the M6850. A complete description is available on a Motorola data sheet in *The Complete Motorola Microcomputer Data Library*. The M6850 is designed for the Motorola microcomputer. It can also be used in other microcomputers, and other microcomputer manufacturers have special chips like the M6850 for their systems. Compared to a UART like the IM6403, the M6850 has the following differences. To save pins, a bit of the transmitter buffer input, a bit of the receiver buffer output, a bit of the control register, and a bit of the buffer/error status register output are internally connected, and connected to a single pin on this chip. Thus, only eight pins are used to connect to the data bus. An external clock is needed to set the baud rate, and the transmitter can have a different clock than the receiver. Also, this chip is designed to connect to a modem, which was discussed in a previous section. It has three pins to control the modem so that the program can control it. Finally, it has a status register with interrupt request logic so that the M6809 can easily examine it in its interrupt handler. The M6850 is shown in figure 7-8; for simplicity, the system is configured so that this chip is addressed at locations $8000 and $8001.

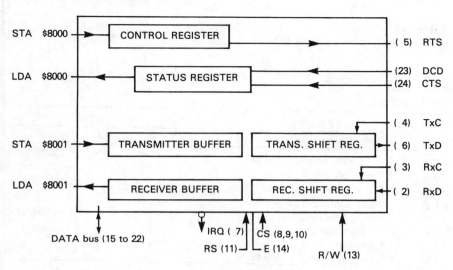

Figure 7-8.   The M6850

The transmitter, with its buffer and shift register, and the receiver and its shift register, operate just as in the UART. They are addressed in the same location because the transmit buffer is write only, while the receive buffer is read only. Once the control register is set up, a word is transmitted simply by writing it in location $8001, and an incoming word is picked up by reading it from location $8001.

The control register written into at location $8000 sets up the baud rate (it is also set by the frequency of the external clocks), the frame format, and the interrupt mechanism. The transmitter interrupt control also controls a signal called request to send RTS on an output pin, which can be used to control a modem. These control values are shown in table 7-2a. The user determines the bit pattern from the protocol and sets this register up in a ritual. An example will be given shortly that uses this table.

The frame format is controlled by bits four to two in an obvious way. Note that the UART has more combinations, but the most popular combinations of data, parity, and stop bits are available in the M6850. The clock frequency is divided to get the baud rate under control of bits one and zero. If division is by one, the baud rate is the same as the frequency of the clock input, which is set by an external oscillator. Each clock cycle shifts out one bit of data. This is useful for high baud rates, such as would be used to communicate between two microcomputers a short distance apart. Normally, division is by sixteen, as discussed in earlier sections; however, division by sixty-four is useful if a slow baud rate is desired. The external clock would have to be divided by four in another (counter) chip to get that frequency. The last code for this field is the master reset. Unfortunately, this

Table 7-2
M6850 Control and Status Bits

Table 7-2a
Control Register

Bits	Function
4,3,2	Frame Format
0 0 0	7 bits, even parity, 2 stop bits
0 0 1	7 data, odd parity, 2 stop bits
0 1 0	7 data, even parity, 1 stop bit
0 1 1	7 data, odd parity, 1 stop bit
1 0 0	8 data, 2 stop bits
1 0 1	8 data, 1 stop bit
1 1 0	8 data, even parity, 1 stop bit
1 1 1	8 data, odd parity, 1 stop bit

Bits	Function
7	Receiver Interrupt
0	Disable
1	Enable

Bits	Function
1,0	Clock Frequency
0 0	Divide by 1
0 1	Divide by !6
1 0	Divide by 64
1 1	Master Reset

Bits	Function	
6,5	Trans. Int.	RTS
0 0	Disable	Low
0 1	Enable	Low
1 0	Disable	High
1 1	Disable	Low[a]

[a]Transmit data output is low.

Table 7-2b
Status Register

IRQ	PE	OVRN	FE	CTS	DCD	TDRE	RDRF

chip does not have a reset pin, as do most of the other I/O chips in the M6809 family. Before it can be used, the M6850 must be reset by putting 11 into bits one and zero. The other bits can be zero. So the first thing to do with this chip is to store $03 into the control register. This is usually done just before the control register is set up with the bits that determine the modes of operation. Be warned, moreover, that if this is not done, the chip will appear to be bad. The author spent a frustrating week and several chips finding this out. The transmitter is controlled by bits six and five. If interrupts are enabled, each time the transmit buffer is empty an interrupt will be generated so that the software can refill it. Interrupts should be enabled, and an appropriate device handler should be used, when a sequence of words is to be output as to a typewriter, if the microcomputer can do some useful work while the M6850 tends to transmitting the message. Interrupts should be disabled when the microcomputer uses the gadfly technique to transmit one word at a time. The RTS signal is often used to control a modem. This (negative logic) signal is set by bits six and five. If these control bits are 11, the transmitter outputs a low signal. This is used to test and to control a modem. Finally, bit seven controls the receiver interrupt. If it is true, an interrupt is requested whenever the receive buffer is full (data is available), so the software can move the word, or whenever there is an error in the receiver such as parity, framing, overrun, or a problem with the modem indicated by a low signal on the data carrier detect DCD pin. This bit should be true if interrupts are used to service the reader, and false if the gadfly technique is used.

Suppose that a simple program is to be written to test the transmitter of the M6850, using an oscilloscope to view the output. The word $C5 has an instructive pattern, so it will be continuously transmitted. The transmitter clock input is 1,600 hertz, and the data is to be sent at 100 baud, with eight data bits, parity, and one stop bit. Neither the transmitter nor the receiver should generate interrupts, and RTS should be low. Consulting table 7-2a, the control bits should be as follows: bit seven should be zero, to disable the receiver interrupt. Bits six and five should both be zero, to disable the transmitter interrupt and set RTS low. Bits four, three, and two should be one, one, and zero to select eight data, even parity, and one stop bit. Bits one and zero should be zero and one to divide the clock rate, 1,600 hertz, by sixteen, to deliver bits at 100 baud. The control word should be $19. The following program initializes the M6850 by first resetting it, then putting in the control word. Then a constant, $C5, is put into accumulator A. The constant is stored into the transmitter buffer in a program loop so that every time the buffer is empty it is immediately refilled with the constant. (If the buffer is already full, writing another word into it does not cause an error but the word that was in it is lost. Normally the program checks a status bit to be sure this buffer is empty before filling it, but in this case there is no harm in constantly writing the same word into it.) The output of the shift register would appear on an oscilloscope as shown in figure 7-9.

```
        LDA   #$03
        STA $8000
        LDA   #$19
        STA $8000
        LDA   #$C5
   L STA $8001
        BRA       L
```

The status bits of the M6850 can be read from location $8000. See table 7-2b. RDRF (bit zero) is true if the receive buffer is full. TDRE (bit one) is true if the transmit buffer is empty. Bits two and three indicate the signals from a modem, DCD and CTS, that normally indicate the data carrier is present and the channel is clear to send. FE, OVRN, and PE, (bits four, five, and six) are the framing overrun and parity error indicators. IRQ (bit seven) is a composite interrupt request bit, which is true if the interrupt enable, control bit seven, is true and any one or several of the status bits zero, two, four, five, or six are true, or if control bits six and five are zero and one and status bit one is true. FE and OVRN are cleared by reading the data register, but PE is cleared when the next character arrives.

In order to show the use of the M6850 status bits, a portion of an interrupt handler will be written to check this device. It will branch to NEXT if

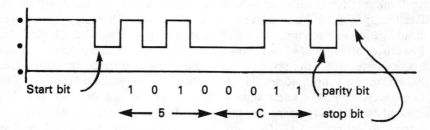

Start bit   1 0 1 0 0 0 1 1   parity bit
        ◄── 5 ──►◄── C ──►   stop bit

Figure 7-9. Output of a Test Program

the M6850 does not request an interrupt: NEXT is some routine to check other I/O devices. If the chip is not in its socket, we want to jump to NEXT too. We test for all ones to see if the chip is not in its socket. We would like to check for a zero bit to insure that the chip is in its socket, but none of the status bits can be guaranteed to be zero. So we check for all ones. While this pattern could conceivably show up, it would require so many coincidences that are far less likely than the chip not being in its socket that we use this test. If the receiver buffer is full, it will branch to a routine STORE that will store the word in the receive buffer in some table or character string. If an error is made upon reception, however, it will branch to a routine ERROR to correct the error or to report it. Lastly, if the transmitter buffer is empty, it will branch to LOAD, which will read another word from some character string or file into the buffer register.

```
LDA      $8000
BPL      NEXT
CMPA     #$FF
BEQ      NEXT
BITA     #$74
BNE      ERROR
LSRA
BCS      STORE
LSRA
BCS      LOAD
```

The M6850 is connected to the M6809 system in the standard way. See figure 7-8 for the pin connections. Pins fifteen to twenty-two are connected to the data bus, pin seven to the IRQ bus line if interrupts are used, pin fourteen to the E clock, and pin thirteen to the R/W line. To select the chip, pins eight, nine, and ten must be high, low, and high, respectively. These are normally connected to an address decoder, and, if it is used, VMA must be true to select the chip because reading or writing in the data buffer registers clears the associated interrupts. VMA can be connected directly to pin eight or ten for convenience. Pin eleven is normally connected to address bit zero, to select control/status if this bit is false, or a data buffer is true. An external clock is connected to pins three and four to set the baud rate for the receiver and transmitter, respectively. While the two clocks can be different, they are usually the same. Finally, pins five, twenty-three, and twenty-four are available to connect to a modem, as discussed in section 7-2.2. If not used, pins twenty-three and twenty-four should be grounded to prevent false interrupts.

7-3.4 The M14469

The M14469 is a "UART" specially designed for a remote station. A short description is given below. A full description is given in appendix C. A CMOS chip, it can use an unregulated supply whose voltage can vary between 4.5 and 18 volts, and it uses very little current. It features a self-contained oscillator and an address comparator that permits the selection of a station when multiple stations are on the same link. A UART protocol is supported, in which the frame has even parity and one stop bit. The baud rate is determined by the crystal (or ceramic resonator) connected between pins one and two, or an external oscillator can drive pin one. The crystal (oscillator) frequency is divided by sixty-four to set the baud rate. A diagram of the M14469 is shown in figure 7-10.

The receiver is a standard UART receiver with an address comparator. A seven-bit address is sent as the low order seven bits of an eight-bit word, the most significant bit being true. The station has a seven-bit address, which is selected by strapping pins ten to four low if a zero bit is needed, or leaving them open if a one bit is needed in the address (these pins have an internal pull-up resistor to make them high if they are not connected). If the incoming address is equal to the station address, the valid address pulse VAP (pin thirty-one) is made high momentarily and the station is said to be *selected*. A seven-bit data word is sent as the low order seven bits of a word, the most significant bit being false. A station that has been selected will put any data word into its receive buffer when the word is completely shifted in,

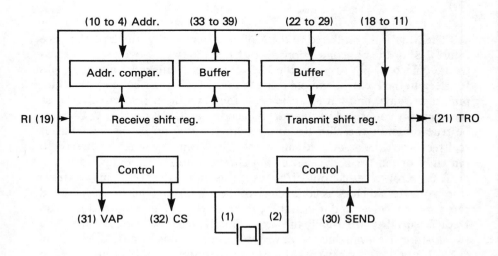

Figure 7-10. The M14469

and make a command strobe CS (in thirty-two) high momentarily just after this happens. Error status is not available on a pin, but if a parity or framing error is detected, an address will not select a station, data will not be transferred to the receive buffer, and VAP or CS will not be pulsed.

Note that a typical message will consist of a frame with an address (most significant bit true) followed by zero or more frames with data (most significant bit false). A single address frame can be used to trigger a remote station to do something, by asserting VAP in it when the address is recognized, or a message with an address frame followed by a number of data frames will cause the data to be stored in the receive buffer each time a data frame arrives and will pulse CS to command something to be done with the data.

The transmitter is a conventional UART transmitter that is modified to send out sixteen bits of data in two consecutive frames if SEND is made high when VAL or CS is asserted (or within eight data bit time units after that) and if it is not currently transmitting a pair of frames. Sixteen bits are sent from the signals on pins eleven to eighteen and twenty-nine to fifteen by transferring the data on pins eleven to eighteen directly into the transmitter shift register, and simultaneously transferring the data on pins twenty-nine to fifteen into the transmitter buffer. The data in the shift register is sent out (pin eleven data first) in the first UART frame, and the data in the buffer (pin twenty-nine data first) is sent out immediately after that in the next frame. The data appears on the transmitter output TRO (pin twenty-one) in negative logic. This output is in negative logic so that it can drive a transistor, which inverts the signal, to power the link out of the station.

The chip is designed for full duplex and for half duplex and has some special provisions for the latter application. In full duplex applications, a master (likely an M6850 in a microcomputer) sends to all the slave stations (several M14469s) on one line (M6850 TxD output to RI input of each slave), while all the slave stations send to the master on another line (slave TRO output into transistor base, transistor collectors in each slave tied together, in a wire-AND bus line, to RxD input of M6850), so that the master can be sending to a slave at the same time that a slave is sending to the master. In this case, VAP can be connected to SEND to send back the two frames as quickly as possible after a station is selected. The master should take care that it does not send two address frames, one right after another, so that two slaves will send overlapping frames back. In the half-duplex mode, a single bus line is used between master and all slaves so that the master can send data to the slaves, or the slaves can send data to the master, but not at the same time. TxD and RxD in the master, and RI and the transistor collector in each slave, would be connected to this single line. In this application, SEND should be connected to CS, so that the slave that was selected will wait for an address frame and a data frame to be sent over the line from the master before the slave returns its two frames. The master should wait for both frames to be returned before it tries to send more data on the same line.

In order to insure that the data has been received, handshaking is often used, and to permit handshaking, the M14469 is designed to prevent difficulties in the half-duplex mode. The slave can be implemented so that the first frame it returns has its own station address. When the master sends a message, it can wait for the slave to respond with a frame having the address of the slave. If that frame is returned, the message must have been received without error and the slave must be active (as opposed to being shut off). This is a simple handshake protocol; however, if the M14469 is used in the half-duplex mode, we do not want the return frame to be received by the same slave and for it to recognize its own address again to trigger itself nor do we want the return message stored in the receive buffer. Therefore, this chip is designed so that it deselects the receiver as soon as it begins transmitting a frame. The frame being transmitted should be a data frame (most significant bit false) to prevent the address decoder from matching it, even though the frame really contains an address. This provision makes handshaking in the half-duplex mode possible. The chip is so designed that way, however, and these peculiarities are apparent in the full-duplex mode too.

Before this section ends, a short program is presented that shows how the M6850 can communicate to several M14469s over a full-duplex line. The object of the program is to select station three, send a word of data to it, and receive a word of data from it. An M14469 is configured as station three by wiring pins ten to four and pins seventeen to eleven to represent the number three. The data to be sent back from this station is connected to pins twenty-three to twenty-nine. Handshaking is used, so the transmission on the link will look as follows. The master will send the address of the slave, then seven bits of data to the slave on the line from master to slave. Then the slave will return its address and seven bits of data on the other line.

The following program sets up an M6850 to send eight bits of data, even parity, and one stop bit per frame, and to divide the clock by sixty-four. The gadfly technique uses a subroutine WTBRE to wait until the transmitter buffer is empty, shown at the bottom of the program, and then to it output the word in accumulator A. Initially, accumulator A has $5A, which is some data for station three. The address is sent first, then the data. Then the receiver is checked for an incoming frame. While checking for the returned frame, the index register is used to keep track of elapsed time. The contents of this frame are compared with the address that was sent out. If too much time elapses before the frame returns or if it contains the wrong address, the program exits to ERROR to report the error. Otherwise, the data in the next frame is left in accumulator B, and this routine is left.

```
              NAM        REMOT
REMOT   PSHS         A     SAVE WORD TO BE OUTPUT
        LDA        #$03    RESET THE M6850
```

```
              STA         $8000      BY PUTTING 3 IN CONTROL
                                     REGISTER
              LDA         #$1A       8 DATA, EVEN PARITY, ONE
                                     STOP
              STA         $8000      DIVIDE BY 64, DISABLE
                                     INTERRUPTS
              LDA         #$83       OUTPUT ADDRESS OF STATION
                                     3 ($80 + $03)
              BSR         WTRBE      CHECK AND OUTPUT WORD IN
                                     ACCUMULATOR A
              PULS          A        GET SUBROUTINE ARGUMENT
                                     BROUGHT IN
              BSR         WTRBE      CHECK AND OUTPUT WORD IN
                                     ACCUMULATOR A
              LDX          #0        PUT LARGEST COUNT IN INDEX
                                     REGISTER X
L1            LDB         $8000      CHECK STATUS
              LSR           B        RDRF IS LEAST SIGNIFICANT
                                     BIT
              BCS          L2        WHEN TRUE, READ REGISTER
                                     IS FULL, GO ON
              LEAX        – 1,X      DECREMENT X
              BNE          L1        LOOP UNTIL WORD IS READ OR
                                     WAIT TOO LONG
              BRA         ERROR      LOOP HAS TIMED OUT THE
                                     WAIT FOR RETURN WORD
L2            CMP A       $8001      CHECK TO SEE IF THE RETURN-
                                     ED ADDRESS IS CORRECT
              BNE         ERROR      IF NOT, ERROR
L3            LDB         $8000      CHECK STATUS BIT RDRF
                                     AGAIN
              LSR           B
              BCC          L3        WAIT FOR IT TO BE TRUE
              LDA         $8001      GET DATA WORD
              RTS
*
WTBRE         LDB         $8000      CHECK STATUS OF TRANSMIT
                                     BUFFER
              BITB        #$02       TDRE IS BIT 1, TRUE WHEN YOU
                                     CAN TRANSMIT
              BEQ         WTBRF      IF FALSE, LOOP
              STA         $8001      SEND WORD TO TRANSMIT
                                     BUFFER REGISTER

              RTS
              END
```

7-4 Other Protocols

Beside the UART protocol, the two most important protocols are the synchronous-bit-oriented protocols—including the SDLC, HDLC, ADCCP, and X.25—and the IEEE-488 bus protocol.

These are important protocols. We fully expect that many if not most of your interfaces will be designed around these protocols. If you are designing an I/O device to be used with a large mainframe computer, you will probably have to interface to it using a synchronous-bit-oriented protocol. If you are designing a laboratory instrument, you will probably interface to a minicomputer using the IEEE-488 protocol so the minicomputer can remotely control your instrument. Motorola has two integrated circuits, the M6854 for the synchronous-bit-oriented protocol and the M68488 for the IEEE-488 bus protocol.

These are complex protocols. The chips are correspondingly complex. The M6854 has four control registers—thirty-two control bits to be initialized in a ritual to configure the device. It has two status registers—sixteen bits—to be analyzed in an interrupt handler. The M68488 has six command/address/polling registers with a lot of rituals to control the bus and seven status/address/polling registers to analyze. While a full discussion of these chips and the communications protocols is not within the scope of this book on I/O interfaces, you should be prepared to handle them based on your thorough understanding of the UART protocol and of the fairly challenging initialization rituals needed to configure the M6840. We will survey the key ideas of these protocols in this section. The first subsection describes the bit-oriented protocols. The second subsection will discuss the 488 bus.

7-4.1 Synchronous-Bit-Oriented Protocols

Synchronous protocols are able to move a lot of data at a high rate. They are primarily used to communicate between *remote job entry* terminals (which have facilities to handle line printers, card readers, and plotters) and computers, and between computers and computers. The basic idea of a synchronous protocol is that a clock is sent, either on a separate wire, or else along with the data in the Manchester coding scheme. Since a clock is sent with the data, there is little fear that the receiver clock will eventually get out of sync after a lot of bits have been sent, so we are not restricted to short frames as we are in the UART. Once the receiver is synchronized, we will try to keep it in synchronization with the transmitter, and we can send long frames without sending the extra control pulses needed to resynchronize the receiver that reduce the efficiency of the channel.

Asynchronous protocols, like the UART protocol discussed in the last section, are more useful if small amounts of data are generated at random times, such as by a computer terminal. Synchronous protocols would have to get all receivers into synchronization with the transmitter when a new transmitter gets control of the channel anyhow, so their efficiency could be poor for short random messages. Synchronous protocols are more useful when a lot of data is sent at once because they do not require the overhead every few bits, such as start and stop bits, that asynchronous protocols need.

Bit-oriented synchronous protocols were developed as a result of the weaknesses in byte- or character-oriented synchronous protocols that were used in applications requiring the movement of large amounts of data. We begin with a short and greatly simplified discussion of the precurser protocol, which will introduce the bit-oriented protocols.

The precurser to the bit-oriented protocol is the binary synchronous *Bisync* protocol, which is primarily character-oriented and is extended to handle arbitrary binary data. This protocol can be used with the ASCII character set. The thirty-two nonprinting ASCII characters include some that are used with the Bisync protocol in order to send sequences of characters. SYN—ASCII $16 is sent whenever nothing else is to be sent. It is a null character used to keep the receiver(s) synchronized to the transmitter. This character can be used to establish which bit in a stream of bits is the beginning of a character. Two Bisync protocols are used, one for sending character text and the other for sending binary data, such as machine code programs, binary numbers, and bit data.

Character text is sent as follows. A Header can be sent: its purpose and format are user-defined. It begins with the character SOH—ASCII $01. An arbitrary number of characters of text is sent after the character STX—ASCII $02, and the text is terminated by the character ETX—ASCII $03. After the ETX character, a kind of checksum is sent. See figure 7-11a.

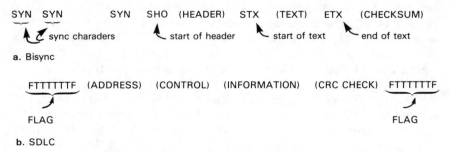

SYN   SYN   SYN   SHO (HEADER) STX   (TEXT)   ETX   (CHECKSUM)

sync charaders   start of header   start of text   end of text

a. Bisync

FTTTTTTF (ADDRESS) (CONTROL) (INFORMATION) (CRC CHECK) FTTTTTTF

FLAG   FLAG

b. SDLC

Figure 7-11. Synchronous Formats

In order to allow any data to be sent, such as a machine code program, including characters that happen to be identical to the character ETX, a character DLE—ASCII $10 is sent before the characters STX and ETX. A byte count is established in some fashion. It may be fixed, so that all frames contain the same number of words, or it may be sent in the header, or it may be sent in the first word or two words of the text itself. Whatever scheme is used to establish this byte count, it is used to disable the recognition of DLE-ETX characters that terminate the frame, so such patterns could be sent without confusing the receiver. This is called the *transparent mode* because the bits sent as "text" are transparent to the receiver controller and can be any pattern.

Bisync uses error correction or error detection and retry. The end of text is followed by a kind of checksum, which differs in differing Bisync protocols. One good checksum is to exclusive-OR the bytes that were sent, byte by byte. If characters have a parity bit, that can identify the byte that is incorrect. The checksum is a parity byte computed "at ninety degrees" from the parity bits and can identify the column that has an error. If you know the column and the row, you know which bit is wrong, so you can correct it. Another Bisync protocol uses a *cyclic redundancy check* (CRC) that is based on the mathematical theory of error correcting codes. The error detecting "polynominal," $X^{**}16 + X^{**}15 + X^{**}2 + 1$, called a CRC-16 polynominal, is one of several good polynominals for detecting errors. The CRC check feeds the data sent out of the transmitter through a shift register that shifts bits from the fifteenth stage towards the zeroth stage. The shift register is cleared and the data bits to be transmitted are exclusive-ORed with the bit being shifted out of the zeroth stage; then this bit is exclusive-ORed into some of the bits being shifted in the register at the inputs to the fifteenth, thirteenth, and zeroth stages. The original data and the contents of the shift register (called the CRC check bits) are transmitted to the receiver. The receiver puts the received data, including the CRC check bits, through the same hardware at its end. When all done, the hardware should produce a zero in the shift register. If it does not, an error (CRC error) has occurred. The Bisync protocol has means to request the frame be sent over again if a CRC error is detected. If the frame is good, an ACK—ASCII $06 is sent, but if an error is detected a NAK—ASCII $15 is sent from the receiver back to the sender. If the sender gets an ACK, it can send the next frame, but if it gets a NAK, it should resend the current frame.

Though developed for communication between a computer and a single RJE station, Bisync has been expanded to include *multi-drop*. Several RJE stations are connected to a host computer on a half-duplex line (bus). The host is a master. It controls all transfers between it and the RJE stations. The master *polls* the stations periodically, just as we polled I/O devices after an interrupt, to see if any of them wanted service. Polling involves the master sending a short packet to each station, so that each station can send back a short message as the master waits for the returned messages.

Bisync protocols had some serious shortcomings. They are set up for and are therefore limited to half-duplex transmission. After each frame is sent, you have to wait for the receiver to send back an acknowledge or a negative acknowledge. This causes the computer to stutter, as it waits for a message to be acknowledged. These shortcomings are improved in bit-oriented protocols. Features that are used for polling and multi-drop connections are improved. The information has been bit-oriented to handle characters, machine code programs, or variable width data efficiently.

The first significant synchronous bit oriented protocol was the *Synchronous Data Link Control* (SDLC) protocol developed by IBM. The American National Standards Institute, ANSI, developed a similar protocol, ADCCP, and the CCITT developed another protocol, HDLC. These are all quite similar at the link control and physical levels that we are studying. We will take a look at the SDLC link, the oldest and simplest of the bit-oriented protocols.

The basic SDLC frame is shown in figure 7-11b. If no data is sent, either a true bit is continually sent (idle condition) or a *flag* pattern, $7E (FTTTTTTF), is sent. The frame itself begins with a flag pattern and ends with a flag pattern, with no flag patterns inside the frame. The flag pattern that ends one frame can be the same flag pattern that starts the next frame.

The frame can be guaranteed free of flag patterns by a five-Ts detector and F inserter. If the transmitter sees that five Ts have been sent, it sends a F regardless of whether the next bit is going to be a T or a F. That way, the data FFTFFTTTTTTF is sent as FFTFFTTTTTFTTF, and the data FFTFFTTTTTFTF is sent as FFTFFTTTTTFFTF, free of a flag pattern. The receiver looks for five Ts. If the next bit is F, it is simply discarded. If the received bit pattern were FFTFFTTTTTFTTF, the F after the five Ts is discarded to give FFTFFTTTTTTF, and if FFTFFTTTTTFFTF is received, we get FFTFFTTTTTFTF; but if the received bit pattern were FTTTTTTF the receiver would recognize the flag pattern and end the frame.

The frame consists of an eight-bit station number address, for which the frame is sent, followed by eight control bits. Any number of information bits are sent next, from zero to as many as can be expected to be received comparatively free of errors or as many as can fit in the buffers in the transmitter and receiver. The CRC check bits are sent next. The address, control, information, and CRC check bits are free of flag patterns as a result of the five-Ts detection and F insertion discussed above.

The control bits identify the frame as an *information frame, supervisory frame*, or *nonsequenced frame*. The information frame is the normal frame for sending a lot of data in the information field. The control field of an information frame has a three-bit number N. The transmitter can send up to eight frames, with different values of N, before handshaking is necessary to verify the frames have arrived in the receiver. Like the ACK and NAK characters in Bisync, supervisory frames are used for retry after error. The receiver can send back the number N of a frame that has an error, requesting that it be sent again, or it can send another kind of supervisory frame with N to indicate that all frames up to N have been received correctly. If the receiver happens to be sending other data back to the transmitter, it can send this number N in another field in the information frame that it sends back to the transmitter of the original message to confirm that it has received all frames up to the Nth frame, rather than sending an acknowledge supervisory frame. This feature improves efficiency, since most frames will be correctly received.

The SDLC link can be used with multi-drop (bus) networks, as well as with a ring network of the same structure as the GPC optical link (figure 7-4). The ring network permits a single main, *primary*, station to communicate with up to 255 other *secondary* stations. Communication is full duplex, since the primary can send to the secondary over part of the loop, while the secondary sends other data to the primary on the remainder of the loop. The SDLC has features for the primary to poll the secondary stations, and for the transmitting station to abort a frame if something goes wrong.

The SDLC link, and the other bit-oriented protocols provide significant improvements over the character-oriented Bisync protocols. Full-duplex communication, allowing up to eight frames to be sent before they are acknowledged, permits more efficient communication. The communication is inherently transparent, because of the five-Ts detection feature, and can handle variable length bit data efficiently. It is an excellent protocol for moving large frames of data at a high rate of speed.

The *X.25* protocol is a three-level protocol established by the CCITT for high-volume data transmission. The physical and link levels are set up for the HDLC protocol, a variation of the SDLC bit-oriented protocol, but synchronous character-oriented protocols can be used so that the industry can grow into the X.25 protocol without scrapping everything. This protocol, moreover, specifies the network level as well. It is oriented to packet switching. Packet switching permits frames of a message to wander through a network on different paths. This dynamic allocation of links to messages permits more efficient use of the links, increases security (since a thief would have to watch the whole network to get the entire message) and enhances reliability. It looks like the communication protocol of the future. While we do not cover it in our discussion of I/O device design, we have been using its terminology throughout this chapter as much as possible.

7-4.2 IEEE-488 Bus Standard

The need to control instruments like voltmeters and signal generators from a computer in the laboratory or factory has led to another kind of protocol, an asynchronous byte-oriented protocol. One of the earliest such protocols was the CAMAC protocol developed by French Nuclear Scientists for their instruments. Hewlett-Packard, a major instrument manufacturer, developed a similar standard, which was adopted by the IEEE and called the IEEE-488 standard. Although Hewlett-Packard owns patents on the handshake methods of this protocol, it has made the rights available on request to most instrument manufacturers, and the IEEE-488 is becoming available on most sophisticated instruments and minicomputers and microcomputers.

Communications to test equipment has some challenging problems. The communications link may be strung out in a different way each time a different experiment is run or a different test is performed. The lengths of the lines can vary. The instruments themselves do not have as much computational power as a large mainframe machine or even a terminal, so the communications link has to do some work for them such as waiting to be sure that they have picked up the data. A number of instruments may have to be told to do something together, such as simultaneously generating and measuring signals, so they cannot be told, one at a time, when to execute their operation. These characteristics lead to a different protocol for instrumentation buses.

The IEEE-488 bus is fully specified at the physical and link levels. A sixteen-pin connector, somewhat like the RS232 connector, is prescribed by the standard, as is the function of the sixteen signals and eight ground pins. The sixteen signal lines include an eight-bit parallel data bus, three handshaking lines, and five control lines. The control lines include one that behaves like the system reset line in the M6809 microcomputer. Others are used to get attention and perform other bus management functions. The heart of the bus standard is the asynchronous protocol used to transmit data on the bus. This is described below.

An asynchronous bus protocol uses a kind of stretchable clock signal, which can be automatically stretched when the bus is longer or shortened if the bus is shorter. The way this happens is that the "clock" is sent from the station that transmits the data to the station that receives the data on one line and back to the transmitter on another line. The transmitter waits for the return signal before it begins another transmission. If the bus is lengthened, so are the delays of this "clock" signal. The IEEE-488 bus uses this principle a couple of times to move a word on an eight-bit bus from a transmitter to a receiver reliably. See figure 7-12.

The handshake cycle is like a clock cycle. Each time a word is to be moved, the bus goes through a handshake cycle to move the word, as shown in figure 7-12. The cycle involves (negative logic) *data available* DAV, sent by the transmitter of the data, (positive logic) *ready for data* RFD, and (positive logic) *data accepted* DAC sent by the receiver of the data.

If the receiver is able to take data, it has already asserted RFD (high). When the transmitter wants to send a data word, it first puts the word on the bus and then it begins the handshake cycle. It checks for the RFD signal. If RFD is asserted at the transmitter, the transmitter asserts DAV (low) to

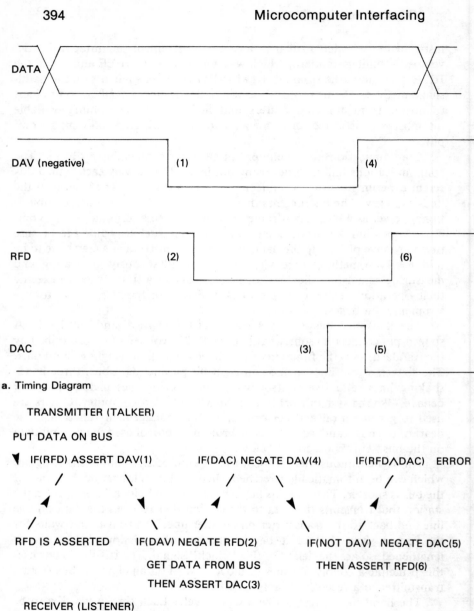

a. Timing Diagram

b. Handshaking Sequence

Figure 7-12. IEEE = Bus Handshaking Cycle

indicate the data is available. This is step (1) in figures 7-12a and 7-12b. When the receiver sees DAV asserted, it negates RFD (low) in step (2) because it is no longer ready for data. When the processor picks up the data from the interface, the receiver asserts DAC (high) to indicate data is accepted. This is step (3). When the transmitter sees DAC asserted, it negates DAV (high) in step (4) because it will soon stop sending data on the data bus. When the receiver sees DAV negated, it negates DAC in step (5). The data is removed sometime after the DAV has become negated. When the receiver is ready to accept new data, it asserts RFD (high) in step (6) to begin a new handshake cycle.

The IEEE-488 bus is designed for some special problems in busing data to and from instruments. First, the bus is asynchronous. If the receiver is far away and the data will take long to get to it the DAV signal will also take a long time and the other handshake signals will be similarly delayed, so long cables are automatically accounted for by the handshake mechanism. Second, the instrument at the receiver may be slow or just busy when the data arrives. DAC is asserted as soon as the data gets into the interface to inform the transmitter that it got there, but RFD is asserted as soon as the instrument gets the data from the interface, so the interface will not get an overrun error that a UART can get. Third, although only one station transmits a word in any handshake cycle, a number of different stations can be transmitters at one time or another. Fourth, the same word can be sent to more than one receiver and the handshaking should be able to make sure all receivers get the word. These last two problems are solved using open collector bus lines for DAV, RFD, and DAC. DAC, sent by the transmitter, is negative logic so the line is wire-OR. That way, if any transmitter wants to send data, it can short the line low to assert DAV. RFD and DAC, on the other hand, are positive logic signals so the line is a wire-AND bus. RFD is high only if all receivers are ready for data, and DAC is high only when all receivers have accepted data.

The IEEE-488 bus is well suited to remote control of instrumentation and is becoming available on many of the instruments being designed at this time. You will probably see a lot of the IEEE-488 bus in your design experiences.

7-5 Conclusions

Communications modules are among the most important I/O modules in a microcomputer. The microcomputer communicates with its keyboards, displays, and typewriters as well as with remote control stations using the

UART protocol. The microcomputer can be in a large computer system and may have to communicate with other parts of the system using the SDLC protocol. It might be in a laboratory and have to communicate with instrumentation on an IEEE-488 bus. Or it might have to talk to different computers in different protocols.

If you would like additional reading, we recommend the excellent *Technical Aspects of Data Communication* by John McNamara, published by Digital Equipment Corporation (DEC). It relates an exceptional amount of practical experience, especially at the physical level, and covers the protocols too. Motorola offers some excellent applications notes for the SDLC protocol using the M6854—*MC6854 ADLC, An Introduction to Data Communication* by M. Newman—and for the IEEE-488 protocol using the M68488—*Getting Aboard the 488-1975 Bus*. These applications notes are well written and can take you from where you left off in this book, if you have to design systems that use these powerful protocols.

This chapter covered the main concepts of communications systems at the physical and link control levels. You should be aware of these concepts so that you can understand the problems and the capabilities of specialists in this field. You should be able to handle the UART, which is the simplest and most widely used communications module, and you should be prepared to connect it to control remote devices or to connect it to a computer. You should be able to connect an M6850 to an M6809 microcomputer and to write initialization rituals, interrupt handlers, and gadfly routines to input data or output data through this chip. These kinds of hardware and software techniques should be adequate for most of your designs and should prepare you well for designing with SDLC and IEEE-488 protocol systems.

Problems

Note

Starred problems are paragraph-correction problems. See the instructions in the problem section at the end of chapter 1 for guidelines. The guidelines for software problems are given there, and those for hardware problems are at the end of chapter 2. Special guidelines for problems using the M6840 counter-timer are presented at the end of chapter 6.

1.*The peer-to-peer interfaces in communications systems are specified in terms of all lower level interfaces in order to avoid any ambiguity. The physical level, at the lowest level, is concerned with the transmission of signals, such as voltage levels, with multiplexing schemes, and with the clocking of data if the clock has to be sent with the data or on a separate line. The baud rate is the number of bytes of user data that can be sent per second. A channel is a data path between entities at the link control level. It is half duplex if every other bit is a data bit, and the remainder are clock bits. Protocols are conventions used to manage the transmission and reception of data at the link control level and to negotiate for and direct communications at the network level. A handshake protocol is one in which congratulations are extended whenever a frame is correctly sent, but the receiver is silent if the data does not look correct. A store-and-forward network is one that sends frames, called packets, from node to node and stores a frame in a node before negotiating to send it to the next node closer to its destination. The bus is a particularly common half-duplex store-and-forward network.

2. Design a one-bit input/output port using the SN75119 differential transciever that is connected to a full-duplex differential line. Reading location $693F will put the data on the incoming line into the sign bit, and the sign bit can be output on the outgoing line by writing in location $693F, but will only be output in the later half of the memory cycle when the M6809 writes in the output register.

3. Design a differential line transmitter using two CA3140s. Both lines should be driven with the low impedance outputs of the OP AMPs. Design a differential line receiver using a CA3140. In both designs, show all pin numbers and component values.

4. Design an RS232-C level translator to drive an RS232-C line from a TTL level using a CA3140. Design a level translator to provide a TTL level output from an RS232-C line using a CA3140. In both designs, show all pin numbers and component values.

5. A "null modem" is a simple module that permits an RS232-C plug from a computer to connect to another RS232-C plug from another computer that has the same connections. Suppose the computer uses only

transmit and receive data, request to send, data set ready, and signal ground. Show connections between the two sockets in the "null modem" that can correctly interconnect the two computers so that one looks like a terminal to the other, and vice versa.

6. The M6840 and Johnson counter of figure 6-4 can generate the frequencies and detect the frequencies for frequency-shift keyed data transmission on the telephone. Device one will be used to generate the outgoing signal, and device three will measure the incoming signal, after appropriate filtering. A signal will be recognized if its period is within 5 percent of the period the receiver should be getting for at least ten cycles. Show a gadfly program (including initialization ritual) that will implement the handshaking sequence of figure 7-3, supplying the data and ANS commands and monitoring the RI status of the data coupler: (a) in the originate modem, assuming that ANS is the most significant bit of the output register at location $8008; (b) in the answer modem, assuming RI is able to be read as the most significant bit of an input register at location $8009 and ANS is the most significant bit of the output register at $8008.

7. Give the logic diagram of a round-robin priority circuit (section 4-2.2) using the GPC link (figure 7-4). Use the TTL gates in *The TTL Data Book*. Each module has a request input R and a a grant flip-flop G, and all are clocked with a common clock. The modules have no other connections between them. In each clock cycle, the request is determinate for the whole clock cycle, and the grant is determined at the end of the cycle to be put in the G flip-flop for the next cycle. The module that gets a grant, setting G, becomes the lowest priority module. (Hint: use negative logic to inhibit the signal on the output of the module in figure 7-4.)

8. Design a modified *Pierce loop* using a GPC link. A Pierce loop is a big shift register, with, say, eight bits of the shift register in each module (computer). Data circulates in the register synchronously. A frame consists of a three-bit source address, a three-bit destination address, and a two-bit data field. One module sends data to another by putting the address of the destination first, then the address of the module that is sending the data, and then the data, in a frame. When a frame is entirely in a shift register in a module, all modules will have a frame in them, and we say the data is framed. When the frame shifts by the destination module the data is taken from the frame. In a modification of this protocol, the eight-bit segments of the shift register are initially bypassed so the loop appears to be a short-circuited wire. A module desiring to transmit a frame inserts its part of the shift register into the loop, with the frame in it, and lets it be shifted out at a time when the data is framed. As it passes the destination, the destination copies it, but lets it go around the loop. When the frame gets back into the shift register of the sender and the data is framed, the sender takes the shift register out of the loop. (a) Design a module using the A device of an M6821

to read the word in the shift register, using the B device to load the shift register in parallel, and using CA2 to control the P signal of a GPC link and the CB2 to load the shift register from the B device, so the GPC can insert the frame. Use the standard chips in *The TTL Data Book*, and show all pin connections between the M6821, the shift register chips, and the GPC gates. (b) Write a gadfly program (including initialization ritual) to output the word in accumulator A, assuming it is already formatted as a frame, and assuming the clock that shifts the shift register is slow and is connected to the CA1 input. Assume a global variable COUNT whose three low-order bits are zero when data is framed, and show how the frame sent by a module can be detected and deleted from the loop. Assume the M6821 is addressed in the normal way at locations $8000 to $8003.

9. Write a program to input and output UART signals using an M6840 to time the samples. The most significant bit of location $8008 is an input bit from the serial communications link and an output bit to it. (a) Initialize the M6840 for a rate of 110 baud, one to request an interrupt each 1/110 second from device one, and to request an interrupt every 1/1760 second from device three for parts (b) and (c) below. (b) Write a device handler to send the word in global variable URTOUT. Use a global variable TCKOUT to count the occurrences of interrupts to keep track of the timing. On each interrupt from device one, send one bit through the output register, but when the word is sent, send stop bits on each interrupt. (c) Write a device handler to receive a word from the input register into global variable UARTIN. On each interrupt from device three, check the input. First check for a start bit, eight interrupts later check the start bit, and every sixteen interrupts later get another bit from the input port. Use a global variable TICKIN to count the number of interrupts and sequence the sampling of the input signal.

10. Show a logic diagram of an I/O device using an IM6403 connected to an M6809. Use completely specified decoding, so the transmit buffer is at location $8000, the receive buffer at $8001, the control register at $8002, and the OE, FE, PE, DR, and TBRE status bits can be read at location $8003. Connect control and status so that the lower numbered pins on the IM6403 are connected to lower numbered data bits for each I/O word, and use the lower numbered data bits if fewer than eight bits are to be connected. Show all pin connections to the M6809 and the IM6403, and show the address decoder using the standard TTL gates.

11. Show the logic diagram of a remote station that uses an IM6403 UART and a 74LS259 addressable latch so that when the number $I + 2 \times N$ is sent, latch N is loaded with the bit I. Be careful about the timing of DR and DRR signals and the G clock for the 74LS259.

12. Show initialization rituals to initialize the M6850 for: (a) eight data, two stop bits, divide clock by one, all interrupts disabled, RTS high; (b) seven data, even parity, two stop bits, divide clock by sixteen, only receiver

interrupt enabled, RTS low; (c) eight data, one stop bit, divide clock by sixteen, only transmitter interrupt enabled; (d) seven data, even parity, one stop bit, divide clock by sixty-four, all interrupts enabled; (e) seven data, even parity, two stop bits, clock divide by one, interrupts disabled, RTS low.

13. Write a simple word-oriented teletype handler, using the gadfly synchronization technique. The M6850 is at locations $8000 and $8001. (a) Write the initialization routine for parts (b) and (c). Use seven data, odd parity, two stop bits, and divide the clock by sixteen. (b) Write a subroutine OUTCH to output the characters in accumulator A. If the device is busy, wait in OUTCH until the word can be output. (c) Write a subroutine INCH to input a character into accumulator A. If no character has arrived yet, wait in INCH until it comes.

14. Write a background teletype handler. The purpose of this handler is to feed characters to the slow teletype using the interrupt synchronization technique so that you can continue working with the computer as the printing is being done. A $100-word queue contains characters yet to be printed. Part (b) will fill this queue when your program is ready to print something, but the interrupt handler in part (c) will pull words from the queue as they are set through the M6850. (a) Write the initialization routine to configure the M6850 for seven data, even parity and one stop bit, dividing the clock by sixteen, and to initialize the pointers and counter for the queue in global memory. (b) Write a subroutine OUTFL that will output N words, starting at address ADDR, by first pushing them on the queue (if the queue is not full) so they can be output by the handler in part (c). If the queue is full, wait in OUTFL until it has room for all words. (c) Write a device handler that will pull a word from the queue and output it, but if the queue is empty it will output a SYNC character ($16).

15. Write a *Newhall loop* routine, using gadfly synchronization and an M6850 at location $8000 and $8001. A Newhall loop is a ring of modules (microcomputers) in which messages are sent from one module to the next in the loop. The message contains a one-word address to which the message is to be sent, a two-byte word count of the number of words left in the message, and the data words in the message. The number of words is less than $100. Each module will input all the words of a message to a buffer first, then check the address, and if the address is not the address of this module, the message is sent to the next module in the ring. Show the routine that will move a message through the ring, but if the address is $05, the routine will jump to a routine MYMSG to do something with the message.

16. A stereo can be remotely controlled using an M14469. Show the logic diagrams, including pin numbers, TTL circuits from *The TTL Data Book for Design Engineers*, and component values for: (a) a single volume control, whose volume is set by sending a seven-bit unsigned binary number

to the M14469 with address $01, using the duty cycle control technique (figure 5-11b); (b) a source and mode selector, whose source and mode are set by sending a four-bit code to the M14469 with address $02, using the select hardware of figure 5-10.

17. Write a routine using a gadfly loop to find the SYNC character and real-time synchronization to pick up the first word of the text that is sent in Bisync after the STX character. Assume the data is sent at 100 baud, and the clock is not sent with the data. Assume bits arrive at LSB in location $8000.

18. Write a gadfly routine to receive bits and compute the CRC check value for the polynominal $X**16 + X**15 + X**2 + 1$. Data arrives in the least significant bit, and the clock arrives in the most significant bit of the input port at location $8000. Data is determinate when the clock rises from F to T.

19. Write a real-time routine to output the stream of data bits in buffer OUTBUF, most significant bit of lowest addressed word first, checking for five Ts and inserting F as in the SDLC protocol. Send the data at 100 baud.

20. Write a gadfly routine to handshake on the IEEE-488 bus. Data can be read or written at location $8000; and DAV, RFD, and DAC are the three least significant bits of location $8002 in an M6821. (a) Show a routine to initialize the M6821, send a word in accumulator A, and perform the handshake for a transmitter (talker). (b) Show a routine to initialize the M6821, perform the handshake, and get the word received into accumulator A for a receiver (listener).

Appendix A:
The ASCII Character Set

Table A-1
The ASCII Character Set

Bits 0 to 3	Bits 4 to 6							
	0	1	2	3	4	5	6	7
0	NUL	DLE	SP	0	@	P	'	p
1	SOH	DC1	!	1	A	Q	a	q
2	STX	DC2	"	2	B	R	b	r
3	ETX	DC3	#	3	C	S	c	s
4	EOT	DC4	$	4	D	T	d	t
5	ENQ	NAK	%	5	E	U	e	u
6	ACK	SYN	&	6	F	V	f	v
7	BEL	ETB	'	7	G	W	g	w
8	BS	CAN	(	8	H	X	h	x
9	HT	EM	)	9	I	Y	i	y
A	LF	SUB	*	:	J	Z	j	z
B	VT	ESC	+	;	K	[	k	{
C	FF	FS	,	<	L	\	l	
D	CR	GS	–	=	M	]	m	}
E	SO	RS	.	>	N	^	n	~
F	SI	US	/	?	O	–	o	DEL

Appendix B

INTERSIL

IM6402/IM6403
Universal Asynchronous Receiver Transmitter (UART)

FEATURES

- Low Power — Less Than 10mW Typ. at 2MHz
- Operation Up to 4MHz Clock (IM6402A)
- Programmable Word Length, Stop Bits and Parity
- Automatic Data Formatting and Status Generation
- Compatible with Industry Standard UART's (IM6402)
- On-Chip Oscillator with External Crystal (IM6403)
- Operating Voltage —
  IM6402-1/03-1: 5V
  IM6402A/03A: 4-11V
  IM6402/03: 5V

GENERAL DESCRIPTION

The IM6402 and IM6403 are CMOS/LSI UART's for interfacing computers or microprocessors to asynchronous serial data channels. The receiver converts serial start, data, parity and stop bits to parallel data verifying proper code transmission, parity, and stop bits. The transmitter converts parallel data into serial form and automatically adds start, parity, and stop bits.

The data word length can be 5, 6, 7 or 8 bits. Parity may be odd or even, and parity checking and generation can be inhibited. The stop bits may be one or two (or one and one-half when transmitting 5 bit code). Serial data format is shown in Figure 6.

The IM6402 and IM6403 can be used in a wide range of applications including modems, printers, peripherals, and remote data acquisition systems. CMOS/LSI technology permits clock frequencies up to 4.0MHz (250K Baud), an improvement of 10 to 1 over previous PMOS UART designs. Power requirements, by comparison, are reduced from 670mW to 10mW. Status logic increases flexibility and simplifies the user interface.

The IM6402 differs from the IM6403 in the use of five device pins as indicated in Table 1 and Figure 1.

PIN CONFIGURATION

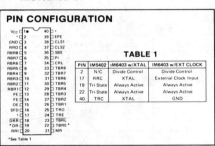

V_CC	1	40	*
	2	39	EPE
GND	3	38	CLS1
RRD	4	37	CLS2
RBR8	5	36	SBS
RBR7	6	35	PI
RBR6	7	34	CRL
RBR5	8	33	TBR8
RBR4	9	32	TBR7
RBR3	10	31	TBR6
RBR2	11	30	TBR5
RBR1	12	29	TBR4
PE	13	28	TBR3
FE	14	27	TBR2
OE	15	26	TBR1
SFD	16	25	TRO
*	17	24	TRE
DRR	18	23	TBRL
* DR	19	22	TBRE *
RRI	20	21	MR

*See Table 1

TABLE 1

PIN	IM6402	IM6403 w/XTAL	IM6403 w/EXT CLOCK
2	N/C	Divide Control	Divide Control
17	RRC	XTAL	External Clock Input
19	Tri-State	Always Active	Always Active
22	Tri-State	Always Active	Always Active
40	TRC	XTAL	GND

ORDERING INFORMATION

ORDER CODE	IM6402-1/03-1	IM6402A/03A	IM6402/03
PLASTIC PKG	IM6402-1/03-1IPL	IM6402/03-AIPL	IM6402/03-IPL
CERAMIC PKG	IM6402-1/03-1IDL	IM6402/03-AIDL	—
MILITARY TEMP	IM6402-1/03-1MDL	IM6402/03-AMDL	—
MILITARY TEMP WITH 883B	IM6402-1/03-1 MDL/883B	IM6402/03-AMDL 883B	—

FUNCTIONAL BLOCK DIAGRAM

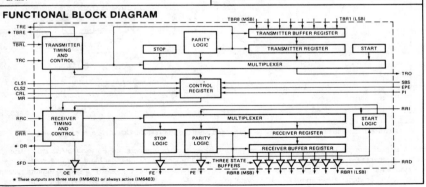

*These outputs are three state (IM6402) or always active (IM6403)

Source: "CMOS/LSI Universal Asynchronous Receiver Transmitter (UART)," Intersil (copyright 1980 Intersil, Inc. All rights reserved.) Reprinted with permission.

405

IM6402/IM6403

IM6402/IM6403

INTERSIL

ABSOLUTE MAXIMUM RATINGS

Operating Temperature
IM6402/03 .... -40°C to +85°C
Storage Temperature .... -65°C to 150°C
Operating Voltage .... 4.0V to 7.0V
Supply Voltage .... +8.0V
Voltage On Any Input or Output Pin .. -0.3V to V$_{CC}$ +0.3V

NOTE: Stresses above those listed under "Absolute Maximum Ratings" may cause permanent device failure. These are stress ratings only and functional operation of the devices at these or any other conditions above those indicated in the operation sections of this specification is not implied. Exposure to absolute maximum rating conditions for extended periods may cause device failures.

D.C. CHARACTERISTICS

TEST CONDITIONS: V$_{CC}$ = 5.0 ± 10%, T$_A$ = -40°C to +85°C

	SYMBOL	PARAMETER	CONDITIONS	MIN	TYP	MAX	UNITS
1	V$_{IH}$	Input Voltage High		V$_{CC}$-2.0			V
2	V$_{IL}$	Input Voltage Low				0.8	V
3	I$_{IL}$	Input Leakage[1]	GND≤V$_{IN}$≤V$_{CC}$	–5.0		5.0	μA
4	V$_{OH}$	Output Voltage High	I$_{OH}$ = –0.2mA	2.4			V
5	V$_{OL}$	Output Voltage Low	I$_{OL}$=1.6mA			0.45	V
6	I$_{OL}$	Output Leakage	GND≤V$_{OUT}$≤V$_{CC}$	–5.0		5.0	μA
7	I$_{CC}$	Power Supply Current Standby	V$_{IN}$=GND or V$_{CC}$		1.0	800	μA
8	I$_{CC}$	Power Supply Current IM6402 Dynamic	f$_C$ = 500 KHz			1.2	mA
9	I$_{CC}$	Power Supply Current IM6403 Dynamic	f$_{CRYSTAL}$=2.46MHz			3.7	mA
10	C$_{IN}$	Input Capacitance[1]			7.0	8.0	pF
11	C$_O$	Output Capacitance[1]			8.0	10.0	pF

NOTE 1: Except IM6403 XTAL input pins (i.e. pins 17 and 40).
NOTE 2: V$_{CC}$ = 5V, T$_A$ = 25°C.

A.C. CHARACTERISTICS

TEST CONDITIONS: V$_{CC}$ = 5.0V ± 10%, C$_L$ = 50pF, T$_A$ = -40°C to +85°C

	SYMBOL	PARAMETER	CONDITIONS	MIN	TYP	MAX	UNITS
1	f$_C$	Clock Frequency IM6402		D.C.	3.0	1.0	MHz
2	f$_{CRYSTAL}$	Crystal Frequency IM6403			4.0	2.46	MHz
3	t$_{PW}$	Pulse Widths CRL, $\overline{DRR}$, $\overline{TBRL}$		225	50		ns
4	t$_{MR}$	Pulse Width MR	See Timing Diagrams	600	200		ns
5	t$_{DS}$	Input Data Setup Time	(Figures 2,3,4)	75	20		ns
6	t$_{DH}$	Input Data Hold Time		90	40		ns
7	t$_{EN}$	Output Enable Time			80	190	ns

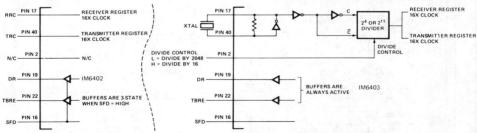

FIGURE 1. Functional Difference Between IM6402 and IM6403 UART (6403 has On-Chip 4/11 Stage Divider)

The IM6403 differs from the IM6402 on three inputs (RRC, TRC, pin 2) as shown in Figure 1. Two outputs (TBRE, DR) are not three-state as on the IM6402, but are always active. The on-chip divider and oscillator allow an inexpensive crystal to be used as a timing source rather than additional circuitry such as baud rate generators. For example, a color TV crystal at 3.579545MHz results in a baud rate of 109.2Hz for an easy teletype interface (Figure 10). A 9600 baud interface may be implemented using a 2.4576MHz crystal with the divider set to divide by 16.

IM6402/IM6403
IM6402A/IM6403A

INTERSIL

ABSOLUTE MAXIMUM RATINGS

Operating Temperature
  Industrial IM6402AI/03AI .... -40°C to +85°C
  Military IM6402AM/03AM .... -55°C to +125°C
Storage Temperature .... -65°C to 150°C
Operating Voltage .... 4.0V to 11.0V
Supply Voltage .... +12.0V
Voltage On Any Input or Output Pin .. -0.3V to V_{CC} +0.3V

NOTE: Stresses above those listed under "Absolute Maximum Ratings" may cause permanent device failure. These are stress ratings only and functional operation of the devices at these or any other conditions above those indicated in the operation sections of this specification is not implied. Exposure to absolute maximum rating conditions for extended periods may cause device failures.

D.C. CHARACTERISTICS
TEST CONDITIONS: V_{CC} = 4.0V to 11.0V, T_A = Industrial or Military

	SYMBOL	PARAMETER	CONDITIONS	MIN	TYP[2]	MAX	UNITS
1	V_{IH}	Input Voltage High		70% V_{CC}			V
2	V_{IL}	Input Voltage Low				20% V_{CC}	V
3	I_{IL}	Input Leakage[1]	GND≤V_{IN}≤V_{CC}	-1.0		1.0	µA
4	V_{OH}	Output Voltage High	I_{OH} = 0mA	V_{CC}-0.01			V
5	V_{OL}	Output Voltage Low	I_{OL} = 0mA			GND+0.01	V
6	I_{OL}	Output Leakage	GND≤V_{OUT}≤V_{CC}	-1.0		1.0	µA
7	I_{CC}	Power Supply Current Standby	V_{IN}=GND or V_{CC}		5.0	500	µA
8	I_{CC}	Power Supply Current IM6402A Dynamic	f_C = 4MHz			9.0	mA
9	I_{CC}	Power Supply Current IM6403A Dynamic	$f_{CRYSTAL}$=3.58MHz			13.0	mA
10	C_{IN}	Input Capacitance[1]			7.0	8.0	pF
11	C_O	Output Capacitance[1]			8.0	10.0	pF

NOTE 1: Except IM6403 XTAL input pins (i.e. pins 17 and 40).
NOTE 2: V_{CC} = 5V, T_A = 25°C.

A.C. CHARACTERISTICS
TEST CONDITIONS: V_{CC} = 10.0V ± 5%, C_L = 50pF, T_A = Industrial or Military

	SYMBOL	PARAMETER	CONDITIONS	MIN	TYP[2]	MAX	UNITS
1	f_C	Clock Frequency IM6402A		D.C.	6.0	4.0	MHz
2	$f_{CRYSTAL}$	Crystal Frequency IM6403A			8.0	6.0	MHz
3	t_{PW}	Pulse Widths CRL, $\overline{DRR}$, $\overline{TBRL}$		100	40		ns
4	t_{MR}	Pulse Width MR	See Timing Diagrams (Figures 2,3,4)	400	200		ns
5	t_{DS}	Input Data Setup Time		40	0		ns
6	t_{DH}	Input Data Hold Time		30	30		ns
7	t_{EN}	Output Enable Time			40	70	ns

TIMING DIAGRAMS

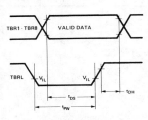

FIGURE 2. Data Input Cycle

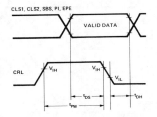

FIGURE 3. Control Register Load Cycle

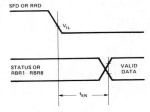

FIGURE 4. Status Flag Enable Time
or Data Output Enable Time

IM6402/IM6403
IM6402-1/IM6403-1

ABSOLUTE MAXIMUM RATINGS

Operating Temperature
Industrial IM6402-1I/03-1I .... -40°C to +85°C
Military IM6402-1M/03-1M .... -55°C to +125°C
Storage Temperature .... -65°C to +150°C
Operating Voltage .... 4.0V to 7.0V
Supply Voltage .... +8.0V
Voltage On Any Input or Output Pin .. -0.3V to V_{CC} +0.3V

NOTE: Stresses above those listed under "Absolute Maximum Ratings" may cause permanent device failure. These are stress ratings only and functional operation of the devices at these or any other conditions above those indicated in the operation sections of this specification is not implied. Exposure to absolute maximum rating conditions for extended periods may cause device failures.

D.C. CHARACTERISTICS
TEST CONDITIONS: V_{CC} = 5.0 ± 10%, T_A = Industrial or Military

	SYMBOL	PARAMETER	CONDITIONS	MIN	TYP[2]	MAX	UNITS
1	V_{IH}	Input Voltage High		V_{CC}–2.0			V
2	V_{IL}	Input Voltage Low				0.8	V
3	I_{IL}	Input Leakage[1]	GND<V_{IN}<V_{CC}	–1.0		1.0	μA
4	V_{OH}	Output Voltage High	I_{OH}=-0.2mA	2.4			V
5	V_{OL}	Output Voltage Low	I_{OL} = 2.0mA			0.45	V
6	I_{OL}	Output Leakage	GND<V_{OUT}<V_{CC}	–1.0		1.0	μA
7	I_{CC}	Power Supply Current Standby	V_{IN}=GND or V_{CC}		1.0	100	μA
8	I_{CC}	Power Supply Current IM6402 Dynamic	f_C = 2MHz			1.9	mA
9	I_{CC}	Power Supply Current IM6403 Dynamic	$f_{CRYSTAL}$=3.58MHz			5.5	mA
10	C_{IN}	Input Capacitance[1]			7.0	8.0	pF
11	C_O	Output Capacitance[1]			8.0	10.0	pF

NOTE 1: Except IM6403 XTAL input pins (i.e. pins 17 and 40).
NOTE 2: V_{CC} = 5V, T_A = 25°C.

A.C. CHARACTERISTICS
TEST CONDITIONS: V_{CC} = 5.0V ± 10%, C_L = 50pF, T_A = Industrial or Military

	SYMBOL	PARAMETER	CONDITIONS	MIN	TYP[2]	MAX	UNITS
1	f_C	Clock Frequency IM6402		D.C.	3.0	2.0	MHz
2	$f_{CRYSTAL}$	Crystal Frequency IM6403			4.0	3.58	MHz
3	t_{PW}	Pulse Widths CRL, $\overline{DRR}$, $\overline{TBRL}$		150	50		ns
4	t_{MR}	Pulse Width MR	See Timing Diagrams	400	200		ns
5	t_{DS}	Input Data Setup Time	(Figures 2,3,4)	50	20		ns
6	t_{DH}	Input Data Hold Time		60	40		ns
7	t_{EN}	Output Enable Time			80	160	ns

IM6402/IM6403

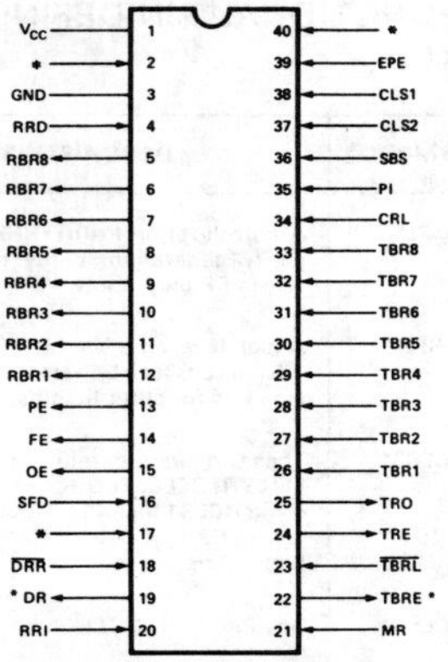

V_CC	1	40	*
*	2	39	EPE
GND	3	38	CLS1
RRD	4	37	CLS2
RBR8	5	36	SBS
RBR7	6	35	PI
RBR6	7	34	CRL
RBR5	8	33	TBR8
RBR4	9	32	TBR7
RBR3	10	31	TBR6
RBR2	11	30	TBR5
RBR1	12	29	TBR4
PE	13	28	TBR3
FE	14	27	TBR2
OE	15	26	TBR1
SFD	16	25	TRO
*	17	24	TRE
DRR	18	23	TBRL
* DR	19	22	TBRE *
RRI	20	21	MR

*DIFFERS BETWEEN IM6402 AND IM6403.

FIGURE 5. Pin Configuration

IM6403 FUNCTIONAL PIN DEFINITION

PIN	SYMBOL	DESCRIPTION
1	V_CC	Positive Power Supply
2	IM6402-N/C IM6403-Control	No Connection Divide Control High: 2^4 (16) Divider Low: 2^{11} (2048) Divider
3	GND	Ground
4	RRD	A high level on RECEIVER REGISTER DISABLE forces the receiver holding register outputs RBR1-RBR8 to a high impedance state.
5	RBR8	The contents of the RECEIVER BUFFER REGISTER appear on these three-state outputs. Word formats less than 8 characters are right justified to RBR1.
6	RBR7	See Pin 5 — RBR8
7	RBR6	See Pin 5 — RBR8
8	RBR5	See Pin 5 — RBR8
9	RBR4	See Pin 5 — RBR8
10	RBR3	See Pin 5 — RBR8
11	RBR2	See Pin 5 — RBR8
12	RBR1	See Pin 5 — RBR8
13	PE	A high level on PARITY ERROR indicates that the received parity does not match parity programmed by control bits. The output is active until parity matches on a succeeding character. When parity is inhibited, this output is low.

IM6403 FUNCTIONAL PIN DEFINITION
(Continued)

PIN	SYMBOL	DESCRIPTION
14	FE	A high level on FRAMING ERROR indicates the first stop bit was invalid. FE will stay active until the next valid character's stop bit is received.
15	OE	A high level on OVERRUN ERROR indicates the data received flag was not cleared before the last character was transferred to the receiver buffer register. The Error is reset at the next character's stop bit if DRR has been performed (i.e., DRR: active low).
16	SFD	A high level on STATUS FLAGS DISABLE forces the outputs PE, FE, OE, DR,* TBRE* to a high impedance state. See Block Diagram and Figure 4. *IM6402 only.
17	IM6402-RRC IM6403-XTAL or EXT CLK IN	The RECEIVER REGISTER CLOCK is 16X the receiver data rate.
18	DRR	A low level on DATA RECEIVED RESET clears the data received output (DR), to a low level.
19	DR	A high level on DATA RECEIVED indicates a character has been received and transferred to the receiver buffer register.
20	RRI	Serial data on RECEIVER REGISTER INPUT is clocked into the receiver register.
21	MR	A high level on MASTER RESET (MR) clears PE, FE, OE, DR, TRE and sets TBRE, TRO high. Less than 18 clocks after MR goes low, TRE returns high. MR does not clear the receiver buffer register, and is required after power-up.
22	TBRE	A high level on TRANSMITTER BUFFER REGISTER EMPTY indicates the transmitter buffer register has transferred its data to the transmitter register and is ready for new data.
23	TBRL	A low level on TRANSMITTER BUFFER REGISTER LOAD transfers data from inputs TBR1-TBR8 into the transmitter buffer register. A low to high transition on TBRL requests data transfer to the transmitter register. If the transmitter register is busy, transfer is automatically delayed so that the two characters are transmitted end to end. See Figure 2.
24	TRE	A high level on TRANSMITTER REGISTER EMPTY indicates completed transmission of a character including stop bits.
25	TRO	Character data, start data and stop bits appear serially at the TRANSMITTER REGISTER OUTPUT.

IM6402/IM6403   INTERSIL

IM6403 FUNCTIONAL PIN DEFINITION
(Continued)

PIN	SYMBOL	DESCRIPTION
26	TBR1	Character data is loaded into the TRANS-MITTER BUFFER REGISTER via inputs TBR1-TBR8. For character formats less than 8-bits, the TBR8, 7, and 6 Inputs are ignored corresponding to the programmed word length.
27	TBR2	See Pin 26 — TBR1
28	TBR3	See Pin 26 — TBR1
29	TBR4	See Pin 26 — TBR1
30	TBR5	See Pin 26 — TBR1
31	TBR6	See Pin 26 — TBR1
32	TBR7	See Pin 26 — TBR1
33	TBR8	See Pin 26 — TBR1
34	CRL	A high level on CONTROL REGISTER LOAD loads the control register. See Figure 3.

IM6403 FUNCTIONAL PIN DEFINITION
(Continued)

PIN	SYMBOL	DESCRIPTION
35	PI*	A high level on PARITY INHIBIT inhibits parity generation, parity checking and forces PE output low.
36	SBS*	A high level on STOP BIT SELECT selects 1.5 stop bits for a 5 character format and 2 stop bits for other lengths.
37	CLS2*	These inputs program the CHARACTER LENGTH SELECTED. (CLS1 low CLS2 low 5-bits)(CLS1 high CLS2 low 6-bits)(CLS1 low CLS2 high 7-bits) (CLS1 high CLS2 high 8-bits)
38	CLS1*	See Pin 37 — CLS2
39	EPE*	When PI is low, a high level on EVEN PARITY ENABLE generates and checks even parity. A low level selects odd parity.
40	IM6402-TRC IM6403-XTAL or GND	The TRANSMITTER REGISTER CLOCK is 16X the transmit data rate.

*See Table 2 (Control Word Function)

TABLE 2. Control Word Function

CONTROL WORD					DATA BITS	PARITY BIT	STOP BIT(S)
CLS2	CLS1	PI	EPE	SBS			
L	L	L	L	L	5	ODD	1
L	L	L	L	H	5	ODD	1.5
L	L	L	H	L	5	EVEN	1
L	L	L	H	H	5	EVEN	1.5
L	L	H	X	L	5	DISABLED	1
L	L	H	X	H	5	DISABLED	1.5
L	H	L	L	L	6	ODD	1
L	H	L	L	H	6	ODD	2
L	H	L	H	L	6	EVEN	1
L	H	L	H	H	6	EVEN	2
L	H	H	X	L	6	DISABLED	1
L	H	H	X	H	6	DISABLED	2
H	L	L	L	L	7	ODD	1
H	L	L	L	H	7	ODD	2
H	L	L	H	L	7	EVEN	1
H	L	L	H	H	7	EVEN	2
H	L	H	X	L	7	DISABLED	1
H	L	H	X	H	7	DISABLED	2
H	H	L	L	L	8	ODD	1
H	H	L	L	H	8	ODD	2
H	H	L	H	L	8	EVEN	1
H	H	L	H	H	8	EVEN	2
H	H	H	X	L	8	DISABLED	1
H	H	H	X	H	8	DISABLED	2

X = Don't Care

IM6402/IM6403

INTERSIL

TRANSMITTER OPERATION

The transmitter section accepts parallel data, formats it and transmits it in serial form (Figure 6) on the TROutput terminal.

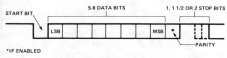

FIGURE 6. Serial Data Format

Transmitter timing is shown in Figure 7. Ⓐ Data is loaded into the transmitter buffer register from the inputs TBR1 through TBR8 by a logic low on the $\overline{TBR}$Load input. Valid data must be present at least t_{DS} prior to and t_{DH} following the rising edge of $\overline{TBRL}$. If words less than 8 bits are used, only the least significant bits are used. The character is right justified into the least significant bit, TBR1. Ⓑ The rising edge of $\overline{TBRL}$ clears TBREmpty. 0 to 1 clock cycles later, data is transferred to the transmitter register, TREmpty is cleared and transmission starts. TBREmpty is reset to a logic high. Output data is clocked by TRClock, which is 16 times the data rate. Ⓒ A second pulse on TBRLoad loads data into the transmitter buffer register. Data transfer to the transmitter register is delayed until transmission of the current character is complete. Ⓓ Data is automatically transferred to the transmitter register and transmission of that character begins.

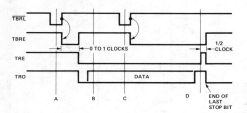

FIGURE 7. Transmitter Timing (Not to Scale)

RECEIVER OPERATION

Data is received in serial form at the RI input. When no data is being received, RI input must remain high. The data is clocked by the RRClock, which is 16 times the data rate. Receiver timing is shown in Figure 8.

Ⓐ A low level on $\overline{DRR}$eset clears the DReady line. Ⓑ During the first stop bit, data is transferred from the receiver register to the RBRegister. If the word is less than 8 bits, the unused most significant bits will be a logic low. The output character is right justified to the least significant bit RBR1. A logic high on OEError indicates an overrun which occurs when DReady has not been cleared before the present character was transferred to the RBRegister. A logic high on PError indicates a parity error. Ⓒ 1/2 clock cycle later, DReady is set to a logic high and FError is evaluated. A logic high on FError indicates an invalid stop bit was received. The receiver will not begin searching for the next start bit until a stop bit is received.

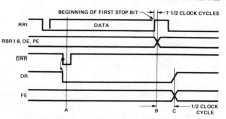

FIGURE 8. Receiver Timing (Not to Scale)

START BIT DETECTION

The receiver uses a 16X clock for timing (see Figure 9.) The start bit Ⓐ could have occurred as much as one clock cycle before it was detected, as indicated by the shaded portion. The center of the start bit is defined as clock count 7½. If the receiver clock is a symmetrical square wave, the center of the start bit will be located within ±1/2 clock cycle, ±1/32 bit or ±3.125%. The receiver begins searching for the next start bit at the center of the first stop bit.

FIGURE 9. Start Bit Timing

TYPICAL APPLICATION

Microprocessor systems, which are inherently parallel in nature, often require an asynchronous serial interface. This function can be performed easily with the IM6402/03 UART. Figure 10 shows how the IM6403 can be interfaced to an IM6100 microcomputer system with the aid of an IM6101 Programmable Interface Element (PIE). The PIE interprets Input/Output transfer (IOT) instructions from the processor and generates read and write pulses to the UART. The SENSE lines on the PIE are also employed to allow the processor to detect UART status. In particular, the processor must know when the Receive Buffer Register has accumulated a character (DR active), and when the Transmit Buffer Register can accept another character to be transmitted.

In this example the characters to be received or transmitted will be eight bits long (CLS 1 and 2: both HIGH) and transmitted with no parity (PI:HIGH) and two stop bits (SBS:HIGH). Since these control bits will not be changed during operation, Control Register Load (CRL) can be tied high. Remember, since the IM6402/03 is a CMOS device, all unused inputs should be committed.

The baud rate at which the transmitter and receiver will operate is determined by the external crystal and DIVIDE CONTROL pin on the IM6403. The internal divider can be set to reduce the crystal frequency by either 16 (PIN 2:HIGH) or 2048 (PIN 2:LOW) times. The frequency out of the internal divider should be 16 times the desired baud rate. To generate 110 baud, this example will use a 3.579545MHz color TV crystal

IM6402/IM6403   INTERSIL

and DIVIDE CONTROL set low. The IM6402 may use different receive (RRC) and transmit (TRC) clock rates, but requires an external clock generator.

To ensure consistent and correct operation, the IM6402/03 must be reset after power-up. The Master Reset (MR) pin is active high, and can be driven reliably from a Schmitt trigger inverter and R-C delay. In this example, the IM6100 is reset through still another inverter. The Schmitt trigger between the processor and R-C network is needed to assure that a slow rising capacitor voltage does not re-trigger RESET. A long reset pulse after power-up (~100ms) is required by the processor to assure that the on-board crystal oscillator has sufficient time to start.

The IM6402 supports the processor's bi-directional data bus quite easily by tying the TBR and RBR buses together. A read command from the processor will enable the RECEIVER BUFFER REGISTER onto the bus by using the RECEIVER REGISTER DISABLE (RRD) pin. A write command from the processor clocks data from the bus into the TRANSMITTER BUFFER REGISTER using TBRL. Figure 10 shows a NAND gate driving TBRL from the WRITE₂ pin on the PIE. This gate is used to generate a rising edge to TBRL at the point where data is

stable on the bus, and to hold TBRL high until the UART actually transfers the data to it's internal buffer. If TBRL were allowed to return low before TBRE went high, the intended output data would be overwritten, since the TBR is a transparent latch.

Although not shown in this example, the error flags (PE, FE, OE) could be read by the processor, using the other READ line from the PIE. Since an IM6403 is used, TBRE and DR are not affected by the STATUS FLAGS DISABLE pin, thus, the three error flags can be tied to the data bus and gated by connecting SFD to READ₂.

If parity is not inhibited, a parity error will cause the PE pin to go high until the next valid character is received.

A framing error is generated when an expected stop bit is not received. FE will stay high after the error until the next complete character's stop bit is received.

The overrun error flag is set if a received character is transferred to the RECEIVER BUFFER REGISTER when the previous character has not been read. The OE pin will stay high until the next received stop bit after a DRR is performed.

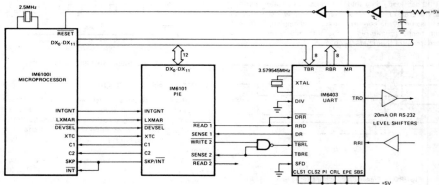

FIGURE 10. 110 Baud Serial Interface for IM6100 System

PACKAGE DIMENSIONS

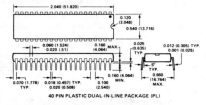

40 PIN PLASTIC DUAL-IN-LINE PACKAGE (PL)

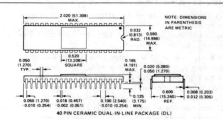

NOTE: DIMENSIONS ARE IN PARENTHESIS METRIC

40 PIN CERAMIC DUAL-IN-LINE PACKAGE (DL)

INTERSIL

10710 N. Tantau Ave., Cupertino, CA 95014 (408) 996-5000 TWX: 910-338-0171

Appendix C

MC14469

ADDRESSABLE ASYNCHRONOUS RECEIVER/TRANSMITTER

The MC14469 Addressable Asynchronous Receiver Transmitter is constructed with MOS P-channel and N-channel enhancement devices in a single monolithic structure (CMOS). The MC14469 receives one or two eleven-bit words in a serial data stream. One of the incoming words contains the address and when the address matches, the MC14469 will then transmit its information in two eleven-bit-word data streams. Each of the transmitted words contains eight data bits, even parity bit, start and stop bit.

The received word contains seven address bits and the address of the MC14469 is set on seven pins. Thus 2^7 or 128 units can be interconnected in simplex or full duplex data transmission. In addition to the address received, seven command bits may be received for data or control use.

The MC14469 finds application in transmitting data from remote A-to-D converters, remote MPUs or remote digital transducers to the master computer or MPU.

- Supply Voltage Range — 4.5 Vdc to 18 Vdc
- Low Quiescent Current — 75 μAdc maximum @ 5 Vdc
- Data Rates to 4800 Baud
- Receive — Serial to Parallel
  Transmit — Parallel to Serial
- Transmit and Receive Simultaneously in Full Duplex
- Crystal or Resonator Operation for On-Chip Oscillator

CMOS LSI
(LOW-POWER COMPLEMENTARY MOS)

ADDRESSABLE ASYNCHRONOUS RECEIVER/TRANSMITTER

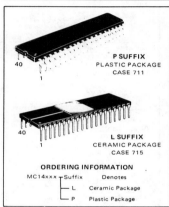

P SUFFIX
PLASTIC PACKAGE
CASE 711

L SUFFIX
CERAMIC PACKAGE
CASE 715

ORDERING INFORMATION

MC14xxx Suffix Denotes
  L Ceramic Package
  P Plastic Package

BLOCK DIAGRAMS

PIN ASSIGNMENTS

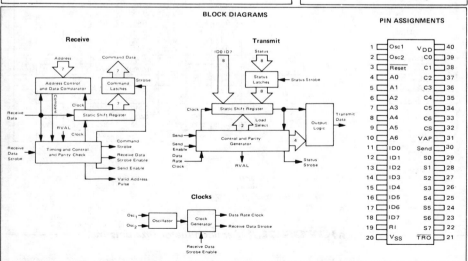

Source: "Motorola Semiconductors," courtesy of Motorola Inc., MOS Integrated Circuit Division. Reprinted with permission.

413

MC14469

MAXIMUM RATINGS (Voltages referenced to V_{SS}, Pin 20.

	Symbol	Value	Unit
DC Supply Voltage	V_{DD}	–0.5 to +18	Vdc
Input Voltage, All Inputs	V_{in}	–0.5 to V_{DD} + 0.5	Vdc
DC Current Drain per Pin	I	10	mAdc
Operating Temperature Range	T_A	–40 to +85	°C
Storage Temperature Range	T_{stg}	–65 to +150	°C

This device contains circuitry to protect the inputs against damage due to high static voltages or electric fields; however, it is advised that normal precautions be taken to avoid application of any voltage higher than maximum rated voltages to this high impedance circuit. For proper operation it is recommended that V_{in} and V_{out} be constrained to the range $V_{SS} \leq (V_{in}$ or $V_{out}) \leq V_{DD}$.

Unused inputs must always be tied to an appropriate logic voltage level (e.g., either V_{SS} or V_{DD}).

ELECTRICAL CHARACTERISTICS

Characteristic	Symbol	V_{DD} Vdc	T_{low}* Min	T_{low}* Max	25°C Min	25°C Typ	25°C Max	T_{high}* Min	T_{high}* Max	Unit
Output Voltage "0" Level	V_{OL}	5.0	–	0.05	–	0	0.05	–	0.05	Vdc
V_{in} = V_{DD} or 0		10	–	0.05	–	0	0.05	–	0.05	
		15	–	0.05	–	0	0.05	–	0.05	
"1" Level	V_{OH}	5.0	4.95	–	4.95	5.0	–	4.95	–	Vdc
V_{in} = 0 or V_{DD}		10	9.95	–	9.95	10	–	9.95	–	
		15	14.95	–	14.95	15	–	14.95	–	
Input Voltage # "0" Level	V_{IL}									Vdc
(V_O = 4.5 or 0.5 Vdc)		5.0	–	1.5	–	2.25	1.5	–	1.5	
(V_O = 9.0 or 1.0 Vdc)		10	–	3.0	–	4.50	3.0	–	3.0	
(V_O = 13.5 or 1.5 Vdc)		15	–	4.0	–	6.75	4.0	–	4.0	
"1" Level	V_{IH}									Vdc
(V_O = 0.5 or 4.5 Vdc)		5.0	3.5	–	3.5	2.75	–	3.5	–	
(V_O = 1.0 or 9.0 Vdc)		10	7.0	–	7.0	5.50	–	7.0	–	
(V_O = 1.5 or 13.5 Vdc)		15	11.0	–	11.0	8.25	–	11.0	–	
Output Drive Current (Except Pin 2)	I_{OH}									mAdc
(V_{OH} = 2.5 Vdc) Source		5.0	–1.0	–	–0.8	–1.7	–	–0.6	–	
(V_{OH} = 4.6 Vdc)		5.0	–0.2	–	–0.16	–0.35	–	–0.12	–	
(V_{OH} = 9.5 Vdc)		10	–0.5	–	–0.4	–0.9	–	–0.3	–	
(V_{OH} = 13.5 Vdc)		15	–1.4	–	–1.2	–3.5	–	–1.0	–	
(V_{OL} = 0.4 Vdc) Sink	I_{OL}	5.0	0.52	–	0.44	0.88	–	0.36	–	mAdc
(V_{OL} = 0.5 Vdc)		10	1.3	–	1.1	2.25	–	0.9	–	
(V_{OL} = 1.5 Vdc)		15	3.6	–	3.0	8.8	–	2.4	–	
Output Drive Current (Pin 2 Only)	I_{OH}									mAdc
(V_{OH} = 2.5 Vdc) Source		5.0	–0.19	–	–0.16	–0.32	–	–0.13	–	
(V_{OH} = 4.6 Vdc)		5.0	–0.04	–	–0.035	–0.07	–	–0.03	–	
(V_{OH} = 9.5 Vdc)		10	–0.09	–	–0.08	–0.16	–	–0.06	–	
(V_{OH} = 13.5 Vdc)		15	–0.29	–	–0.27	–0.48	–	–0.2	–	
(V_{OL} = 0.4 Vdc) Sink	I_{OL}	5.0	0.1	–	0.085	0.17	–	0.07	–	mAdc
(V_{OL} = 0.5 Vdc)		10	0.17	–	0.14	0.28	–	0.1	–	
(V_{OL} = 1.5 Vdc)		15	0.50	–	0.42	0.84	–	0.3	–	
Maximum Frequency	f_{max}	4.5	400	–	365	550	–	310		kHz
Input Current	I_{in}	15	–	±0.3	–	±0.00001	±0.3	–	±1.0	µAdc
Pull-Up Current (Pins 4-18)	I_{up}	15	12	120	10	50	100	8.0	85	µAdc
Input Capacitance (V_{in} = 0)	C_{in}	–	–	–	–	5.0	7.5	–	–	pF
Quiescent Current (Per Package)	I_{DD}	5.0	–	75	–	0.010	75	–	565	µAdc
		10	–	150	–	0.020	150	–	1125	
		15	–	300	–	0.030	300	–	2250	
Supply Voltage	V_{DD}	–	+4.5	+18.0	+4.5	–	+18.0	+4.5	+18.0	Vdc

*T_{low} = –40°C
T_{high} = +85°C
=Noise immunity specified for worst-case input combination.
Noise Margin both "1" and "0" level = 1.0 Vdc min @ V_{DD} = 5.0 Vdc
2.0 Vdc min @ V_{DD} = 10 Vdc
2.5 Vdc min @ V_{DD} = 15 Vdc

 MOTOROLA *Semiconductor Products Inc.*

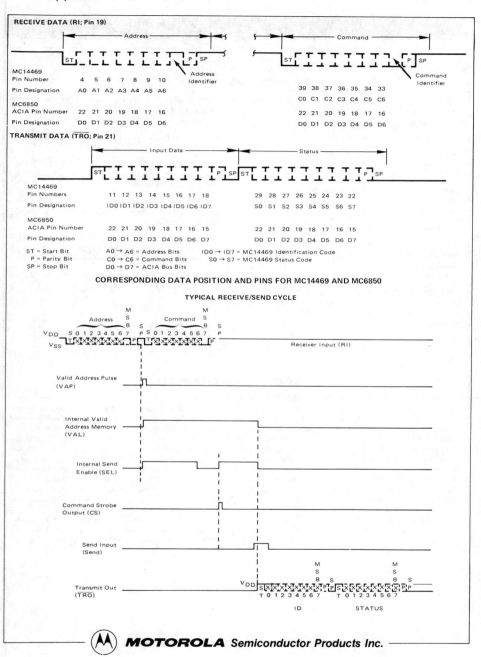

RECEIVE DATA (RI; Pin 19)

| | Address | Command |

MC14469
Pin Number   4 5 6 7 8 9 10
Pin Designation   A0 A1 A2 A3 A4 A5 A6

                                              39 38 37 36 35 34 33
                                              C0 C1 C2 C3 C4 C5 C6

MC6850
ACIA Pin Number   22 21 20 19 18 17 16   22 21 20 19 18 17 16
Pin Designation   D0 D1 D2 D3 D4 D5 D6   D0 D1 D2 D3 D4 D5 D6

TRANSMIT DATA (TRO; Pin 21)

| | Input Data | Status |

MC14469
Pin Numbers   11 12 13 14 15 16 17 18   29 28 27 26 25 24 23 22
Pin Designation   ID0 ID1 ID2 ID3 ID4 ID5 ID6 ID7   S0 S1 S2 S3 S4 S5 S6 S7

MC6850
ACIA Pin Number   22 21 20 19 18 17 16 15   22 21 20 19 18 17 16 15
Pin Designation   D0 D1 D2 D3 D4 D5 D6 D7   D0 D1 D2 D3 D4 D5 D6 D7

ST = Start Bit   A0 → A6 = Address Bits   ID0 → ID7 = MC14469 Identification Code
P = Parity Bit   C0 → C6 = Command Bits   S0 → S7 = MC14469 Status Code
SP = Stop Bit   D0 → D7 = ACIA Bus Bits

CORRESPONDING DATA POSITION AND PINS FOR MC14469 AND MC6850

TYPICAL RECEIVE/SEND CYCLE

Valid Address Pulse (VAP)

Internal Valid Address Memory (VAL)

Internal Send Enable (SEL)

Command Strobe Output (CS)

Send Input (Send)

Transmit Out (TRO)

ID   STATUS

MOTOROLA *Semiconductor Products Inc.*

DEVICE OPERATION

OSCILLATOR (Osc1, Osc2; Pins 1, 2) — These pins are the oscillator input and output. (See Figure 1.)

RESET (Reset; Pin 3) — When this pin is pulled low, the circuit is reset and ready for operation.

ADDRESS (A0-A6; Pin 4, 5, 6, 7, 8, 9, 10) — These are the address setting pins which contain the address match for the received signal.

INPUT DATA (ID0-ID7; Pins 11, 12, 13, 14, 15, 16, 17, 18) — These pins contain the input data for the first eight bits of data to be transmitted.

RECEIVE INPUT (RI; Pin 19) — This is the receive input pin.

NEGATIVE POWER SUPPLY (V$_{SS}$; Pin 20) — This pin is the negative power supply connection. Normally this pin is system ground.

TRANSMIT REGISTER OUTPUT SIGNAL (TRO; Pin 21) — This pin transmits the outgoing signal. Note that it is inverted from the incoming signal. It must go through one stage of inversion if it is to drive another MC14469.

SECOND or STATUS INPUT DATA (S0-S7; Pins 22, 23, 24, 25, 26, 27, 28, 29) — These pins contain the input data for the second eight bits of data to be transmitted.

SEND (Send; Pin 30) — This pin accepts the send command after receipt of an address.

VALID ADDRESS PULSE (VAP; Pin 31) — This is the output for the valid address pulse upon receipt of a matched incoming address.

COMMAND STROBE (CS; Pin 32) — This is the output for the command strobe signifying a valid set of command data on pins 33-39.

COMMAND WORD (C0-C6; Pins 33, 34, 35, 36, 37, 38, 39) — These pins are the readout of the command word which is the second word of the received signal.

POSITIVE POWER SUPPLY (V$_{DD}$; Pin 40) — This pin is the package positive power supply pin.

OPERATING CHARACTERISTICS

The receipt of a start bit on the Receive Input (RI) line causes the receive clock to start at a frequency equal to that of the oscillator divided by 64. All received data is strobed in at the center of a receive clock period. The start bit is followed by eight data bits. Seven of the bits are compared against states of the address of the particular circuit (A0-A6), while the eighth bit signifies an address word "1", or a command word "O". Next, a parity bit is received and checked by the internal logic for even parity. Finally a stop bit is received. At the completion of the cycle if the address compared, a Valid Address Pulse (VAP) occurs. Immediately following the address word, a command word is received. It also contains a start bit, eight data bits, even parity bit, and a stop bit. The eight data bits are composed of a seven-bit command, and a

"0" which indicates a command word. At the end of the command word a Command Strobe Pulse (CS) occurs.

A positive transition on the Send input initiates the transmit sequence. Again the transmitted data is made up of two eleven-bit words, i.e., address and command words. The data portion of the first word is made up from Input Data inputs (ID0-ID7), and the data for the second word from Second Input Data (S0-S7) inputs. The data on inputs S0-S7 is latched before the start of transmit of the first of the second two words. The transmitted signal is the inversion of the received signal, which allows the use of an inverting amplifier to drive the lines.

The oscillator can be crystal controlled or ceramic resonator controlled for required accuracy. Pin 1 may be driven from an external oscillator. See Figure 1.

 MOTOROLA *Semiconductor Products Inc.*

MC14469

FIGURE 1 — OSCILLATOR CIRCUIT

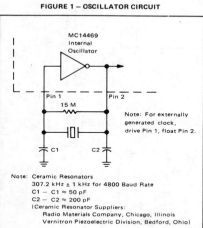

MC14469
Internal
Oscillator

Pin 1   Pin 2

15 M

Note: For externally
generated clock,
drive Pin 1, float Pin 2.

C1   C2

Note: Ceramic Resonators
307.2 kHz ± 1 kHz for 4800 Baud Rate
C1 — C1 ≈ 50 pF
C2 — C2 ≈ 200 pF
(Ceramic Resonator Suppliers:
Radio Materials Company, Chicago, Illinois
Vernitron Piezoelectric Division, Bedford, Ohio)

FIGURE 2 — RECTIFIED POWER FROM DATA LINES CIRCUIT

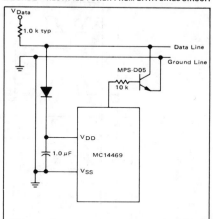

V_{Data}

1.0 k typ

Data Line

Ground Line

MPS-D05

10 k

V_{DD}

1.0 μF   MC14469

V_{SS}

FIGURE 3 — A-D CONVERTER INTERFACE

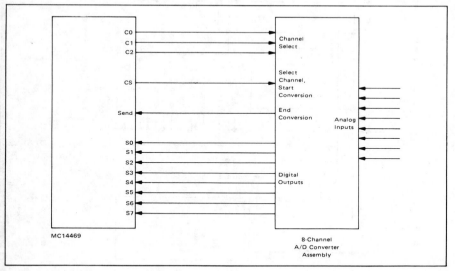

C0
C1   Channel
C2   Select

CS   Select
                      Channel,
                      Start
                      Conversion

Send   End
                      Conversion   Analog
                                          Inputs
S0
S1
S2
S3   Digital
S4   Outputs
S5
S6
S7

MC14469   8-Channel
                                  A/D Converter
                                  Assembly

 MOTOROLA *Semiconductor Products Inc.*

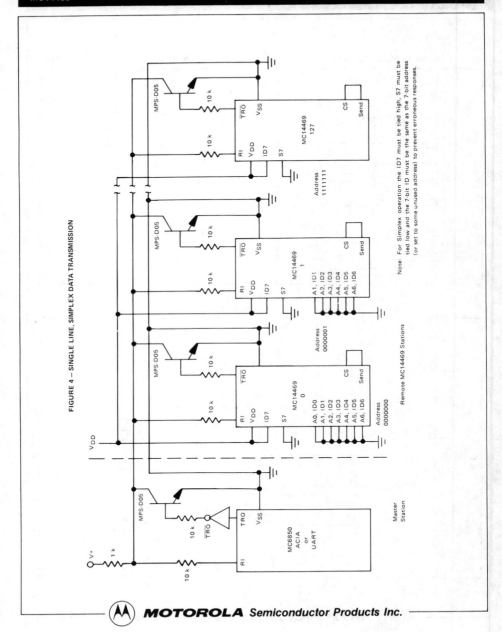

FIGURE 4 — SINGLE LINE, SIMPLEX DATA TRANSMISSION

Note: For Simplex operation the ID7 must be tied high, S7 must be tied low and the 7-bit ID must be the same as the 7-bit address (or set to some unused address) to prevent erroneous responses.

MOTOROLA *Semiconductor Products Inc.*

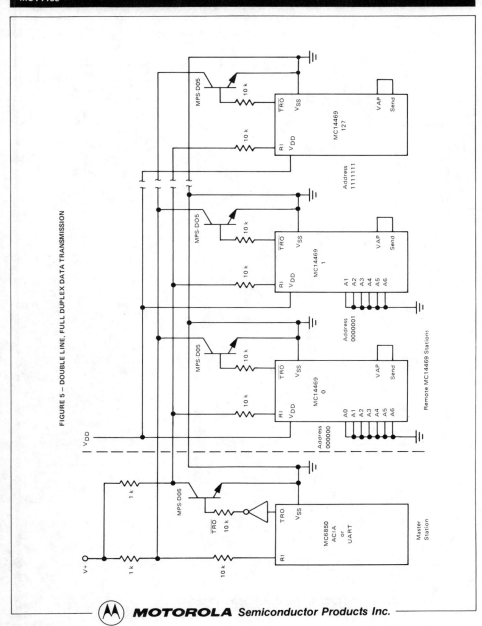

FIGURE 5 – DOUBLE LINE, FULL DUPLEX DATA TRANSMISSION

MOTOROLA Semiconductor Products Inc.

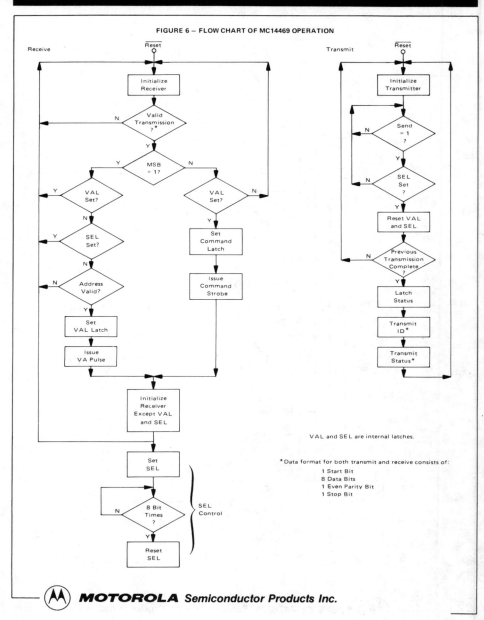

FIGURE 6 — FLOW CHART OF MC14469 OPERATION

VAL and SEL are internal latches.

* Data format for both transmit and receive consists of:
    1 Start Bit
    8 Data Bits
    1 Even Parity Bit
    1 Stop Bit

MOTOROLA *Semiconductor Products Inc.*

Index

About the Author

G. Jack Lipovski has taught electrical engineering and computer science at the University of Texas at Austin since 1976. He is a computer architect internationally recognized for his design of the pioneering data-base computer, CASSM, and of the Texas Reconfigurable Array Computer, TRAC. His expertise in microcomputers is also internationally recognized, as indicated by the fact that he is a director of EUROMICRO, the European microcomputing professional society. Dr. Lipovski has published more than fifty papers, largely in the proceedings of the annual symposium on computer architecture, the IEEE transactions on computers, and the National Computer Conference, and has edited two books. He has served as chairman of the IEEE Computer Society Technical Committee on Computer Architecture, as chairman of the special-interest group on architecture (SIGARCH) of the Association for Computing Machinery (ACM), and is currently a member of the Computer Society Governing Board and the coordinator of conferences and meetings. He received the Ph.D. degree from the University of Illinois in 1969, taught at the University of Florida from 1969 to 1976, and designed a microcomputer for Harris Semiconductor in 1973. His current interests include array processing, data-base processing, microcomputing, hardware-description languages, optical computing, and almost any other hot topic in computer architecture.